Oceans

Oceans

An Atlas-History of Man's Exploration of the Deep

General Editor   G. E. R. Deacon, C.B.E., F.R.S.

Director, National Institute of Oceanography, England

PAUL HAMLYN   LONDON

Contents

Acknowledgment is made for various quotations appearing in this book: pp. 66–73 from *Nautilus 90 North*, by Commander William Anderson and Clay Blair, Jr., by permission of Hodder & Stoughton Ltd., London; pp. 57 from *The First Crossing of Greenland*, by F. Nansen, by permission of Longmans, Green & Co. Limited, London; pp. 57–65 from *Farthest North*, by F. Nansen, by permission of Constable and Company Limited, London; pp. 36–45 from the *Journals of Captain Cook on his Voyage Of Discovery*, ed. by J. C. Beaglehole, by permission of the Hakluyt Society.

Published by
PAUL HAMLYN WESTBOOK HOUSE FULHAM BROADWAY LONDON
First published in 1962 by Paul Hamlyn, London
© Geographical Projects Limited, London 1962
Printed in Germany by Chr. Belser, Stuttgart

To an observer in space the planet Earth would appear as a globe largely covered by water. The continental gardens and lesser islands rising out of the sea occupy only 29 per cent of the total surface area of the planet and are surrounded by water with an average depth ranging from two to three miles. Throughout geological time there have been many dramatic changes in the level of the sea in relation to the land. At times a substantial portion of the oceans has been locked up as ice, and coast lines everywhere have been altered. At other times subsidence has drowned coastal areas and cities – sometimes overnight. Today about half of the three hundred major ports and coastal cities built between 3000 B. C. and the fall of the Roman Empire are submerged and many are being excavated by underwater archaeologists.

Man's exploration of the oceans began long before recorded history. Curiosity must have been one of the motives but the main inducements were the search for food and wealth. During the fifteenth and sixteenth centuries the search for trade routes to the East and the discovery of new lands were the main driving forces. Soon after James Cook's famous voyages in the late eighteenth century most of the great geographical puzzles of the oceans had been solved. In the following century oceanography was to receive its greatest stimulus from science, which sponsored expeditions like the three-year voyage around the world of the research ship H. M. S. *Challenger*. Today the scientific exploration of the oceans is being carried out by many nations. Like the earlier explorers, the scientist-explorers of the twentieth century continue to search the sea for food, but in addition they are looking for ways to tap the vast mineral wealth and to harness the energy locked up in the oceans; but perhaps more important are the basic studies that are refining our knowledge of the great chain of life in the seas, the currents, the action of waves and tides, and geological and geophysical aspects of the sea floor.

The shadow relief maps appearing throughout this book stress the features of the ocean floor rather than those of the land. In most of the maps, therefore, the coloring of the land has been subdued or treated in such a way that the reader's eye is directed to the sea areas. Wherever physical configuration of the ocean floor is important, relief coloring has been used: the lighter blues denoting shallower water and the darker blues deeper water. In many maps color is used to provide additional information. For example, a range of red tones on the currents map (pages 204-05) shows the surface temperature of the sea. On another map a sequence of colors ranging from yellow to green denotes the relative fertility of the sea. Keys accompanying all such maps explain the meanings of the colors.

Wolfgang Foges   EDITORIAL DIRECTOR
Roy A. Gallant   EDITORIAL ADVISER
Shirley Carpenter   GEOGRAPHICAL DIRECTOR
Hans Erni   ART DIRECTOR
Judy Hannington   ART EDITOR

About this Book

The world map on pages 6 and 7 shows the main features of the ocean floor – the great abyssal plains, mountain ranges, ridges, and continental shelves. The coloring of the water ranges from light blue (shallow water) to deep blue (deeper water). ▶

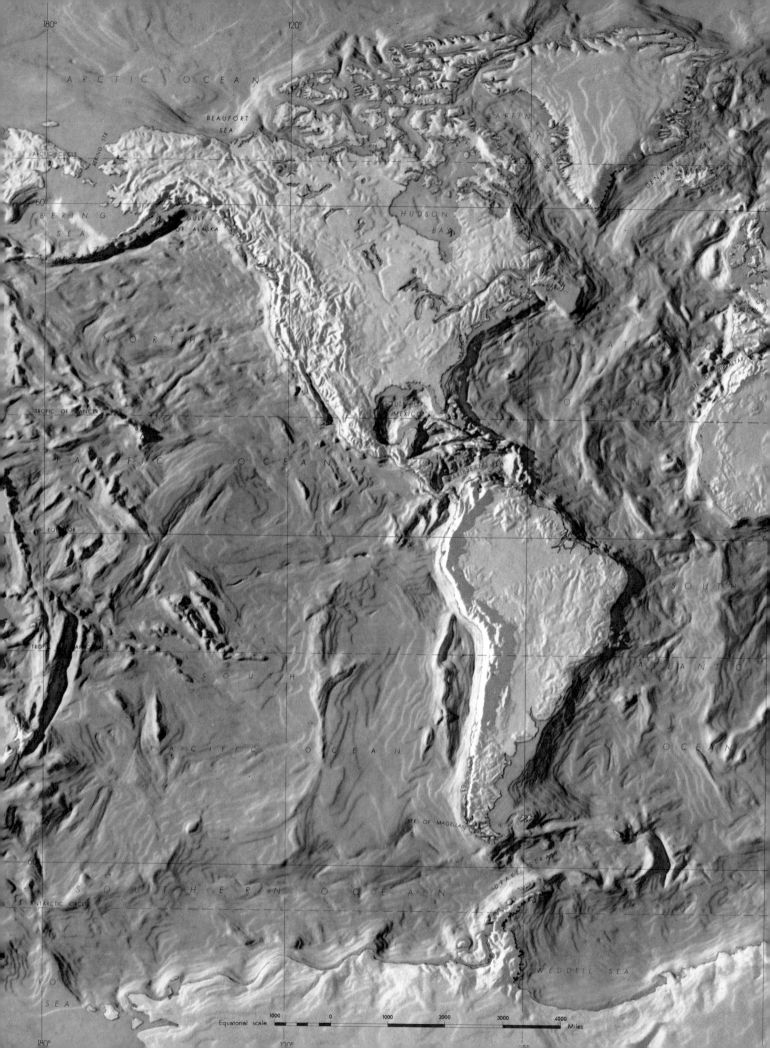

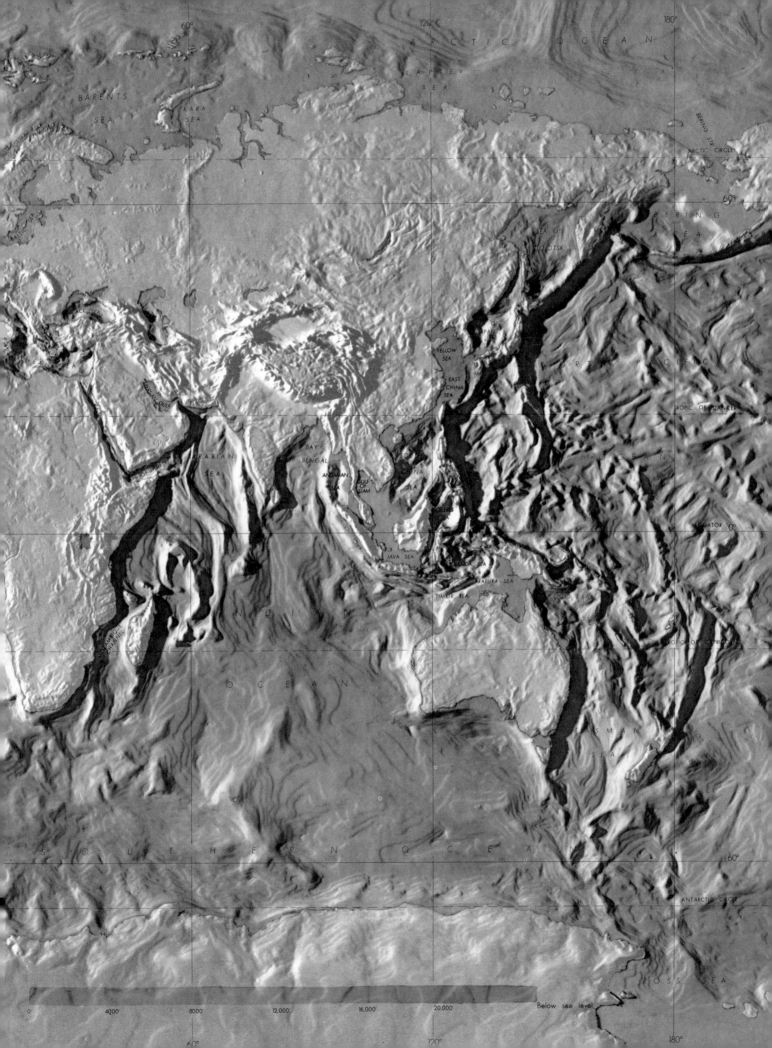

ARCTIC OCEAN

LAPTEV SEA

BARENTS SEA

KARA SEA

BALTIC SEA

BLACK SEA

RED SEA

PERSIAN GULF

GULF OF ADEN

ARABIAN SEA

BAY OF BENGAL

ANDAMAN SEA

GULF OF SIAM

MOZAMBIQUE CHANNEL

INDIAN OCEAN

JAVA SEA

TIMOR SEA

ARAFURA SEA

BANDA SEA

CELEBES SEA

SOUTH CHINA SEA

EAST CHINA SEA

YELLOW SEA

SEA OF JAPAN

SEA OF OKHOTSK

BERING SEA

BERING STR.

ARCTIC CIRCLE

NORTH PACIFIC OCEAN

TROPIC OF CANCER

EQUATOR 0°

TROPIC OF CAPRICORN

TASMAN SEA

SOUTHERN OCEAN

ROSS SEA

ANTARCTIC CIRCLE

60°

120°

180°

60°

60°

0   4000'   8000'   12,000'   16,000'   20,000'   Below sea level

The Earth and its Oceans
T. F. Gaskell

If the Earth were formed from four to five thousand million years ago, as we now believe, and if the oceans were formed soon afterwards, then our planet's mantle of water is very old. Even though we have no direct evidence of what happened in those misty beginnings, we can deduce a sequence of events that might account for the formation of our planet and its restless seas.

On the one hand, the Earth and its companion planets making up the solar system could have been formed cold – as a result of large nuclei of matter sweeping up gas, dust, and solid particles spread out around the newborn Sun. Over millions of years this sweeping-up process would have continued, each planetary nucleus capturing and drawing into itself larger and larger aggregates of matter.

On the other hand, according to a quite different theory, the Earth was formed hot, having condensed from a whirling mass of hot gaseous material thrown off from the Sun. Whether the Earth was formed hot *or* cold, there is little doubt that soon after its formation it became a molten globe. If not, then we have no satisfactory way to explain the distribution of heavy and light matter within our planet. We now know that the core is made up of the densest material, iron-nickel, and has a diameter of about 4000 miles. Surrounding the core is the mantle, 2000 miles deep and made up of lighter silicate rocks rich in iron and magnesium. The outer shell of the Earth, a five- to twenty-mile-thin crust, is made up of still lighter rocks – the kinds we see at the surface.

As a molten globe, the Earth would have lost heat rapidly. In about 10,000 years it would give off enough heat to allow a substantial part of the crust to solidify. It was sometime during this infant stage in the Earth's life that the oceans began to form. At first, the water that later flowed into land basins was locked up in the molten rock since at high temperatures and pressures water and rock can mix in any proportion. But as the primordial rock cooled and solidified, the water was squeezed out, evaporated, and added to the Earth's primeval atmosphere. It was a fortunate chance that the Earth was large enough to retain its atmosphere, for unless a planet is of a certain minimum size it cannot hold an appreciable atmosphere by gravitational attraction, so the atmosphere will leak off into space. There is no atmosphere to speak of on the Moon, and relatively little on Mars.

While the crust was cooling and giving off water vapor to the atmosphere, massive clouds formed and released rain in torrents. For how many tens or hundreds of years the first rains poured down onto the cooling crust – first steaming back into the atmosphere because the surface rocks were still above the boiling point of water – we cannot say. But gradually the surface rocks grew cool enough so that the rains no longer boiled away. The waters collected in pools, cascaded into depressions and flowed as rivers, sculpturing the land and ever seeking the lowest levels. Gradually the first basins began to fill, but they were not the sea and ocean basins we know today.

"And the spirit of God moved upon the face of the waters." This medieval impression of the Creation Story is depicted in a mosaic of 1182 in the dome of Monreale Cathedral, Sicily. (Only a section is shown here.)

These chalk cliffs at Etretat, Normandy, are slowly being cut away by wave action. It is in sedimentary rocks like these, which have been uplifted from the sea floor, that fossils of sea creatures are found. Below is a fossil of a sea lily which grew on the sea floor in Mesozoic times.

The distribution of water over the Earth has changed throughout geological time. Today 70.8 per cent of our planet's surface is covered by oceans that average two to three miles deep, the total water area being 139,480,000 square miles. The rocks composing the floors on which the deep water rests are quite different from the rocks making up the continental gardens that rise out of the seas. The floors of the large, deep oceans appear to be permanent and not to change places with the continents by buckling and rising up to the surface, but this is not to say that the ocean floors are flat, featureless expanses. Wrinkling of the deep-ocean crustal rocks has formed a network of great mountains and valleys ranging over the floors of the oceans. Valleys like the Marianas Trench in the Pacific could accommodate Mount Everest with room to spare. But the crustal rocks under these deep oceans are only a few miles thick compared with the twenty miles or so of the continental gardens.

When geologists examine rocks they try to picture what forces were at work inside our planet when the rocks were formed. Solidified lavas are the result of great outpourings from ancient fissures or from volcanoes. Other rocks, such as limestones and sandstones, are shallow water deposits compressed by their own weight in the course of time, and they often contain abundant remains of animal life that existed when the fine deposits began to rain down. These animal remains provide wonderful markers for the geologist. While some plants or animals continue to evolve gradually, others suddenly die out and may be replaced by still others, so the existence of certain characteristic fossil remains of past life gives the geologist proof that a rock was formed during a certain period in geological history.

By examining rocks from different parts of the world we can tell which parts of the continents were covered by water at any particular time. About a hundred million years ago the whole of southeast England was a shallow sea in which thick deposits of chalk were being laid down. This sea extended across the present site of the English Channel into Europe. In a similar way large parts of the North American continent have been submerged by shallow water at one time or another. The continental areas have been subjected to a continuous series of warpings and tiltings. Great mountain ranges such as the Rockies and the Himalayas were formed of shallow water deposits together with volcanic lavas which forced their way to the surface when these deposits were being folded and pushed upward. These mountains are already being worn away by wind, frost, and rain to form new sedimentary rocks. And so the process of reworking the continental rocks goes on inexorably with the world distribution of shallow seas varying from one geological period to another.

Some of the geological reconstructions of the shallow seas of the past do not make sense, and there is a large body of evidence suggesting that entire blocks of continental rock have moved as a whole relative to each other. A glance at the map here will show, for example, that Africa and South America would fit together very well if we could move them toward each other across the Atlantic. And the fit is even better if the continents are joined at the edges of their continental shelves, rather than at the present-day coast lines.

We can carry this exercise even further by grouping all the continents to form one large land mass, which has been called Pangaea. Such a reconstruction fits India neatly between south Africa and Antarctica, with Madagascar and Ceylon forming useful space-fillers. The German geologist Alfred Wegener and his associates worked very hard on this type of jigsaw puzzle, and Pangaea is only one of the super-continent possibilities that exist. Their arguments do not rest merely on the fitting together of shapes. Rock formations of some of these separate land masses show a strong correspondence both in the continuity of mountain ranges and in the composition of the rocks themselves.

This theory of continental drift has attracted strong criticism because it is difficult to visualize solid granitic continents moving about through the dense, basaltic rock floor of the oceans. However, the most recent evidence shows that time seems to be on the side of some kind of slow drifting. Possibly there have been heat changes in the past which permitted large-scale continental movement.

Although the Earth has been cooling since it was first formed, there is a built-in heat generator in the crust and mantle rocks — the inexorable decay of radioactive atoms. Rock is a poor conductor of heat and it forms a blanket which keeps heat inside the Earth. There may, therefore, be periods when the upper part of the mantle is warming up. Earthquake studies have shown that there is a layer of rock about a hundred miles within the mantle which appears to be softer than the normal mantle rock above and below. This could be the effect of a zone of excessive heating, and it may be that from time to time this zone slowly moves toward the surface of the mantle. When it reaches the crust it provides a soft layer on which the continents can move about. There would then be enormous volcanic activity, and heat would be released to such an extent that the mantle would become completely solid, and once more another steady regime of slow accumulation of heat would begin.

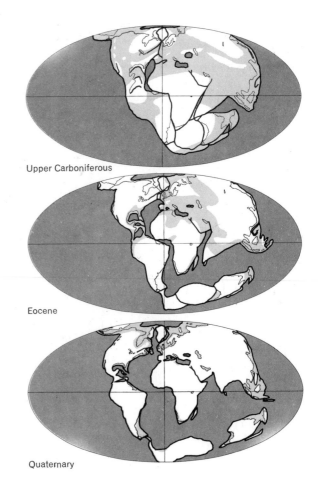

Upper Carboniferous

Eocene

Quaternary

According to Wegener's theory of continental drift, the continents known to us today were once a unified land mass that separated into segments, which drifted to their present positions. Pale blue indicates shallow seas; deep blue, deeper oceans. Present coast lines are shown for identification.

As the distribution of the seas has changed imperceptibly through time, so has their composition. The primeval seas became salty as streams and rivers feeding them washed and dissolved minerals from the land. Although common salt is the main dissolved material in sea water, many other compounds and elements exist in varying proportions. Since the volume of the sea is so great – 330 million cubic miles – the total weight of valuable metals (although they are present in very small concentrations) exceeds that to be found on the land. Industries thrive on the bromine mined from sea water, and fish grow fat and healthy with the help of small amounts of cobalt, nickel, and vanadium that are circulated from the sea-bed sediments by the ponderous underwater movements that form the ocean currents.

From the early days of oceanographic studies we have known that the salinity of sea water varies from place to place, and from shallow to deep water in any one location. As we shall find in the last chapter of this book, salt is one of the markers which tell the oceanographer where the currents are flowing, but the sea is not well stirred; each individual current, like the famous Gulf Stream, keeps its entity for thousands of miles, although a little mixing occurs at the fringes. But the body of water moves on, labeled by its salinity and its temperature until it loses its identity in the shallow seas. In general, cold, salty water sinks and warm water, together with fresh water from rivers, floats on top. These different streams of water circulate round the oceans. Not only do they affect navigation, but their continual stirring and upwelling bring the necessary nutrients for animal life up from the nutrient-rich deep layers. In the relatively still subtropical areas there is usually a dearth of plankton – the basic food of larger fishes. There are few plankton because there are few fresh chemicals brought to the surface layers.

Because the surface of the oceans is exposed to the air and to the warmth of the Sun's rays, evaporation takes place. However, since the oceans are so deep, and because water has a large capacity for holding heat, the temperature of the water stays more or less the same. But in inland lakes like the Dead Sea evaporation leaves great concentrations of dissolved salts, and eventually thick deposits of valuable materials containing sodium, potassium, iodine, and other elements are laid down. A similar process sometimes takes place near shore when deposits of mud form shallow pools, the water of which alternately evaporates and is replenished. In such cases salt deposits are interleaved between the clays and limestones that are formed.

In the deep oceans the deposits are different. Sometimes shallow water material is carried far out onto the abyssal plains of the deep ocean floor by turbidity currents which tumble as underwater avalanches down the continental slopes, but the general picture is one of slow and steady settlement of minute, solid particles from the water. This rain of material includes the skeletal remains of small animals, pebbles carried by ice or by floating tree trunks, fragments of pumice from volcanic outbursts, and dust from outer space. The rate of accumulation of this material on the sea bed is unimaginably slow.

Age after age such material has been filtering down continuously to the sea floor. Once it is encased in sediments, which can

At Batz, near St. Nazaire, Brittany, sea water is pumped into large enclosures called "pans," where it is allowed to evaporate. The remaining salt is then raked into piles.

Within historical times the land has gained over the sea in the Persian Gulf area. Over the years the Tigris and Euphrates rivers have altered the coast line by carrying sediments far out into the gulf. Coast line positions since 3000 B.C. are shown according to various authorities.

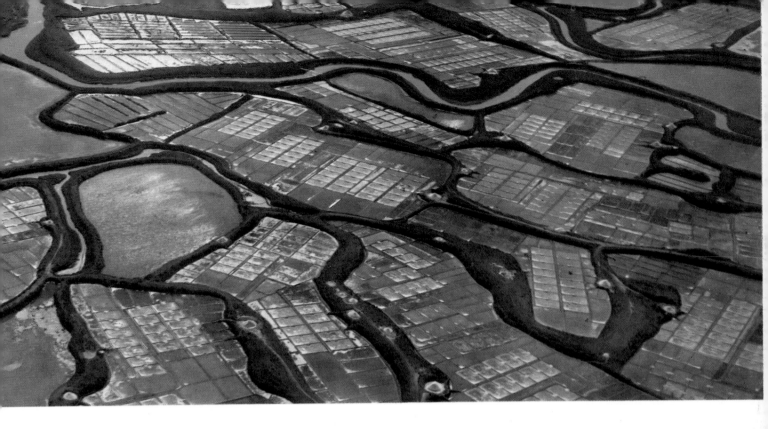

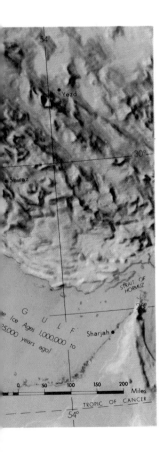

be dredged up and studied by the oceanographer, it becomes a book to the past, providing a record of twenty-million-year-old volcanic eruptions, or spasms of prolific animal life. But recently an even more subtle way has been devised to trace back into geological history and reveal past surface temperatures of the oceans. When water evaporates, those water molecules that contain the lighter isotope of oxygen are lost more rapidly to the atmosphere than are the heavier water molecules. During warm conditions the surface water contains an extra abundance of heavy oxygen isotopes, and this is reflected in the composition of animals which grow and live near the surface. When the animals die and sink to the sea floor their skeletons have locked up inside them the oxygen isotope ratio from which the surface temperature can be calculated. So besides the qualitative evidence of cycles of activity in geological history, the sediments of the ocean floor contain a history of the environmental conditions.

The oceanographer must take great care when he collects samples of these ocean sediments. Deposits from turbidity currents can mislead him; also, there are burrowing animals that live in the top few feet of the sea floor. These creatures have been brought up in core samples, and they have been seen by oceanographers who have penetrated the deeps in bathyscaphes. The difficulty of selecting an undisturbed sediment hunting ground is one with which geologists are familiar in their work on land.

Seismic measurements in the oceans show that more than a thousand feet of claylike material covers the deep, flat parts of the oceans. Compared with the rate of sedimentation in shallow water – 40,000 feet have accumulated in the Persian Gulf in the last hundred million years alone – this is only a thin veneer of material. Until we can study cores brought up from the bottom part of the

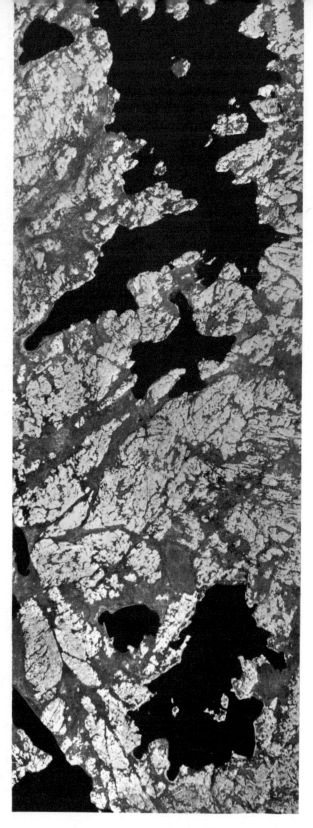

In parts of northern Canada and Europe great stretches of barren rock lie exposed. These areas were scraped clean by the massive ice sheets that advanced southward during the last ice age. As the ice melted, thousands of lakes were formed in the rock hollows.

sea-bed sediments, we cannot be certain of the history of the oceans. Such a core sample down to the rock bed of the sediments is the oceanographer's dream, and we seem to be on the verge of realizing it. In March 1961, oceanographers working on the Mohole Project (an attempt to drill a hole right through the Earth's crust to the mantle) at Guadalupe Island went through two miles of water, 500 feet of sediments, and fifty feet of rock. More core samples of such great depths would add enormously to our knowledge of the oceans' history.

From time to time throughout geological history great quantities of the Earth's water have been locked up as ice during ice ages. We are, in fact, today living in the dying grips of an ice age which reached its fourth climax about 10,000 years ago, and which began between 500,000 and a million years ago. About one-tenth of the total land surface is glaciated today.

While the continents move up and down on a time scale represented by tens to hundreds of millions of years, invasions and retreats of ice over large parts of the land may take place over periods of tens of thousands of years. Although there is no general agreement about the mechanisms that touch off an ice age, we do not have to take them on trust, as we do wandering continents. The Greenland and the Antarctic icecaps and the glaciers of the Alps and other mountains are there for us to examine, and we can see the marks that glaciation leaves behind. These same marks — rocks scarred by ice, valleys with rounded slopes, deposits of material at the foot of glaciers — can be seen in ancient rocks. At least three other major periods of glaciation have been discovered, ranging back to the Pre-Cambrian of 700 million years ago.

The amount of water locked up as ice during an ice age is an appreciable fraction even of the enormous volume of the oceans. For example, if the Greenland and Antarctic icecaps should melt suddenly, the level of the sea would rise by about 300 feet — enough to turn New York, London, and Paris into underwater cities. But the picture is not quite so simple; as the great weight of ice is removed from the land, the land rises up, causing subsidence elsewhere. By examining old shore lines we find that interglacial periods have taken place in the past, during which most of the Earth's ice must have melted. We can estimate the dates of these warming-up periods from fossil evidence and carbon-14 dating, which is more precise for recent times (the last 20,000 years). From 18,000 to 6000 years ago the seas have risen nearly 300 feet, so it is not surprising that early records of man's history mention floods and deluges. A sea-level rise of 300 feet today would alter all but the steepest rising coast lines and flood many of our most concentrated centers of population, simply because such a great percentage of the land is relatively low. This has undoubtedly happened at least once during man's period of habitation of the planet. At the end of the last interglacial period, such large-scale flooding over the earth must have taken place. Although the rise of sea level averaged only one foot in forty years during a warming-up period, the past encroachment of water over certain areas would almost certainly have been in catastrophic bursts, when rain and wind and tide conspired to produce great floods.

The present sea level has been maintained within about ten feet either way for the past 6000 years, but that does not mean that the present cycle of ice ages has come to an end. There could be another advance of ice over the land with the consequent reduction of sea level by about 300 feet. On the other hand, the ever-present threat of the Antarctic and Greenland ice melting, with a consequent rise of 300 feet in sea level, is still with man.

Although we do not know just what controls the delicate balance, it seems probable that both the major icecaps provide some sort of stability. They appear to be held in deep basins by rings of mountains, whereas the ice sheets which covered Canada, part of the United States, Asia, and northern Europe were not held and could spread out thinly and so be more readily dispersed. It is important, then, to measure the present-day rate of snow accumulation on the icecaps and compare it with the rate of evaporation, and to measure the escape of ice that plunges over the rims of the containing mountains and tumbles into the sea.

It is an easy matter to explain the rise and fall in sea level: glacial ice simply melts and becomes part of the sea or water freezes. But the mechanisms that touch off these processes are much more difficult to explain. We have already seen that the radioactivity of the mantle rocks may provide a periodic heating up of the Earth's crust and so alter world climate from time to time, and there are other mechanisms that may be associated with warming our planet. Changes in the carbon dioxide content of the atmosphere, for instance, may affect world climate. An atmospheric blanket of carbon dioxide would produce a greenhouse effect and trap the reflected long-wave (heat) radiations of the Earth and so trigger off a warming up period which would melt the remaining ice and drown all the low-lying land. However, carbon dioxide is absorbed in sea water, and circulation of the large volume of water in the oceans may be adequate to preserve a fairly constant balance of carbon dioxide between air and water and thus provide a steadying influence.

But there are other ways of shielding the Earth from the Sun's rays and thus upsetting the delicate balance which controls climate. The Earth could become enveloped in a cloud of meteoric dust; continuous volcanic activity over a long period of time could throw up a screen of fine ash in the sky; or there could be a long-term change in the intensity of solar radiation. Also, a change in inclination of the Earth's axis could cause the regions of ice to shift location. It would seem that any number of these conditions could conspire and touch off another period of cooling. A cooler Earth would have longer and more severe winters. Snow rather than rain would fall and would tend to remain rather than be melted and washed away. Thick accumulations of snow would form ice patches and in turn these would grow into icecaps or glaciers, which creep downhill forcing a retreat of life before them.

But the slow march of glaciers does not constitute the entire invasion of ice. The extension of winter conditions far away from the polar regions, plus the slow accumulation of snow, are the real mechanisms that advance an ice age. And the sea is the provider of the snow. During an ice age it may give up as much as two to five per cent of its volume in the form of ice and snow, but when the mechanisms that touch off the ice age reverse, the sea reclaims its loss as the ice melts. And so the cycle goes on, apparently without end, from water to rain and snow and ice and then back to water again.

If the Greenland and Antarctic icecaps should melt suddenly, the level of the oceans would rise about 300 feet. This would turn New York, London, Paris, and Tokyo into submerged cities, leaving only the tops of the highest buildings rising out of the water.

Men against the Sea

Edward Shackleton

*When men have set out on the sea, whether
in search of new lands, new trade routes,
or against an enemy, they have had to choose
their ships well. We know relatively little
about ships of the classical world. Not
until the fifteenth century do we begin to
find detailed records. The Unicorn, a large
galley of Henry VIII's navy, is shown here.*

Left: Part of the North Sea map showing trade routes, made c. 1535 by the Swedish priest Olaus Magnus. At this time monsters were believed to exist, and are shown here on the map where they were last reported.

The first men who ventured to the ocean shores must have regarded the vast expanse of water before them as an endless barrier extending to the very edge of creation. Aware of their limitations as swimmers, they must have made their first voyages on tree trunks or limbs lashed together as a raft. Later, with the experience of several voyages behind them, they became bold enough to venture out to sea in hollowed logs, or in skin boats like the umiaks still used by Eskimos. Without navigational aids they would have been careful never to go beyond the sight of land if they could help it, yet sometimes storms must have driven them out to sea.

Although we have no records of the earliest sea voyages, we do have records of Eskimos having crossed all the way from Greenland to the north of Scotland. And we accept as fact that in the South Seas the Polynesians sailed from Asia, crossing the wide ocean via the islands of Indonesia to New Zealand and beyond. To guide them toward land they had only the stars and the flights of birds to follow.

Next came the traders – the Phoenicians, the Arabs, and the Chinese. Galleys and sailing boats soon opened many of the sea lanes familiar to us today. Even though there were tremendous hazards at sea, when the winds were unfavorable or the seas tempestuous, a ship could wait for good sailing conditions. It was not long after the traders established themselves that the highways of the sea also began to draw explorers – and so began the great age of discovery. But discovery, like invention, has all too often been rediscovery. The Vikings had discovered America some 500 years before Columbus rediscovered it. And when Bartholomew Diaz in 1487 – and ten years later Vasco da Gama – rounded the Cape of Good Hope, they were doing from west to east only what the Phoenicians in 600 B.C. had done from east to west. In fact we can say that nearly all the inhabited parts of the world had already been discovered when they were rediscovered by the explorers and navigators who belong to the fifteenth century's great age of discovery.

In this chapter we have singled out of the hundreds of sea explorers six whose voyages have special significance for our story

This engraving of a seventeenth-century Dutch school of navigation shows a variety of instruments then in use: globes, hourglasses, cross-staffs, astrolabes, dividers, compasses, and charts.

of the sea. It can be argued that any choice of six is bound to be arbitrary and to raise the question: Why have others been omitted? Our narrative begins with Pytheas, an outstanding traveler who well represents the many unrecorded journeys of the classical world, and he was a suitable forerunner of the scientific explorers of latter days. In the eighteen hundred years that passed from the time of Pytheas to the great age of discovery, little advance in sea exploration was made, if we exclude the remarkable voyages of the Vikings. In their long ships they traveled not only round the north of Norway to the White Sea, but also to Iceland; and from Iceland, Eric the Red traveled to Greenland. Later, his son Leif visited the mainland of America in the vicinity of Labrador, Newfoundland, and possibly penetrated even as far south as Virginia.

Inspired by Prince Henry the Navigator, of Portugal, and by national interests in colonizing new lands, European sea explorers sailed the waters east round the Cape of Good Hope, and west across the Atlantic. This period is well represented by Ferdinand Magellan, the second explorer we meet in this chapter. His voyage was the first circumnavigation of the globe and led to exploration of much of the Pacific.

Other explorers and travelers of many European nations continued during the following two hundred years to add to the charts, until the time of James Cook. This English sea captain towers as a giant among navigators and explorers, and his work filled in most of the remaining gaps in man's knowledge of the Pacific, leaving only the Arctic and the Antarctic still to be explored. And so we come to James Clark Ross in the Antarctic and then to Fridtjof Nansen of Arctic fame. Finally, to complete our narrative, we have chosen the remarkable voyage under the North Pole of the *Nautilus*, commanded by William Anderson.

In this twentieth-century vessel may lie the key to the real exploration of the sea that is yet to come. When I sailed in the *Nautilus* not long ago, I was aware that I was as much in a new element and in a new means of transport as a man traveling in a spaceship to the stars.

Pytheas
Into the Unknown World

When the Greek explorer Pytheas set out on his famous voyage about 325 B.C., he most likely sailed in a ship resembling the one (above) depicted on this Greek vase dated about 530 B.C. Since no original account of his voyage exists, there are several theories about the route he followed. The map shows routes suggested by different authorities.

Pytheas, courageous man that he was, sailed beyond the limits of the world known to Greek civilization. By the end of his major voyage the extent of the island of Britain, great stretches of the coast of western Europe, and part of the Arctic regions had been added to the sum total of civilized man's knowledge of the world.

Because there is no record of the earliest sea explorers, the voyage of Pytheas, about whom we have at least some accounts, is important in the history of sea exploration. The travels of this Greek astronomer, navigator, and inventor have never ceased to be a source of controversy and of interest to geographers. Unfortunately, Pytheas' own accounts of his travels have long been lost, so we must rely on those early writers who had either seen his book or had some knowledge of it.

The date of Pytheas' expedition is fairly accurately fixed at about 325 B.C., yet his motives for setting out are less certain. Some think that he ventured northward in search of knowledge for its own sake; others, that he set out to investigate a Phoenician blockade; and still others, that Greek merchants encouraged him to search for the source of tin which from time to time appeared in the market place of his native town, Massilia (now Marseilles). Until that time tin had been filtering down from the north, probably by the overland trade route following the Rhône through Gaul. Whatever Pytheas' motives, he was to venture into the unknown, "haunted" seas and penetrate far beyond the boundary of the Habitable World known to the Greeks.

Around the time Pytheas set out on his epic voyage there were Phoenician ships blockading the western approach to the Mediterranean. For hundreds of years the Greeks and Phoenicians had been trade rivals, each seeking fortunes in the Mediterranean, and the Phoenicians outside it, but until Pytheas' time the Phoenicians had managed to keep secret their routes to the rich tin and silver markets discovered by Himilco around 500 B.C.

Because many of Pytheas' statements about his voyage contradicted Greek philosophy and geographical theory of the time, he became thoroughly discredited – the Münchhausen of the classical world – and most of the statements attributed to him were chosen by geographers and historians who considered him an exaggerator and liar; Strabo and Polybius, for instance. Yet Diodorus, Timaeus,

ROUTES FOLLOWED BY PYTHEAS ACCORDING TO DIFFERENT AUTHORITIES:

{
A V. Stefansson "Ultima Thule"
B G. E. Broche "Pytheas Le Massaliote"
b Areas where Broche differs from Stefansson
{
C Sir C. R. Markham "Lands of Silence"
D M. B. Synge "A Book of Discovery"
d Return journey where Synge differs from Markham
E P. Hermann "Conquest of Man"
Russian "Atlas of the History of Geographical Discoveries and Explorations"

and Eratosthenes looked upon Pytheas with at least some respect.

What, exactly, do we know about the man? There is no doubt of his abilities as an astronomer and mathematician; even Strabo allows him this, saying that "with regard to astronomy and mathematical research he will appear to have used his data sensibly enough." We are also told that Pytheas constructed a gnomon with which he was able to fix the latitude of Massilia so accurately that it was not improved on for many centuries. At that time the Greek method of working out latitude was based on the length of the longest and shortest days of the year, and latitude was determined by the number of hours the Sun appeared above the horizon. For example, the farther north or south of the Equator you travel on Midsummer Day, the longer the Sun remains above the horizon, until finally you reach the Arctic Circle, where the Sun remains above the horizon throughout the day. It was this method of determining latitude that Pytheas himself used on his travels.

Another contribution of Pytheas was that he contradicted the belief that the celestial north pole coincided with a particular star. Instead, he said that it was associated with a formation of three stars. He was also the first Greek to observe and describe the movements of ocean tides and relate spring and neap tides to phases of the Moon, tides at that time being a phenomenon strange to peoples living on the shores of the almost tideless Mediterranean.

While we have some knowledge of Pytheas himself, we know practically nothing about his ship. We can presume that it was seaworthy since it was bound for unknown northern waters, and that it was equipped to defend itself against possible attack. Fridtjof Nansen, one of the later explorers we will meet in this chapter, suggested that it was probably more than a hundred feet long, and in some ways better equipped than the Viking galleys that crossed to Greenland and America about A.D. 1000. Sir Clements Markham, president of the Royal Geographical Society at the turn of the century, gave a detailed description of the type of ship she might have been: a large trireme of four or five hundred tons, 150 to 170 feet long. Although fitted with sails (yards with square sails laced to them), she had auxiliary rowing power – 54 bottom rowers, 58 middle, and 62 upper, a total of 174. Such ships could average fifty miles or more a day.

Pytheas set out from Massilia, sailed through the Pillars of Hercules, passed Cape St. Vincent and beyond the limit of the world known to the Greeks. From there his course lay north. He made his first recorded observation at a place where the longest day was fifteen hours, which would be about the latitude of Oporto (40°59′ N.). Continuing northward through the Bay of Biscay he rounded Brittany and then crossed to Britain, either to Cantium (Kent) or Belerium (Land's End), both of which he undoubtedly visited at some stage of his circumnavigation of the whole of Britain. Pytheas' description of Britain probably was taken originally from his book and reported by Diodorus:

"This land is in shape triangular like Sicily, but its sides are not equal; it stretches out along Europe slantwise, and they say that the headland, which they call Cantium and which is least distant from the Continent, is about 100 stadia [1 Attic stadium = 607 English feet] from the land at the place the sea makes a current. Another promontory, which is called Belerium, is said to be distant

By the first century B.C. the tin miners of Cornwall were casting tin in 150-pound ingots. When the Phoenicians traded with them earlier, the Britons had not yet begun to use a furnace to smelt the ore.

The Greeks highly valued the amber which they obtained in trade with people from northern and western Europe. Shown here is a fifth-century B.C. amber carving of Athena, goddess of wisdom, found in south Italy.

The Hecateaus map (left) shows the extent of the world known to the Greeks around 500 B.C. By about 300 B.C. maps (one below, by Eratosthenes) included the British Isles, India, the mysterious "Thule," and parts of southern Russia.

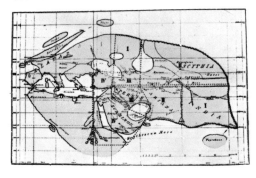

a voyage of four days from the Continent. While the remaining one, they record, runs out into the sea and is named Orka [Duncansby Head?]. The shortest of the sides has a measurement of 7500 stadia, and runs out along Europe; the second stretching from the Strait to the apex, 15,000 stadia; and the remaining one 20,000 stadia. So that the whole circumference of the island is 42,500 stadia."

While this is about twice the circumference of Britain, we must make allowances for Pytheas; it is quite possible that he was misquoted.

We also have from Diodorus a description of the tin industry, based on Pytheas' observations. "The natives of Britain by the headland of Belerium are unusually hospitable, and thanks to their intercourse with foreign traders have grown gentle in their manner. They extract the tin from its bed by a cunning process . . . Having smelted the tin and refined it, they hammer it into knucklebone shape and convey it to an adjacent island, Ictis [St. Michael's Mount]. They wait until the . . . tide has drained the intervening firth, and then transport whole loads of tin on wagons. The merchants buy the metal from the natives and carry it from [St. Michael's Mount] to Galatia [France]." Pliny, quoting Timaeus, also refers to Ictis and remarks that ". . . the Britons sail to it in boats made of wickerwork sewn round with hides."

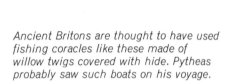

Ancient Britons are thought to have used fishing coracles like these made of willow twigs covered with hide. Pytheas probably saw such boats on his voyage.

At low tide a causeway links St. Michael's Mount to the mainland. It was across this causeway that ancient Britons carried tin for export to the Continent. At that time the island was known as Ictis.

As Pytheas sailed up the coast of Britain, he took three more sets of observations. The first, where the longest day was seventeen hours, would be at about Flamborough Head at latitude 54° 2′ N.; the second, where the longest day was eighteen hours, at Tarbat Ness in northern Scotland, at latitude 57° 58′ N.; and finally at a place where the longest day was nineteen hours, bringing him to the northernmost part of the Shetland Islands, at latitude 61°N. Pytheas called this place Orkas, and it was here that he heard about a land called Thule.

This is the most mysterious part of Pytheas' voyage. Even today we cannot be certain where his Thule is, or whether he actually visited it. Some have associated Thule with the Shetlands and the Orkneys, but more likely possibilities are Iceland or part of Norway. Both Strabo and Pliny quote Pytheas as saying that Thule is six days north of Britain. But due north, or northeast? There is, however, more evidence, and evidence of a very significant kind. Strabo reports that "Thule . . . is near to the congealed sea"; and Solinus writes that "beyond Thule we meet with a sluggish and congealed sea"; and according to Pliny, "after one day's sail from Thule the frozen sea is reached called by some Cronium." These references would seem to strengthen Iceland's claim, for the pack ice off the coast of Greenland in Denmark Strait and down past the western coast of Iceland is very much nearer than any area off Norway.

Strabo gives us a remarkable description of Pytheas' congealed sea: ". . . There was no longer any distinction of land or sea or air, but a mixture of the three like a sealung in which [Pytheas says] land and sea and everything floats, and this binds all together and can neither be traversed on foot or by boat. . . ." The key word *sealung* could very well refer to the ice at the edge of the main pack, flexible and having the appearance of jellyfish, especially on a misty day when sea, ice, and sky seem to merge into one. The writer himself has been caught in a boat in this sort of loose, new sea ice and found it impossible to walk over because of its soft, rubbery consistency.

Pytheas also tells us that "the barbarians revealed to us the

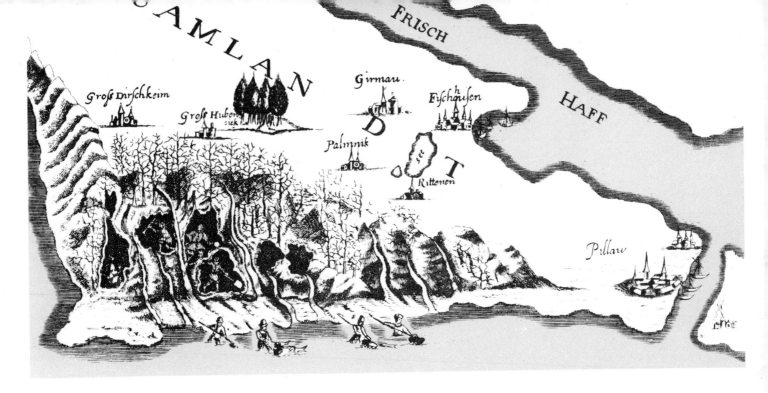

Pytheas probably visited this region of north Prussia, "Samland," where men gathered amber from the sea. It was so plentiful along the shore that it was used as fuel.

sleeping place of the Sun," meaning the Arctic Circle. "It was found in those regions that the night was very short lasting, in some places two hours, in others three." A Midsummer Day of twenty-one or twenty-two hours would indicate latitudes between 63°N. and 65°N. It is not difficult to see in Strabo's account what is probably the first description of the edge of the Arctic pack, and it is reasonable to conclude that Pytheas probably saw it himself a day's journey north of Iceland. We could continue to speculate indefinitely, as many geographers have, but we would be little the wiser for it. At this stage we should mention the other, and equally frustrating, part of his travels.

This one is no easier to follow than his circumnavigation of Britain, and possibly it was part of a separate voyage. According to Strabo, "Pytheas states that having returned thence [from Thule] he visited the whole of the ocean coasts of Europe from Gadina to Tanais [the Don]." This is bound to be a rather fanciful statement, for the Don was generally regarded as being the border of Asia.

We do know, however, that Pytheas voyaged beyond the Rhine and came to an island where amber was to be found. Although this particular island has never been definitely identified, it could have been either Helgoland or one of the islands off the coast of Schleswig, a borderland between Germany and Denmark. Nonetheless, this was an important report in its time, for amber was prized by the Greeks. Pliny, again referring to earlier reports, described how Pytheas had encountered the Teutones, a Germanic people, and he referred to amber being washed up by the waves, the belief then being that amber was solidified sea water.

Unfortunately, there was no way to confirm Pytheas' voyages, even while his records were still available. The Phoenician blockade apparently tightened and there are no further reports of Greek voyages either to Britain or Thule, or to the north at all. We have few figures in history whose claim to fame rests on such scanty records, yet we must regard Pytheas as one of the early explorers whose discoveries and scientific observations added significantly to man's knowledge of the Habitable World.

Ferdinand Magellan
Break-through to the Pacific

Although we have no accurate representation of Magellan's ships, this 1532 drawing by Holbein shows a ship thought to be similar to those of Magellan's fleet in 1519.

During the eighteen hundred years that separate Pytheas from Magellan, the old world was mapped and important journeys were made – but chiefly by land. The first great burst of exploration by sea came in the fifteenth century, with the high-spirited voyages sponsored by Spain and Portugal. Probably the most astonishing of all these undertakings was Ferdinand Magellan's circumnavigation of the earth.

Magellan made his magnificent voyage in the service of Charles V of Spain. Ironically, though, in view of the rivalry between the two countries at that time, he himself was a native of Portugal, born about 1480 in the arid and mountainous district of Traz-os-Montes. At the age of fifteen young Ferdinand became a page at the queen's court, where he remained until he was twenty-four, at which time, stirred by the conquests of explorers such as Da Gama, Cabral, and Gaspar Corte-Real, he decided to take part in the great adventure.

He signed on as a *sobresaliente* (an extra officer) with a twenty-ship armada that set out in 1504 to annihilate the fleets and armies of the Sultan of Egypt and hostile Indian rulers. The operation was completely successful. While Portugal emerged as a great world empire, Magellan emerged with the scars of his first battle wounds and with an undiminished appetite for the sea.

During the next few years he risked his life in one nautical venture after another. Yet when he returned to Lisbon in 1512, he had little material gain to show for his seven years' apprenticeship, apart from a slave he had bought somewhere in the Moluccan islands. Magellan next found himself caught up in legal battle (a breach of trust when some captured cattle and horses, which had been partially under his charge, disappeared). Furious, he stormed back to Lisbon to put his case before the king, but he was refused audience and was ordered back to his post. The charge was later dropped. At thirty-seven Magellan, already one of the most experienced seamen and campaigners in Europe, was told that he was free to offer his services wherever he wished, for they were not wanted in his own country.

During the next year or so he remained in Portugal, giving himself over to an intensive study of navigation. During these months he met Ruy Faleiro, an astronomer and fellow student of navigation whose brilliant treatises on determining latitude were to be entrusted to Magellan. The art of navigation had come a long way since the days of Pytheas, and Magellan was determined to learn as much as he could. Although the cross-staff and the astrolabe were in common use for finding latitude, there was still no reliable means of calculating longitude (which depends on a clock that can accurately record the difference between local and Greenwich time).

Sixteenth-century portrait of Magellan.

Toward the end of 1517 Magellan was ready to strike out. Since Portugal did not want him, perhaps the emperor of Spain, Charles V, would. Renouncing his Portuguese citizenship, he now went to Seville, followed a few months later by Faleiro. Magellan was lucky enough to meet and establish close friendship with a fellow Portuguese, Diogo Barbosa (whose daughter became Magellan's wife). In March 1518 the two friends presented a bold plan to the emperor: If Charles V would give them ships and men, Magellan and Faleiro would undertake to find the shortest route to the Moluccas – the highly prized Spice Islands in the South Seas. Also they would prove that the Moluccas lay within Spain's boundaries.

What was more, Magellan maintained that he could sail to the Moluccas by a westerly route. This meant that he staked everything on a conviction that there was a strait linking the Atlantic and Pacific oceans. At that time, it was generally thought that the huge land mass of the Americas continued unbroken to the South Pole. There is no way of knowing whether Magellan actually knew that this assumption was false.

Charles V was so impressed by the plan that he agreed to fit out an armada of five ships with a company of about 268 officers and men and a two-year store of provisions. The emperor also promised that Magellan and Faleiro would be granted a good share of any profits that resulted from their discoveries. If they discovered more than six islands, they could choose two from which they might receive one-fifteenth of the profits.

Many weary and frustrating months were to pass before the armada could be assembled. For one thing, Faleiro was a man of unstable and jealous temperament; he made so many enemies that Magellan must have been relieved when Faleiro finally withdrew from the venture, warned off by a gloomy astrological prediction. And when news of the expedition reached Portugal, the Portuguese king instructed his ambassador to prevent the expedition sailing.

The map on these pages shows the routes of the five ships that set out on Magellan's voyage around the world. Before the voyage had ended Magellan was killed, and only one of the five ships completed the voyage. The woodcut at left shows sailors of about the time of Magellan in a storm at sea.

————————	1519—1521 Voyage of Magellan
—·—·—·—·—	1520— ? *Santo Antonio* flees to Spain
—··—··—··—	1521 (?) *Trinidad* attempts to return to Spain via America forced to return to Spice Islands
———— ————	1521—1522 *Victoria* sails back to Spain under Del Cano

Equatorial scale   1000   0   1000   2000   3000   Miles

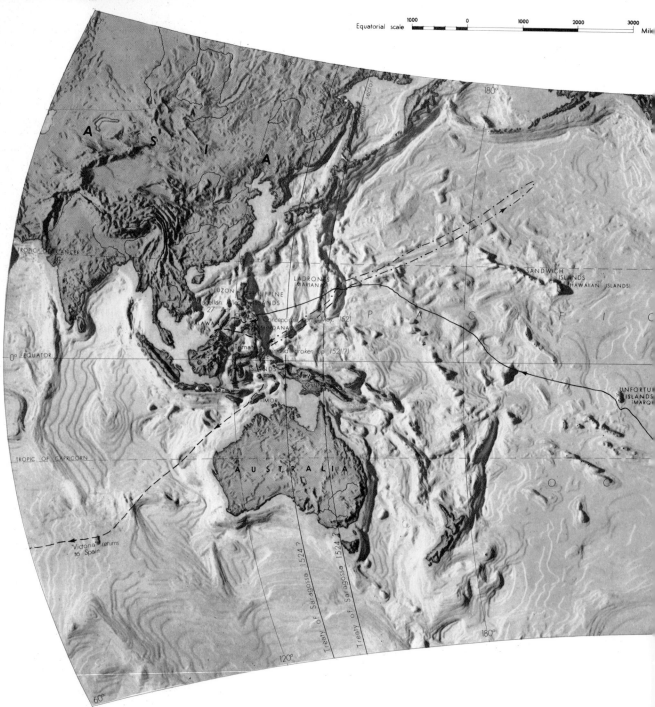

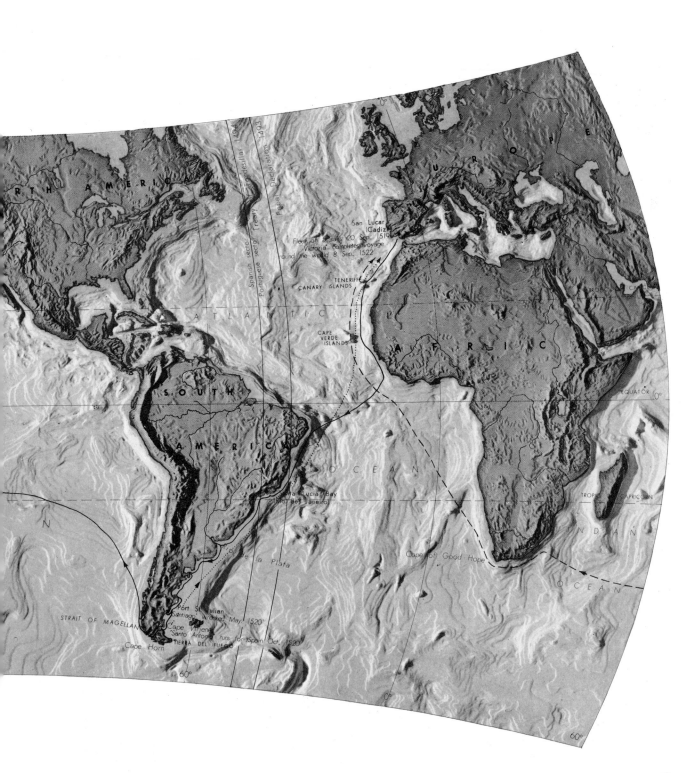

NORTH AMERICA

San Lucar
(Cadiz)
Fleet of 5 sails 20 Sep. 1519
Victoria completes voyage
round the world 8 Sep. 1522

TENERIFE
CANARY ISLANDS

CAPE
VERDE
ISLANDS

ATLANTIC

SOUTH

AMERICA

OCEAN

Santa Lucia Bay
(Rio de Janeiro)

Rio de la Plata

Port St. Julian
Santiago wrecked May 1520
Cape
'Santo Antonio' runs for Spain Oct. 1520
STRAIT OF MAGELLAN   TIERRA DEL FUEGO
Cape Horn

EUROPE

AFRICA

Papal Declaration 1493

Treaty of Tordesillas 1494
Spanish sector / Portuguese sector

EQUATOR 0°

TROPIC OF CANCER

Cape of Good Hope

INDIAN

OCEAN

TROPIC OF CAPRICORN

60°

0°

60°

60°

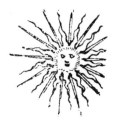

Although we know little about the ships beyond their names and tonnage – *Santo Antonio*, 120 tons; *Trinidad*, 110 tons (the flagship); *Concepcion*, 90 tons; *Victoria*, 85 tons; and *Santiago*, 75 tons – we do have detailed lists of the instruments, stores, armament, and trade goods they carried. There were twenty-four parchment charts, six pairs of compasses, twenty-one wooden quadrants, seven astrolabes, thirty-five compass needles, eighteen hour glasses, and Faleiro's invaluable treatises on latitude. The main items among the ships' stores were biscuits, wine, olive oil, anchovies, dried pork, cheeses, sugar, and a surprisingly large variety of medicines. There was also a plentiful supply of fighting equipment, among which were a thousand lances, boarding pikes, ten dozen javelins, 95 dozen darts, 60 crossbows, and 360 dozen arrows and sundry swords. The list of trade goods was as modern as those carried in the nineteenth century, except perhaps for "20,000 small bells of three kinds." There were cloths, caps and kerchiefs, combs, mirror glasses, brass basins, knives, scissors, fishhooks, and 500 pounds of crystals, "which are diamonds of all colours."

It was easier to outfit the ships than to find men to sail them. The final complement of about 268 men included Spaniards, Basques, Genoese, Corfiotes, Negroes, Malayans, Englishmen, Sicilians, and thirty-seven Portuguese, among whom were all the pilots and Magellan's brother-in-law and cousin. There were four captains in addition to Magellan himself. The most graphic account of the epic voyage comes from the pen of a young Italian, Antonio Pigafetta, who went on the expedition "desirous of seeing the wonderful things of the ocean." From him, and from a few histories based on information collected first-hand from the survivors, we have a remarkably full story of what happened.

On Tuesday, September 20, 1519, the five ships got under way and shaped their course for the Canaries. By then Magellan had done all the careful planning he could to assure the success of his great venture. He was already recognized by Pigafetta as "a discreet and virtuous man careful of his honour." On September 26 the five ships arrived at Tenerife, where they remained for a few days to take on wood, water, and pitch. It was well that they did delay for they were overtaken by a caravel from Spain bearing a secret message to Magellan from his father-in-law. The Captain General, warned Diogo Barbosa, should keep a close watch on his captains, since they had told their friends and relations that if they had any trouble with Magellan they would kill him. The ringleader apparently was Juan de Cartagena, captain of the *Santo Antonio*.

After leaving Tenerife the fleet sailed down the African coast with fair winds as far as Cape Verde. Then came twenty days of calms and baffling winds as they sailed on to Sierre Leone, followed by a full month of head winds and storms. "In these tempests," Pigafetta wrote, "the *corpo santo*, or Saint Elmo's fire, often appeared, and in one which we experienced on a certain very dark night it showed itself at the summit of the mainmast with such brightness that it seemed like a burning torch, remaining there for the space of more than two hours . . . ."

For nearly sixty days they sailed through torrential rains along the Equator, " . . . a thing very strange . . . to be seen," wrote Pigafetta, "large fishes with terrible teeth and a bird that makes no nests because it has no feet, and the hen lays her eggs on the back

of the cock and there hatches them [possibly a man-of-war]." About this time they began to run short of provisions, and water had to be rationed. But more serious were the growing dissensions between Magellan and his captains. At one meeting on the flagship the discord flared to a climax when De Cartagena, who had several times before ignored orders of the day, sneered openly at the Captain General's choice of course. Magellan was not the man to permit such insubordination. He promptly arrested De Cartagena, deprived him of his command, and put him under custody.

The fleet now steered a more westerly course; and sighted the coast on November 29, at Cape St. Augustin near Pernambuco. Fourteen days later it anchored in the Bay of Santa Lucia (now Rio de Janeiro) and a fortnight of rest and fresh food revived the battered company. The natives – "a good people and numerous" – bartered pineapples, sweet potatoes, fowls, and tapir for combs, knives, and other small gifts. They were even ready to barter their children for an axe or a large knife. The five ships next pushed on down the coast through constant storms and increasingly cold weather.

At the beginning of February 1520 they arrived at the estuary of the Río de la Plata, which they followed for two days on the chance that it might be the hoped-for passageway from the Atlantic to the Pacific. After they had put out to sea again, Magellan kept prudently examining every stretch of coastline, "to see if there was not an outlet for the Moluccas." About this time Magellan was also searching for suitable winter quarters. After a month of endless

Two pages from Pigafetta's 1525 manuscript describing Magellan's voyage. This section relates how the Spanish met with natives of the "Thieves'" Islands and bartered combs, mirrors, and bells for food.

European visitors to Patagonia were amazed at the size of the Indians, as Pigafetta pointed out in his journal of Magellan's voyage. Here, an officer accompanying Cook on a voyage to the Pacific gives a string of beads to a Patagonian woman.

storms – during some of which the ships were temporarily scattered – he found on March 31 a sheltered anchorage at Port St. Julian. Once again he put his men on reduced rations, in anticipation of the long period that they must wait before resupplying themselves with fresh food – though there were, says Pigafetta, "a great plenty of fish" in the sea around them.

This time the reduction in rations broke the spirit of the men. They were cold, tired, frightened, and discouraged. The future seemed too hideous to face, and there was a general demand for the restoration of full rations and return home. Although Magellan managed to shame the rank and file into some degree of acquiescence, his captains were bent on mutiny. On Easter Day, only the new captain of the *Santo Antonio* obeyed a summons to dine on the flagship, and that night the *Santo Antonio* was captured by the disloyal captains. Realizing that the situation was critical, Magellan took swift and desperate action in order to crush the mutiny.

One captain was killed during the affair, a second died of wounds, a third was later beheaded, and Juan de Cartagena and a priest were condemned to be marooned on that bleak coast when the armada moved on. Soon there was another crisis, this time an accident that resulted in the loss of one of the ships. Toward the beginning of May the *Santiago*, which had gone south on a reconnaissance, was wrecked some seventy miles away from St. Julian. Luckily, only one man was drowned; the thirty-seven survivors managed to struggle back to the anchorage over land. Soon afterward a tall savage appeared on the beach; "so tall was this man," writes Pigafetta, "that we came only to the level of his waistbelt." Friendly relations were soon established with the tribe, whom the Spaniards called Patagão, from the size of their feet.

With the return of warmer weather, on October 18 the four remaining ships resumed the voyage. Three days later they saw "an opening like unto a bay." They were off Cape Virgenes and the long-dreamed-of strait was before them. Whether or not he realized that success was at hand, Magellan must have been a very hopeful man as his eyes followed the inviting water stretching toward the western horizon. The *Santo Antonio* and the *Concepcion* were sent ahead to reconnoiter. Meanwhile the other two ships waited anxiously, riding the storms that swept into the strait. At last the two ships hove in sight, flags flying, guns saluting, bringing the welcome news that they had sailed up the passage for three days without seeing an end to it. All along the way soundings had remained deep, in some places "bottomless," and the flood tide was stronger than the ebb – all surely proof that a through passage had been found.

The accounts of the voyage through the Todos los Santos (All Saints Strait), as Magellan called it, are somewhat confused. To navigate the Strait of Magellan at any time takes considerable skill. The fact that Magellan was able to accomplish it without charts, and in only thirty-eight days, is a measure of his genius. The direct link for the passage is about 320 miles, but the little fleet must have covered a much greater distance. In addition to exploring the maze of sounds and channels bordering the Strait, Magellan had to waste several days searching for the *Santo Antonio*, which had slipped away and deserted when the ships had split into two parties to explore alternate channels.

Earlier, when they were part way through the Strait and

Magellan had asked the opinion of his officers on the future course of the expedition, the pilot of the *Santo Antonio* had advised retreat. Magellan had calmly replied that even if he and his men had to eat the leather on the ships' yards, he would still go on and discover what he had promised the emperor. The men on the *Santo Antonio* clearly had no taste for leather.

After more than a month of slow, cautious, and probing movement through the Strait, Magellan sent a small boat to explore a likely-looking channel. Three days later the boat returned with exciting news. It had come to a very long cape, and beyond the cape there must be open sea! Wrote Pigafetta: "At the joy which the Captain General had at this, he began to cry and he gave the name of Capo Deseado to this cape, as a thing that had been much desired for a long time."

On the evening of November 28 the three remaining ships entered the waters of the Pacific Ocean. Now they turned and sailed northwest along the wild, western coast of southern Chile, staying fairly close to land until December 16. After their past months of

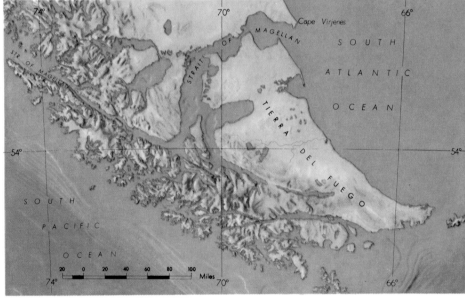

heavy weather, the steady breezes blowing them over calm seas must have been welcome.

As a northwesterly track took the fleet farther and farther away from the mainland, Magellan's men relaxed, feeling that they were on the threshold of the Moluccas, but gradually they began to sense the vastness of the Pacific. Their spirits began to sink as they sailed on and on over calm, empty seas and as day by day their water and food diminished. Pigafetta described them as follows: "Such a dearth of bread and water was there that we ate by ounces and held our noses as we drank the water from the stench of it. . . . We ate biscuit, but in truth it was biscuit no longer but a powder full of worms. . . and in addition it was stinking with the urine of rats. . . . [We were forced to eat] the hides covering the main yards; these, exposed to the sun and rain and wind, had become so hard that we were forced first to soften them by putting them overboard

The Vaz Duardo map (1568) shows the Strait of Magellan as deceptively open and free of the many small islands which we now know to exist (above). Patagonian Indians appear on the right of the old map, and the coat of arms of Spain hangs from the tree.

for four or five days. We were also forced to eat the sawdust of wood and rats which became such a delicacy that we paid half a ducat apiece for them."

During two long months they sighted only two atolls, then came a third terrible month when nothing was sighted. Finally, on March 6, ninety-eight days after losing sight of South America, they came to a wooded island and, hardly able to believe their eyes, saw canoes manned by curious savages racing toward them. For three days they rested there, eating fresh food bartered from the inhabitants and trying to foil the islanders' incessant attempts to steal everything they could lay their hands on. For a long time afterward the islands — which are the modern Marianas — were known as the Ladrones (Thieves') Islands.

A week more on a westward course and they reached Samar and Malkou, in what are now the Philippine Islands. There they anchored for several days and their dreams of wealth seemed on the verge of coming true when they noticed gold ornaments being worn by some of the chiefs. After tending to their sick and taking on fresh supplies, they sailed on to Mazzava (now Limassawa) where the Malay spoken by Magellan's Moluccan slave was understood by the natives. El Dorado seemed just over the horizon, and everything appeared to be working toward the success of Magellan's great adventure.

Piloted by the chief of these amiable people, the fleet went on to the nearby island of Cebu, which was a large trading center for spices; and once more the natives gave them a cordial welcome. In fact, Cebu's rajah, who was accustomed to exacting tribute from visiting ships, decided to waive his dues and offer friendship instead. He visited the Spanish flagship in state and was so overwhelmed by what he heard and saw of the power of Spain, and the consolations of the Spaniards' religion, that he gladly entered into a treaty with them. He even asked to be baptized. It must have seemed to Magellan and his men that the end of their trials was at hand, and that little more remained for them to do but load their ships with rich cargo and sail happily home. But within a few days disaster was to strike.

The rajah of Cebu had been planning an attack on Mactan, a small neighboring island whose chief had refused to pay his customary homage. Magellan, driven by some luckless impulse, offered to make the attack with Spanish arms, and to lead it himself. With only fifty men, he attacked the island at midnight on April 26, 1521, and set fire to the main village. But then things went wrong. The little company was surrounded by hosts of infuriated savages and driven back by sheer weight of numbers. Although armor protected the white men's bodies, their limbs were exposed to the hundreds of arrows and stones that hailed down on them.

Pigafetta has left a vivid account of the tragic end: "Thus we fought for an hour or more, until at length an Indian succeeded in wounding the captain in the face with a bamboo spear. He, being desperate, plunged his lance in the Indian's breast, leaving it there. But, wishing to use his sword, he could only draw it halfway from the sheath because of a spear wound he had received in his right arm. Seeing this, the enemy all rushed at him; and one of them with a long terzado, like a large scimitar, gave him a heavy blow on the left leg, which caused him to fall forward on his face. Then

J. de los Ladrones.

As Magellan's ship neared the Ladrones – or "Thieves' Islands" – (the modern Marianas), he was greeted by dozens of islanders in canoes. The islands were so named because the natives attempted to steal nearly everything within sight. This engraving is from Hulsius' book of 1603.

34

the Indians threw themselves upon him with iron-pointed bamboo spears, scimitars, and every weapon they had, and ran him through – our mirror, our light, our comforter, our true guide – until they killed him."

In confusion the Spaniards returned to Cebu, the legend of their invincibility gone. It was not long before the rajah turned against them and then fled – after massacring twenty-seven of the company that had been his ally. Since there were now too few to man the ships, the *Concepcion*, least seaworthy of the three, was scuttled. During the following months the *Trinidad* and *Victoria* wandered through the archipelago almost as if they had lost their sense of purpose and direction; with Magellan's death the expedition had fallen to pieces. On November 8, 1521, the two ships entered Tidore, center of the Moluccas and Magellan's goal. (As an interesting footnote, on touching land, Magellan's Moluccan slave became the first man to sail around the world.) Six weeks of trading filled the ship's holds and the *Victoria* finally reached Seville in September 1522 with a crew of only forty-seven Europeans and a few natives; strangely, she was commanded by Sebastian del Cano, who had mutinied when the ships were at St. Julian. Because the *Trinidad* had sprung a leak she had to be left behind and return to Spain when she was able, but her ending was a grim one. After attempting to return home by sailing east across the Pacific, she was forced to sail back to the Moluccas and was captured by the Portuguese. Only a handful of her company eventually straggled home, many years later and after many privations.

It is ironic that the first ship to circumnavigate the globe was brought home not by the man who had organized and inspired the expedition, but by a group of mutineers. Charles V heaped Del Cano with honors, while Magellan was at that point all but forgotten. It is also ironic that the Moluccas went to Portugal, not to Spain.

To the end, Magellan had one loyal supporter – Pigafetta. Had it not been for this adventurous man, about whom we know surprisingly little, our knowledge of Magellan would be the poorer. "At sea," wrote Pigafetta, "he endured hunger better than we. Greatly learned in nautical charts, he knew more of the true art of navigation than any other person, in sure proof whereof is the wisdom and intrepidity with which, no example having been offered him, he attempted and almost completed the circumnavigation of the globe."

By the time of Magellan, the early sixteenth century, Portuguese ships were trading around the shores of the Indian Ocean. Here, traders offer some oriental prince bronze cannons in return for spices.

This 1603 engraving shows Magellan being killed by natives on the island of Mactan. The Victoria and Trinidad stand by.

Captain James Cook
In Search of a Continent

A model of Cook's Endeavour bark.
A catbuilt, collier-type ship, she was
capable of a speed of seven to eight knots.

When Magellan sailed through the strait now bearing his name, he saw to the south what he took to be a great land mass. Today we know that land mass – Tierra del Fuego – as simply an island that hugs the tip of South America. But for many years European map makers showed Tierra del Fuego as part of a sprawling southern continent – "Terra Australis Incognita." Pure logic, they felt, required the existence of such a land mass to counterbalance the land lying north of the Equator. They had imagined the Pacific Ocean to be far smaller than the 10,000-mile wide, 9000-mile long body of water it is.

In the years between 1521 and 1769 a number of explorers systematically reduced the size of the mythical Great Southern Continent by sailing across places where it was thought to lie. But it was James Cook, an eighteenth-century English sea captain, who foresaw the real southern continent – Antarctica – and, in so doing, enlarged the boundaries of the Pacific.

Cook was the first man to navigate and chart not only hundreds of islands but thousands of miles of Pacific water and coast line. No other man before or since Cook's time navigated such gigantic expanses of unexplored water. In searching for the fabled Terra Australis, Cook changed the maps of the world and revolutionized the art of seamanship.

In an age when most men could make little progress without money and influence, Cook's remarkable determination enabled him to rise from humble beginnings to a position of world fame. He was born in an obscure Yorkshire village near Whitby on October 28, 1728, and had barely learned his three Rs when he had to leave school to help out on his father's farm. By the time he was seventeen he was serving as an apprentice seaman on board a squat little collier, the *Freelove*, which traded between the north and south of England, and had begun an intensive study of mathematics and navigation. When he finished his apprenticeship, Cook probably knew more navigation than any earlier explorer of the Pacific.

By the age of twenty-four, he had become a mate in the merchant marine and would soon have risen to captain had he been willing to remain in the restricted waters of the North Sea. But in 1755, when war broke out between the English and French colonists in North America, Cook saw his chance to steer a course for wider horizons. Resigning from the merchant marine, he volunteered for the Royal Navy as an ordinary seaman aboard H.M.S. *Eagle*, under Captain Sir Hugh Palliser. Cook's experience at sea and his long evenings over textbooks bore quick fruit. Within a month he was master's mate of the *Eagle* and had won the respect and friendship of Palliser himself.

After two years on the *Eagle*, Cook was promoted and transferred to the *Pembroke*, a ship that was destined to play an important role in capturing Quebec from the French. The success of the British depended on their ability to navigate the St. Lawrence River, and Cook was given the job of charting the river under the very nose of the French. After a week of careful work under cover of darkness he completed a survey that is still the basis for modern charts of the St. Lawrence. And so it was that General Wolfe's famous capture of Quebec was made possible largely by James Cook's skill.

In 1768 the Royal Society was busily planning an expedition to the South Pacific to observe the 1769 transit of Venus. It was hoped that close observation of the event would shed new light on the Earth's distance from the Sun, and the Admiralty had offered to send a ship for this purpose to Tahiti, the South Sea island that England's Captain Samuel Wallis had only recently discovered.

As with most government-sponsored expeditions, scientific knowledge was not the only goal. The British also hoped to find new land to claim, and the possibilities of the Great Southern Continent still loomed large. Despite the fact that Sir Francis Drake and others by this time had found that Tierra del Fuego was only an island, most geographers still believed that the South Pacific *must* contain a continent as big as Europe and Asia combined. It was thought to extend nearly into the tropics in places; and it would almost certainly be a source of great wealth to the first nation to plant its flag there. In 1768 there was still room for such a belief. No vessel had yet approached the Antarctic Circle (lat. 66° 30′ S.), and few had reached even as far as lat. 30° S. So the Society turned to James Cook, who happened to be in England, and whose paper on longitude had proved him a competent scientific observer. In May of that year Cook was transferred from the navigation to the executive branch of the navy and was made a first lieutenant. He then took command of H.M.S. *Endeavour*. At the age of forty — an advanced age for those days — he was finally to begin his great work.

On August 25 the *Endeavour* set sail with ninety-four persons on board, including several scientists. The ship was entirely Cook's choice; like his first ship, the *Freelove*, she was a three-masted vessel of 368 tons, built for the coal trade. Cook felt that she was exactly right for his purpose of charting coast lines. Her large capacity, small draft, and the ease with which she could be hauled ashore for repairs were an ideal combination.

Before following Cook on his first voyage around the world we should clearly establish his mission. His initial objective was Tahiti, where the scientists were to observe the transit of Venus. Next

Maori families like the one shown here were seen by Cook during his explorations of the many inlets along the New Zealand coast. This family is pictured on the shore of Dusky Bay, South Island, which Cook visited.

came the question of the Great Southern Continent; in secret sealed instructions the Admiralty had ordered Cook to proceed from Tahiti "... to the southward in order to make discovery of the continent abovementioned until you arrive in latitude of 40°." Should Cook fail to discover the hoped-for land mass, he was to sail westward "... until you discover it or fall in with the eastern side of the land discovered by Tasman and now called New Zealand." He was to "... carefully observe the latitude and longitude in which that land is situated, and explore as much of the coast as the condition of the bark, the health of her crew and state of your provisions will admit of." He might then return to England either by Cape Horn or the Cape of Good Hope.

This was a formidable program in an age when the fixing of a ship's position at sea was constantly subject to error. Furthermore, Cook had to face the strong probability of an outbreak of scurvy. It was a rare crew that escaped scurvy in those days, but one of the marks of Cook's greatness was his consideration for the health of his men. After making his way down the coast of South America, Cook reached the bleak coasts of Tierra del Fuego. Its inhabitants, he noted in his journal, were "... perhaps as miserable a set of people as are this day upon earth." Rounding Cape Horn, the *Endeavour* set a northwesterly course for Tahiti and sailed right over what the map makers still designated as part of the fabulous Great Southern Continent. In April 1769 the ship dropped anchor off Tahiti.

The expedition spent three months on the island, where, for the first time, Cook displayed his genius for dealing with native peoples. The Tahitians were a high-spirited, friendly race, but their code of ethics differed fundamentally from that of the Europeans. Theft was their chief accomplishment; they are on record as being "prodigious expert" at the art of making off with anything not nailed down. Cook's stockings were stolen from under his pillow one night as he lay on his bunk fully awake. To the Tahitians such imaginative pilfering was a mischievous game, and – unlike captains of an earlier age – Cook understood their attitude. Where other men would have hanged, shot, or flogged a captured culprit, Cook applied psychology. He decreed that any Tahitian convicted of theft would have his head shaved – thus becoming an object of ridicule. Not that James Cook was a soft man. He could be a severe disciplinarian. When two marines tried to desert before the ship sailed, Cook had them flogged, realizing that if he turned a blind eye to such behavior he might risk losing the entire crew.

The long-awaited passage of Venus came at last and all the necessary observations were made. On July 31, 1769, the *Endeavour* set sail from Tahiti, carrying a local chief named Tupia to act as pilot and interpreter. West of Tahiti Cook found and charted a new group of islands, which he named the Society Islands in honor of the Royal Society. Then he headed southward into unknown seas in search of the Great Southern Continent. After reaching lat. 40°S., 1500 miles from Tahiti, without "the least visible signs of land," he altered course to the west, sighting land October 7.

Had he at last reached the great unknown continent? Cook could not be sure; the fact was that he had reached New Zealand, which had first been touched by the Dutch navigator Abel Tasman in 1642. *Could* this land be part of a larger land mass? Tasman had failed to annex the territory for his home country and no other Europeans had set foot on it since his time. It was generally assumed that Tasman's discovery must form part of the Great Southern Continent, so when the *Endeavour* reached the east coast, which Tasman had never seen, Cook decided to explore northward along the coast line and settle the problem for good.

Northward sailed the *Endeavour*, slowly so that Cook could chart the coast line. The ship sailed completely around North Island until it came to the great opening between the two islands that comprise New Zealand. Tasman had charted this opening as a bay, but Cook proved it to be a strait – a strait that bears his name to this day. By March 1770, the *Endeavour* had also circumnavigated South Island. Cook now knew that New Zealand was not the land he had been searching for.

He had circumnavigated a coast line of some 7400 miles in a little over six months, and the charts he made still remain a monument to his accuracy and powers of observation. A French explorer who made his own chart of part of the coast line a year later said: "I carefully compared [my] chart . . . with Captain Cook's. I found it of an exactitude and thoroughness of detail that astonished me beyond all power of expression. I doubt whether our own coasts of France have been delineated with more precision."

By now Cook had carried out the Admiralty's instructions to the letter and could justifiably have made straight for England. Not the man to overlook a chance for further discoveries, Cook next set a course for Australia – New Holland, as it was then known – on the chance that he could find a fair-weather route through to the Indian Ocean. Dutch explorers had already made rough charts of three sides of this vast island, and Tasman had also discovered Van Diemen's Land (now Tasmania). But it was not yet clear whether Tasman's discovery formed part of Australia or was a separate island. The east coast of Australia was quite unknown, and it was thought that New Guinea and Australia were joined.

While collecting botanical specimens for Joseph Banks in Australia, Cook and his men had their first view of a kangaroo. They shot one that weighed eighty-four pounds, prepared it for dinner, but were disappointed with the flavor of the meat.

The Endeavour *bark being refitted after she was damaged on the Great Barrier Reef.*

This aerial view shows Green Island, typical of the many coral formations of the Great Barrier Reef off Australia's east coast.

Cook hoped to resolve all such questions on his homeward voyage, but he failed to answer one when a gale forced him too far to the north of Tasmania to determine whether it was an island; the question was to remain unanswered until 1798.

The *Endeavour* sailed up Australia's unknown east coast to a harbor that Cook named Botany Bay because of the abundance of plants gathered there by one of the scientists on board – Sir Joseph Banks. Continuing up the coast, the expedition escaped utter disaster by a hairbreadth. To the northwest, converging steadily upon the Australian coast, lies the Great Barrier Reef, a wonderful but dangerous mass of coral formations 1200 miles long. On June 10 the *Endeavour* sailed into this trap without warning and impaled herself on a coral ledge.

Water poured in through the torn planks and for a time the pumps labored in vain. But there was no panic and eventually the ship was refloated on the rising tide. Saved as if by a miracle, the the crew made temporary repairs to the gaping holes below decks. Cook's choice of a shallow-draft collier was vindicated; a man-of-war or a merchantman would have been battered to pieces. Even the *Endeavour* would have foundered had not one of its gaping holes been plugged by a great piece of coral that broke off and remained fast in the planking.

After turning the continent's northeast corner, the ship sailed through Torres Strait, the first European vessel to do so since 1606. Finally, they arrived at Batavia, where they put in for provisions and repairs before returning to England. So far, the crew's health had been generally good, but death now stalked the decks of the *Endeavour*. During ten weeks in Batavia more than thirty men (among them the Tahitian chief, Tupia) died of malaria and dysentery, a tragic finale to one of the greatest voyages in history.

On July 12, 1771, James Cook was back in London again, ready to make his report to the Royal Society and the nation. It was a somewhat disappointing report for the Society because the observation of the transit of Venus had not improved existing knowledge of the Earth's distance from the Sun; however, New Zealand and Australia had been added to the British Empire, and the possible location of the Great Southern Continent had been pushed farther south in the Pacific. Since Australia and New Zealand were now clearly delineated as islands, the fabulous unknown land must exist – if it did exist – in as yet unexplored southern latitudes.

Knowing that Britain's colonial rivals, the French and Spanish, were increasing their activity in the Pacific, the Admiralty acted swiftly by sending Cook on a second voyage. This time he was to circumnavigate the globe as far to the south as he could. He was commissioned as a Captain and given two ships, the *Resolution* and *Adventure*, the latter commanded by a Captain Tobias Furneaux. Both were of recent construction and were similar in design to the *Endeavour*.

On July 13, 1772, the ships, far more lavishly equipped than the *Endeavour* had been, sailed from Plymouth bound for the Cape of Good Hope and thence southward and eastward into unknown seas. Early in December, soon after leaving the Cape, the expedition saw its first icebergs – massive flat-topped islands moving silently through the water. Mariners refer to the latitudes through which the ships were sailing as the filthy fifties – and not without reason.

Cook and his men sailed on through appalling weather – rain, sleet, hail, and snow – until on January 17, 1773, they became the first men on record to cross the Antarctic Circle. "We could proceed no further," Cook wrote, "the ice being entirely closed to the south in the whole extent from east to west-southwest, without the least appearance of any opening."

There was still no sign of the longed-for Terra Incognita, so the expedition passed the winter in New Zealand. But Cook was not a man to tolerate idleness. He revisited Tahiti and charted a neighboring group of islands, which he named the Friendly Islands, after which the *Resolution* and *Adventure* headed back toward New Zealand from where they were to renew the southward search. As it turned out, the *Resolution* had to continue the search alone when a violent storm separated the two ships and made it necessary for the *Adventure* to return to England. For the second time now, Cook was to cross the Antarctic Circle. True to her name, the *Resolution* pushed on to lat. 67° 31′ S., but there was still no sign of land. So she pushed farther on until she reached lat. 71° 10′ S. – a farthest-south record that was to stand for nearly half a century.

At this point a solid barrier of ice, apparently extending for hundreds of miles on either side, blocked progress. "I will not say," Cook wrote, "that it was impossible anywhere to get in among this ice, but I will assert that the bare attempting of it would be a very dangerous enterprise and what I believe no man in my situation would have thought of." His ship was defenseless against ice and would have splintered like matchwood if she had been "nipped." And so at last Cook declared himself ". . . well satisfied no continent was to be found in this ocean but must be so far south as to be wholly inaccessible on account of ice."

A few days later, the strain of the voyage on his iron constitution proved too harsh: he fell ill of a "bilious colic." All he needed, according to the ship's doctor, was fresh meat. As it happened, there was a pet dog on board, so the great captain was soon well.

During the next year, Cook filled in a few more of the gaps in the geography of the Pacific Ocean. On the world's charts he now fixed Easter Island, with its enigmatic, brooding statues, New Caledonia, the New Hebrides, and the enchanting Marquesas. On the homeward run he circumnavigated the first typical Antarctic land – the lofty, snow-capped island of South Georgia, a savage and desolate island of glaciers and barren rocks in the South Atlantic.

On July 30, 1775, the *Resolution* reached England after a voyage of some 60,000 miles—more than twice around the world. This second Pacific expedition is the most famous of Cook's voyages and one of the most famous of *all* voyages. While it had struck a death blow to the age-old myth of Terra Australis Incognita, it had shown that there probably was a land of ice centered on the Pole.

Beyond these accomplishments, the second expedition also benefited mankind in two other ways. First, Cook proved that disease and death were not the inevitable fellow-travelers of a ship's crew. During the three years at sea only one of the *Resolution*'s company of 112 men died of disease, although three were killed by accidents. This remarkable record was not the result of sheer good luck: Cook had made a special effort to master the scourge of scurvy, which usually killed up to a third of the men on any long voyage. Aware from his own early experience of the filthy condi-

The world map on the following pages shows the routes that Cook followed on his three major voyages to the Pacific. His early visits to Canada, when he charted the St. Lawrence River and Newfoundland, are also plotted. ▶

ARCTIC OCEAN

ARCTIC CIRCLE

BERING SEA

ALEUTIAN ISLANDS

TROPIC OF CANCER

Macao

PACIFIC

EQUATOR 0°

NEW GUINEA

Batavia

TORRES STR

OCEAN

NEW HEBRIDES

NEW CALEDONIA

FRIENDLY IS. TONGA

INDIAN

TROPIC OF CAPRICORN

NORTH ISLAND

of Hope

OCEAN

NEW ZEALAND

Botany Bay

VAN DIEMEN'S LAND (TASMANIA)

SOUTH ISLAND

KERGUELEN IS.

60°

ANTARCTIC CIRCLE

tions under which the average sailor slept and ate, he saw to it that his men kept their quarters clean and their clothing dry. And he compelled them – often against their will – to vary their diet with fresh meat and vegetables. His ships' stores were always well stocked with preserved soup and vegetables to eke out the salt beef, weevily biscuits, and stinking water that were the sailor's usual lot. Thus, not one of the *Resolution's* crew died of scurvy.

Secondly, Cook made intensive use of recently developed navigation instruments. Longitude had long been difficult to fix, and as a result new discoveries were sometimes lost, but Cook took advantage of two newly perfected methods of establishing longitude: special nautical tables and a highly accurate chronometer. By such means he proved that accurate fixes were possible.

For a year after his return Cook lived ashore. His reputation was now assured. He was presented to King George III, was given a commission as post-captain, and was made a Fellow of the Royal Society, one of the highest scientific honors of the eighteenth century, as it is today. But a last adventure lay ahead for Cook.

For centuries men had dreamed of finding a Northwest Passage, a short cut from the Atlantic to the Pacific that would provide a quick trade route to the East. Although all attempts to find such a passage had failed, the British Admiralty was determined to try again. Rumor had it that there was a through channel leading from what is now British Columbia on the west coast of North America to Hudson Bay, and that the channel might be easier to find from a westward approach than from the east, although Drake had tried and failed. So the Admiralty invited Cook to conduct a new search.

Once again Cook flew his flag in the *Resolution*, accompanied this time by the *Discovery* under the command of Captain Charles Clerke. (The *Resolution's* master, incidentally, was the notorious William Bligh, who was later to command the famous *Bounty*.) Cook's instructions were twofold: he was to seek an entrance to the Northwest Passage, and he was to stock some of Britain's new dominions in the Pacific with livestock for the benefit of the natives – an appropriate gift from George III, the Farmer King.

On July 12, 1776, Cook sailed from Plymouth on his last voyage. For eighteen months he cruised in southern waters, revisiting old haunts in Tonga (the Friendly Islands) and Tahiti. On his northward course he discovered the Hawaiian Islands – or, perhaps, rediscovered them, since there is some reason for believing that white men had visited them nearly two hundred years earlier. Cook named them the Sandwich Islands after Lord Sandwich, the First Lord of the Admiralty, and they were known by that name for a long time.

To the north of Hawaii, across more than a thousand miles of desolate ocean, lies a narrow passage, only fifty-six miles across, that separates Asia from North America. Gateway to the Arctic Ocean, this strait had been discovered in 1728 by a Danish captain, Vitus Bering, sailing under orders from Peter the Great of Russia. Some years later Bering had explored part of the coast line of Alaska. Cook now set out to fill in gaps in Bering's charts.

After stopping to refit at Nootka Sound (on what was later named Vancouver Island), the two ships sailed up the northwest coast of America looking for the long-sought doorway to the Atlantic. They failed to find it, of course. Instead, they rounded the

This chronometer, used by Cook at sea, was made by Kendall in 1769. It is a copy of Harrison's chronometer of an earlier date.

Alaskan peninsula, entered Bering Strait, proceeded into the Arctic Ocean, and sailed northward until stopped by a boundless belt of pack ice. There, at lat. 70°44′N., Cook made up his mind that, with winter approaching, it would be best to return south before attempting a further assault.

But there would be no further encounter with the polar ice for James Cook. The end was at hand. Back in Hawaii the crews of the *Resolution* and *Discovery* met with a magnificent reception at first; the natives evidently believed Cook to be the reincarnation of one of their gods. Then, unaccountably, their friendliness gave way to hostility. When a ship's boat was stolen and Cook tried to retrieve it by the traditional method of taking a tribal chief as hostage, the plan failed to work.

Accompanied by a party of marines, Cook had gone ashore expecting no trouble. But as he and his party were trying to persuade one of the native chiefs to join them aboard ship, an angry crowd gathered and a fight broke out. In the confusion, Cook seemed to have become separated from the others. Accounts of what happened next disagree, but there is no doubt that Cook was clubbed by one native and stabbed by another. When he fell face downward in the water, a shrieking mob of natives then dragged him ashore and hacked him to pieces. When the *Resolution*'s guns finally cleared the beach, not a trace of the captain remained. A few days later the Hawaiians themselves turned over to the sorrowing British the remaining fragments of their captain's body.

Though he was only fifty at the time of his death, Cook's achievements might well have occupied the lifetimes of a dozen lesser men. He had charted the coasts of New Zealand and eastern Australia; he had fixed numerous Pacific islands on the map; he had outlined much of North America's northwestern coast. And he had destroyed two age-old myths: there was no Southern Continent in the South Pacific and there was no easy Northwest Passage linking the Pacific with the Atlantic. Cook left the Pacific looking much as we know it today. Its map is his epitaph.

Friendly Cove, Vancouver, where Cook refitted during his last voyage. Some of the canoes of the Nootka Indians were forty feet long and seaworthy enough to venture out into the Pacific for whales.

James Clark Ross
South to the Antarctic

Sir James Clark Ross.

H.M.S. Fury and Hecla, *painted in 1823, the year Parry and James C. Ross discovered the Fury and Hecla Strait.*

When Captain James Cook was murdered by Hawaiian islanders in 1779, he left two major geographical problems unsolved; both were problems associated with the oceans: Was there an Antarctic continent? And was there a Northwest Passage? Although Cook had crossed the Antarctic Circle, he had not in fact touched any part of the continent or the main islands. At the other end of the world, in the north, he had rediscovered Bering's passage from the Pacific into the Arctic Ocean, but he died before he could prove whether there was a navigable route through to the Atlantic.

During the years that followed, the more urgent problems of war demanded the attention and energy of the nations of Europe. Then in 1805 came Trafalgar, and in 1815 Waterloo and an end to hostilities. The oceans were free again. The British Navy was then at the height of its power and had a cadre of experienced young officers eager for further adventure.

One of these veterans, anxious to try his luck in the Arctic was Lieutenant (later Sir) John Ross. For six years he had had serving under him a young midshipman, his nephew James Clark Ross, who was to add as much, and perhaps more, to our knowledge of the polar regions than any other man.

We know very little of James Ross' early years. His father, George Ross, was a London merchant and it was in London that James was born on April 15, 1800. At the time he volunteered for the navy under his uncle, he was only twelve.

When Sir John Barrow, Secretary of the Admiralty, revived interest in an expedition to find a Northwest Passage and discover the North Pole, Commander John Ross was among the first to volunteer. In 1818, four small whaling vessels sailed down the Thames. Two of them, the *Dorothea* and the *Trent*, were bound for

Spitsbergen and the Pole under the command of Lieutenant (later Sir) John Franklin, whose name, like that of James Clark Ross, was to be famous in polar exploration. His fate and that of Ross were to be curiously interwoven.

Of the other two ships bound for the Northwest Passage the *Isabella* was commanded by John Ross and carried James Ross as a midshipman. Commander of the second ship, the *Alexander*, was a young lieutenant (later Sir) William Edward Parry. Thus did four famous polar explorers make their debut on the stage of history.

Commander Ross' immediate objective was Baffin Bay, which lies to the north of Canada and separates Greenland from the many islands of the Canadian Arctic archipelago. It was off Greenland's west coast that young Ross got his first taste of the grinding, crushing pack ice of the Arctic when both ships were beset and narrowly missed total disaster. Although the voyage proved Baffin's original chart to be right, the expedition failed to find a way through to the Pacific; and for Commander Ross it was an embarrassing failure. As the ships entered Lancaster Sound (a possible gateway to the Pacific), Ross thought a mountain range barred his way. He was not the first to be deceived by clouds. His second in command, Parry, disagreed and wanted to push on, but Ross gave the order to turn back. On his return to England there was an outcry over his failure to press on through Lancaster Sound. Like Parry, the Admiralty was convinced that Ross' "mountains" were nothing more than a mass of clouds.

Within two months two new ships, the *Hecla* and *Griper* had been fitted out for a return voyage – this time with Parry in command and James Clark Ross serving under him. It was his apprenticeship during three expeditions that molded young Ross' character and taught him all the subtle realities of ice. In May 1819 the ships sailed to the Canadian Arctic "to advance the knowledge of geography and navigation and in particular to find the Northwest Passage." Though they failed to find the Passage, they managed to work their way farther west than any ship before them. Two more attempts to find a passage, in 1821 and 1824, also failed.

James Clark Ross' next taste of the Arctic came in 1827 when he again sailed with Parry in the *Hecla*, this time in an attempt to reach the North Pole. Ross was now a full lieutenant. Parry's idea was to sail to Spitsbergen, 600 miles from the Pole, then work his way to the Pole by hauling boats over the intervening ice. When they reached Spitsbergen they anchored the *Hecla* and left her in command of Francis Crozier, who later served with Ross in the South. Parry, Ross, and their party set off in two of the ship's boats, *Enterprise* and *Endeavour*. Their flat-bottom design was intended to make them withstand pressure from ice; in addition each boat had strong metal runners for gliding over long stretches of smooth ice. At first they made good progress through the loose brash ice, but soon they found themselves hauling the two-ton boats over difficult ice floes. We now know how impossible was the task they had set themselves. Even when they reached smooth floes, they found a strong southerly current carrying them back, so they abandoned the attempt after they had reached a latitude of 82°45'N. Not until eighty-two years later, in 1909, did the American admiral Robert E. Peary become the first man to reach the North Pole. This was the last of Edward Parry's Arctic voyages, but for James Clark

Parry and Ross, in the two boats Enterprise *and* Endeavour, *during their attempt to reach the Pole. Here, on August 12, they are caught in a storm off Spitsbergen.*

CAPTAIN ROSS'S ARCTIC EXPEDITION.

ARRIVAL OF CAPTAIN ROSS.

HULL, Quarter before 10, Friday morning.

Captain Ross is this moment landing, having come by the Gazelle steamer from Rotterdam to Hull.

A second edition of the *Hull Advertiser*, dated Friday, half-past 9, has the following:—" We stop the press to announce the arrival at Hull of Captain Ross, who is on board the Gazelle steamer, from Rotterdam. He and Captain Humphreys left the Isabella off the Humber. We had the pleasure of bidding Captain Ross welcome to his native land, and were happy to see that he appeared in excellent health."

(From the *Caledonian Mercury*.)

The following particulars of Captain Ross's arctic expedition have been collected from the verbal statement of one of his crew, and we give them as we received them, without vouching for their entire accuracy, although we have reason to believe that, in the main, they will be found to be correct. In the month of May, 1829, this enterprising officer sailed from this country for the Arctic regions in a steamer prepared and fitted out at his own expense. His crew, we believe, consisted of 19 persons, exclusive of himself and his son, all volunteers. In the first season he only reached Wylie Fiord, on the eastern side of Davis's Straits, where, finding his machinery nearly useless, he resolved on converting his steamer into a sailing vessel, and equipped it as such from the materials of a London whaler which he found abandoned on that part of the coast. Next season he took the earliest opportunity to prosecute his voyage, and having proceeded up Baffin's Bay, entered Sir John Lancaster's Sound, and steered for the spot, in Prince Regent's Inlet, where His Majesty's ship Fury had been abandoned. Here he found only the keel of the Fury, and a few of her timbers, but, what was of more importance to him, he found the greater part of her provisions. Having revictualled his vessel out of the abandoned stores, and left three of his boats at Fury Beach, he made sail for the westward, and succeeded in getting as far as 101 deg. W. L., near the North Georgian Islands, where, unfortunately, his progress was arrested by finding himself embayed and beset with ice. As the season was now far advanced, and he had no hope whatever of extricating his vessel, Captain Ross was compelled to abandon her; and after many difficulties, he and his crew succeeded, by means of sledges and otherwise, in reaching Fury Beach, where the boats had been left, late in the same season. It appears that during the whole of 1831 they were unable to move to any distance from Fury Beach. In 1832, however, they made an attempt to reach the sea in their three boats; but after suffering many privations they failed in accomplishing their object, and were obliged to retrace their steps that winter, being at times thrown upon the beneficence of the few natives whom they chanced to meet with. As early in the present season as they could make any progress they again started for the open sea, and happily fell in with the Isabella, of Hull, at Jacob Teure, just as that ship was about to leave the fishing station. The Clarendon, of Leith, afterwards fell in with the Isabella, and saw both Captain Ross and his crew, who were all well, excepting two or three who were affected with scurvy. Captain Ross lost three men the first year on his voyage out, but no other casualties occurred.

A report from the Times, *October 18, 1833, announces the safe arrival of John Ross after an absence of four years. It was on this expedition that J. C. Ross searched for the North Magnetic Pole.*

Ross it was just a beginning of a long series of ventures.

For the time being the Admiralty lost interest in a Northwest Passage, but John Ross was still anxious to make up for his error about Lancaster Sound. Although the Admiralty refused to back his latest plan, an old friend, Felix Booth, alderman of the City of London, gave him £18,000 toward the cost of a private expedition in search of a Northwest Passage. With part of this money Ross bought the *Victory*, an old steam packet of eighty-five tons, and James Ross, now age twenty-nine, joined the crew. He had a special reason for doing so. He had become interested in the earth's magnetism, then a new field of study. Ross' particular interest was to find the actual positions of the magnetic poles. Until this had been done cartographers could not prepare charts showing variation, which was necessary to get a true compass heading. Encouraging Ross was the acknowledged expert of the time, Edward (later Sir Edward) Sabine, who had been Ross' shipmate on Parry's voyages. It was Sabine who originated the program of magnetic observations which was later to carry Ross into Antarctic waters.

Meanwhile the *Victory* sailed, followed the northward route taken by Parry, and in 1829 entered Prince Regent Inlet, all the time searching for an opening to the west and the Bering Strait. But once again John Ross missed his opportunity. By bad luck he sailed past a "bay" that later proved to be the way through to the Pacific and was named Bellot Strait. Even so, John Ross discovered land to the south, which he called Boothia Felix, and the *Victory* remained there for three summers.

During that time Eskimos visited them and built a village of igloos near the ship. James Ross had already learned some Eskimo, so he was able to talk to them about their country. The Eskimos told him that Boothia Felix was, in fact, linked to the mainland of North America by a narrow isthmus. They lent Ross huskies and guides, and in the course of the many sledge trips he made he was able to plot the position of the North Magnetic Pole. On the last day of May 1831, James Ross attained his objective and stood at what was then considered the Magnetic Pole (but we now know that the position of both magnetic poles varies from year to year). Here at lat. 70° N., long. 96° W. on low-lying land, he raised the Union Jack. "I wish," he later wrote, "that a place so important had possessed more mark or note [such as that envisioned by some people who expect the Magnetic Pole to be] a mountain of iron or of magnets as large as Mont Blanc. But Nature had erected no monument to denote the spot which she had chosen as the centre of one of her great and dark paths."

During the two winters that the *Victory* lay frozen in, James Ross made many other sledge journeys covering extensive unexplored areas. He was the first to sight present-day King William Island and, thinking it part of the mainland, he explored beyond its northern tip, Cape Felix, to Victory Point on the west coast. As the third winter came on, the expedition faced the dreaded threat of scurvy. John Ross' only hope for getting his men alive back to England was to abandon ship and sledge across to the wreck of Parry's old ship, the *Fury*. Here there were boats and supplies. The group spent a fourth winter in the makeshift hut near the *Fury*, then in the spring of 1833 John Ross and his men sailed in their small boats for Lancaster Sound. Then they saw a sail, and after an agony of suspense the ship saw them and hove to. It was the *Isabella*, the ship in which Commander John Ross had sailed to Baffin Bay in 1818.

The explorers received a tremendous welcome on their return home, and John Ross, having made good his reputation, was awarded a knighthood. Never before had an expedition spent four winters in the Arctic. They had charted five hundred miles of new coast line, discovered the northern extremity of the mainland of North America, located the approximate position of the North Magnetic Pole, and brought back a large collection of natural history specimens.

It was now fifteen years since James Clark Ross had first sailed to the Arctic as a midshipman. During that time he had personally helped piece together the jigsaw puzzle of islands and lands that form the northern shores of North America. Another fifteen years were to pass before he would revisit those regions. Meanwhile, plans were afoot which were to give him his first real opportunity for leadership.

Steam navigation was dawning. Marine engineers were speaking of ships of iron that would soon replace ships of wood. Navigation techniques would have to be refined. The Royal Society and the British Association, the two major scientific organizations in England, had been urged by Edward Sabine to fill in the gaps in knowledge of the Earth's magnetism.

While these learned bodies were deliberating, France and the United States sent expeditions to find the South Magnetic Pole. A German mathematician and astronomer, Karl Friedrich Gauss, had calculated that the Pole must be in the region of lat. 66° S., long. 146° E., in that part of the Antarctic continent that faces New Zealand. Eventually, in 1838, the British government authorized a naval expedition to carry out magnetic observations in the southern latitudes. The Admiralty chose as leader Captain James Clark Ross, the man with more Arctic seasons to his credit than any other man alive, and the "discoverer" of the North Magnetic Pole. The choice was a natural one and could scarcely have been bettered. In 1839, when the expedition sailed, Ross was forty years old and in his prime.

The expedition was entirely naval. Two ships, H.M.S. *Erebus*, 370 tons, and H.M.S. *Terror*, 340 tons, were chosen. Both were former mortar-carrying vessels and were strengthened for ice navigation. Francis Crozier, who had been with Ross and Parry on the *Hecla*, commanded the *Terror*, while Ross sailed in the *Erebus*. They took a huge quantity of tinned meats and soups, and mountains of vegetables.

James Clark Ross' instructions were to carry out magnetic observations at various landfalls, and then to sail for Van Diemen's Land (Tasmania), where he was to set up a magnetic observatory at Hobart. From there they were to voyage south, determine the position of the Magnetic Pole, and reach it, if they could. This accomplished, they could then spend a second summer exploring some of the Antarctic coast line.

After months of preparation *Erebus* and *Terror* sailed through the English Channel and south for Van Diemen's Land. Following two months of magnetic observations at the Kerguelen Islands, a dreary sub-Antarctic group in the Indian Ocean, the ships reached Hobart where they were given a warm welcome by the governor,

An engraving of Sir John Ross being greeted by Eskimos of Prince Regent Inlet, 1818. On this voyage Ross mistook clouds for mountains and abandoned his search for a Northwest Passage.

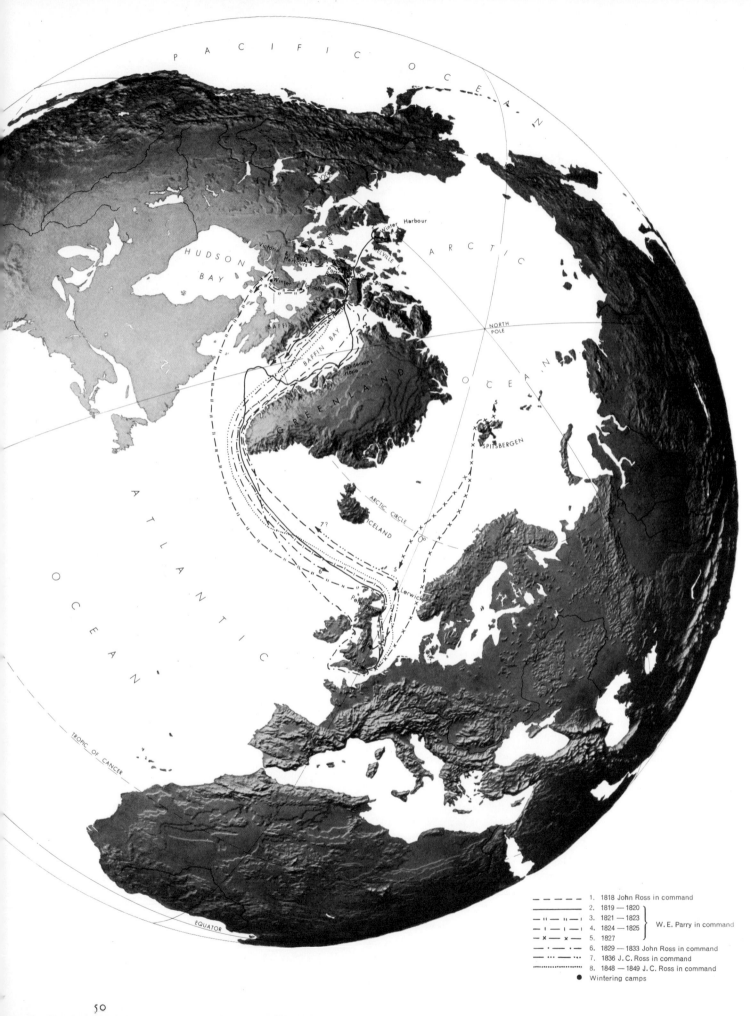

PACIFIC OCEAN

ARCTIC

HUDSON
BAY

Winter Harbour

VICTORIA
Victorial
Harbours
MELVILLE

Winter
Igloolik

BAFFIN ISLAND

Port
BAFFIN BAY

NORTH
POLE

OCEAN

Sanderson's
Hope

GREENLAND

5
Spitsbergen

ARCTIC CIRCLE
0°
ICELAND

7?

5

ATLANTIC

6

Lerwick

OCEAN

Peterhead

TROPIC OF CANCER

EQUATOR

– – – –	1. 1818 John Ross in command
————	2. 1819 — 1820
–‖–‖–‖–	3. 1821 — 1823
–ı–ı–ı–	4. 1824 — 1825
–×–×–×–	5. 1827
–·–·–·–	6. 1829 — 1833 John Ross in command
–··–··–	7. 1836 J. C. Ross in command
············	8. 1848 — 1849 J. C. Ross in command
●	Wintering camps

W. E. Parry in command

polar-explorer Sir John Franklin. Balls at Government House and picnics in the countryside gave the expedition members a last taste of civilization before facing the perils of the Antarctic. During this time they set up their observatory. Then came disturbing news, news that angered Ross.

Dumont d'Urville's expedition and the United States' expedition under Charles Wilkes both claimed to have made important discoveries in the area to be explored by Ross. Wilkes even paid Ross the courtesy of giving him a copy of his own charts. But there, regrettably, Ross the obstinate patriot overshadowed Ross the scientist. He decided to ignore the foreign discoveries and to sail south along a meridian farther east than either Wilkes or d'Urville. He was to be well rewarded.

Shortly after Christmas 1840, *Erebus* and *Terror* met their first icebergs – huge flat-topped islands, so very different from the small pinnacled bergs of the Arctic. Later explorers were to find icebergs many square miles in extent, and it was James Ross who was to discover where they came from. In January they reached the edge of the ice belt which girdles Antarctica, ice which had deterred Captain Cook. But *Erebus* and *Terror* buffeted their way through the pack. On January 5, Ross found himself in the open sea with not a particle of ice to be seen. The way to the South Magnetic Pole lay open, and southward Ross sailed. Eventually a great range of mountains loomed up; the Admiralty Range, Ross called them, and the summits' names still commemorate the board of the Admiralty of that day. Landing on an offshore island, Ross raised the national flag and, in the presence of a large concourse of penguins, claimed the region for the Queen – Victoria Land.

But they were still far from the Magnetic Pole which, according to their best calculations, lay five hundred miles to the southwest. Hugging the ice-fringed coast line, the ships continued through the frigid, uncharted waters. Each day they were rewarded with vistas of even more splendid ranges and summits. Officers and men scarcely slept for fear of missing something new. There was a thirteen-thousand-foot-high volcano which emitted dense smoke and streams of red-hot lava. Ross named it Mt. Erebus, and its smaller neighbor Mt. Terror. These mountains were to be familiar landmarks to later polar explorers.

Farther to the east of the volcanoes another wonder awaited them – a high cliff of ice dazzling white in the sunshine. They were the first men to gaze on this Antarctic ice shelf, which has been a constant source of controversy and mystery. More than 150 feet high, it is the greatest breeding ground of the tabular bergs which the ships had met earlier. It resembled nothing in the Arctic, and Ross called it simply the Barrier, for it was just that to his plans of further progress to the south.

Ross guided his ships along this wall of ice for 250 miles to the east, as far as long. 166° W., yet it continued apparently without end. It was in this area that he decided to look for winter quarters. Turning the ships toward land he began a search for a harbor as close to the Magnetic Pole as possible. At this point he had his first bit of bad luck. Making in the direction of McMurdo Bay, named after the First Lieutenant of the *Terror*, Ross and his officers miscalculated the distance of a mountain range that backed on the bay. They turned in their tracks and missed one of Antarctica's

Ross' observatory at Hobart Town, set up in 1840 when Sir John Franklin was governor of Tasmania. Ross used the observatory to study magnetic variation.

◀ *The globe shows routes followed by Sir James Clark Ross during his exploration of the Arctic regions. (See key for details of each voyage.)*

most wonderful natural harbors. Today, known as McMurdo Sound, it is one of the main centers of operation for Antarctic exploration. By this time the season was too advanced for further work and, having failed to find winter quarters, Ross decided to head back for the comforts of Hobart.

In December 1841, summer for the Southern Hemisphere, *Erebus* and *Terror* once more entered the Antarctic pack ice. Ross was determined to explore his sea further and to trace the seemingly endless ice barrier to its conclusion. Christmas and the New Year were spent with the two ships imprisoned in the ice. Ross then put to practice those lessons in relaxation and morale-raising that he had learned from Parry in the Arctic. An officer of the *Terror*, J. E. Davis, described how they set up a ballroom on the frozen sea between the two ships: "Captain Crozier and Miss Ross opened the ball with a quadrille. After that we had reels and country dances. You would have laughed to see the whole of us with thick overall boots on dancing, waltzing and slipping about and all the fun imaginable going on. Ladies fainting with cigars in their mouths, the cure for which the gentlemen would politely thrust a piece of ice down her back."

But fortune was not to be so kind to Ross this second season. Ice conditions were bad and constant gales battered the ships as they crept painfully against the strong northerly current. When eventually they found open water, they had traveled more than eight hundred miles through the pack. Ross was now able to continue the previous year's survey along the Barrier for a further four hundred miles of continuous ice cliff, too high for the land beyond to be seen. Then the Barrier veered to the northeast, and far beyond loomed the distant mountains of the land which Captain Scott later named Kind Edward VII Land. But Ross had too often been deceived in the past by "mirages." He contented himself with noting on his chart: "appearance of land."

February came and young ice began to form around the ships. On this voyage Ross had reached lat. 78°9′ S.; the time had come to make for the north and warmer latitudes. They made good progress until they were well beyond the Antarctic Circle, but they were still not out of the clutches of the ice. The greatest dangers they were to encounter were bearing down on them. A heavy gale with blinding snow blew up suddenly, reducing visibility to a few yards. Dead ahead of the *Erebus* a huge iceberg reared up. Ross brought the vessel hard over out of the monster's way, but directly across the path of *Terror*. A collision was inevitable. Ross wrote, "We instantly hove all back to diminish the violence of the shock, but the concussion when she struck us was such as to throw almost everyone off his feet. Our bowsprit, topmasts and other smaller spars were carried away, and the ships hanging together and entangled by their rigging, and dashing against each other with fearful violence, were bearing down on the weather face of the lofty berg under our lee." At the very last minute, the *Terror*, seeing a dark space between the closer berg and another closing in, made a dash for it and got through the gap. *Erebus*, helpless with her head-sails gone, drifted till her yardarms scraped the face of the berg. With difficulty Ross brought *Erebus*' head around and aimed it at the now decreasing gap between the two icebergs. The Captain's log continued: "She dashed through the narrow channel between

This water color showing Mount Erebus and Beaufort Island, with the Erebus and Terror *in the foreground, was painted by I. E. Davis during Ross's 1840–43 voyage.*

The telltale flat top of this Antarctic iceberg, tinted by the midnight sun, identifies it as a piece broken off one of the ice shelves. Some of the blocks are a half mile across.

two perpendicular walls of ice, and the foaming breakers which stretched across it, and the next moment we were in smooth water under its lee." When daybreak came they temporarily repaired the wreckage, and the ships continued on without further adventure. On April 6, they reached the Falkland Islands, having been out of sight of land for 136 days.

In December 1842, Ross set sail on his third and last Antarctic cruise, this time hoping to follow in the tracks of a British sealer, Captain James Weddell, who had worked his way to lat. 74° S. in 1823. To the east of the great peninsula that juts out from the Antarctic toward South America, today known as Graham Land or as Palmer Peninsula, Ross discovered several islands. Some of these boasted a microscopic vegetation showing that the Antarctic is not entirely barren. But ice was packing against the coast and it was dangerous to linger there. They were now in the heart of one of the most dangerous of all Antarctic seas, the Weddell Sea. Farther east he succeeded in reaching lat. 71°30′ S., but where Weddell had been lucky enough to report open sea, Ross found solid pack, so he decided to turn back.

The expedition reached England in September 1843 after an absence of two and a half years and with a clean bill of health – not a single case of scurvy or other serious sickness. With nine winters in the Arctic and seventeen seasons of navigating behind him, Ross had been able to get the best results out of a well-equipped expedition. Not only had he found an open sea leading deep into the Antarctic continent, but he had also charted hundreds of miles of the sea along the coast. They were impressive scientific results, for James Clark Ross combined the qualities of a first-class naval officer with those of a first-class scientist. Ross' was the last great voyage of Antarctic discovery to be made in sailing ships, and another fifty years were to pass before anyone attempted to explore the Antarctic continent itself. When the time came, it was in the Ross sector and the McMurdo Sound area that the effort was to be directed. Ross returned home to a knighthood and marriage, and would have been happy to settle down with his family, write his memoirs, and follow his scientific interests but he was to become involved in a final contest with the ice.

The Admiralty had another polar expedition afoot, this time to the Arctic. They were anxious once and for all to settle the problem of the Northwest Passage. At the same time they were eager to test their screw propeller under severe conditions. Sir Edward Parry was at this time Comptroller of steam machinery and an ardent promoter of this enterprise. The two ice veterans, *Erebus* and *Terror*, were fitted with steam engines and equipped for a three-year campaign on a lavish scale. Command was offered to Sir James Clark Ross, but he declined, saying that he was too old (at forty-five). Sir John Franklin, who had only recently given up the governorship of Van Diemen's Land, accepted, although he was fifty-nine, and Crozier took command of the *Terror*.

The story of the Franklin expedition is one of the great dramas of polar exploration; in fact, it became the mystery of the century. Franklin's task was to work his way westward or southward as ice conditions permitted, with the Bering Strait his objective. He reached the west coast of Boothia without incident and found himself in a region charted by Ross. Unfortunately Ross' map showed

This 1821 engraving shows John Franklin and his party on an inland expedition crossing the ice of Point Lake, Canada.

this as King William Land, not King William Island. In all good faith he had shown it linked to the North American mainland by an isthmus. But there was a narrow and navigable channel where the isthmus was supposed to lie. Had Franklin chosen this route he might very well have found his way into the waters of the Pacific, but he chose another one, and with fatal results. Both *Erebus* and *Terror* were caught in the main Arctic pack ice, were beset, and never got free. When the crew came to open their vast stock of tinned foods they had the horror of finding that half of it was putrid. Food poisoning and scurvy claimed their victims. Painfully dragging the ships' boats down the shores of King William Island, 105 men made a bid for escape to the mainland and possible rescue. Their route was marked by abandoned supplies and the skeletons of the dead. A few did live to see the channel that could have saved the ships – the last obstacle in the Northwest Passage – but their's was a hollow victory. Not one man survived to tell the tale.

Franklin had sailed in 1845. Not until nearly three years later, a normal waiting period for such an expedition, did the government take action. During the next ten years no less than forty search parties set out to find the missing men. The first of these was a three-pronged action – an expedition by land to the Arctic coast of North America, one by sea to Bering Strait in hopes of greeting Franklin as he completed the Northwest Passage, and another by sea to follow the route taken by Franklin. Ross left the comfort of retirement to take command of this last party. With him in the *Enterprise* was the young lieutenant (later Sir) Francis Leopold McClintock, who eventually solved the mystery of Franklin's missing ships.

Ross' orders were to search by boat and sledge from bases on North Somerset Island and Melville Island. When he reached Barrow Strait he found it blocked with ice so he concentrated his search on North Somerset Island. Ross and McClintock sledged over 250 miles along the north and west coasts, but found nothing. Before he abandoned the search he hit on an ingenious method of conveying news to the missing men. To several foxes he had caught he clipped copper collars engraved with the position of the rescue ships and food caches. His hope was that the crews of *Erebus* and *Terror* would capture the foxes for food and find the glad tidings. Ross had intended to stay out a second winter, but ice conditions were so bad that he was forced to return in September 1849. The Admiralty then decided to divert the search in different directions. If only they had continued Ross' sledge route along Boothia's west coast the mystery might have been solved earlier. This was Sir James Clark Ross' last voyage. He died at the age of sixty-two, on April 3, 1862.

The story of Ross' Arctic and Antarctic adventures leaves no doubt about his fearlessness, resolution, and ability. As an ice navigator he had a supreme record, and his approach to scientific matters was painstaking and thorough. During his Antarctic expeditions, he would not hesitate to go off course for the sake of making weather observations or deep-sea soundings. He came closest to Cook in his regard for the welfare and health of his officers and men. His geographical discoveries were of tremendous significance, opening the road to the Antarctic and preparing the way for the discoveries seventy years later of Scott, Shackleton, and Amundsen.

The globe shows routes followed by Sir James Clark Ross during his three Antarctic voyages. (See key for details of each voyage.) ▶

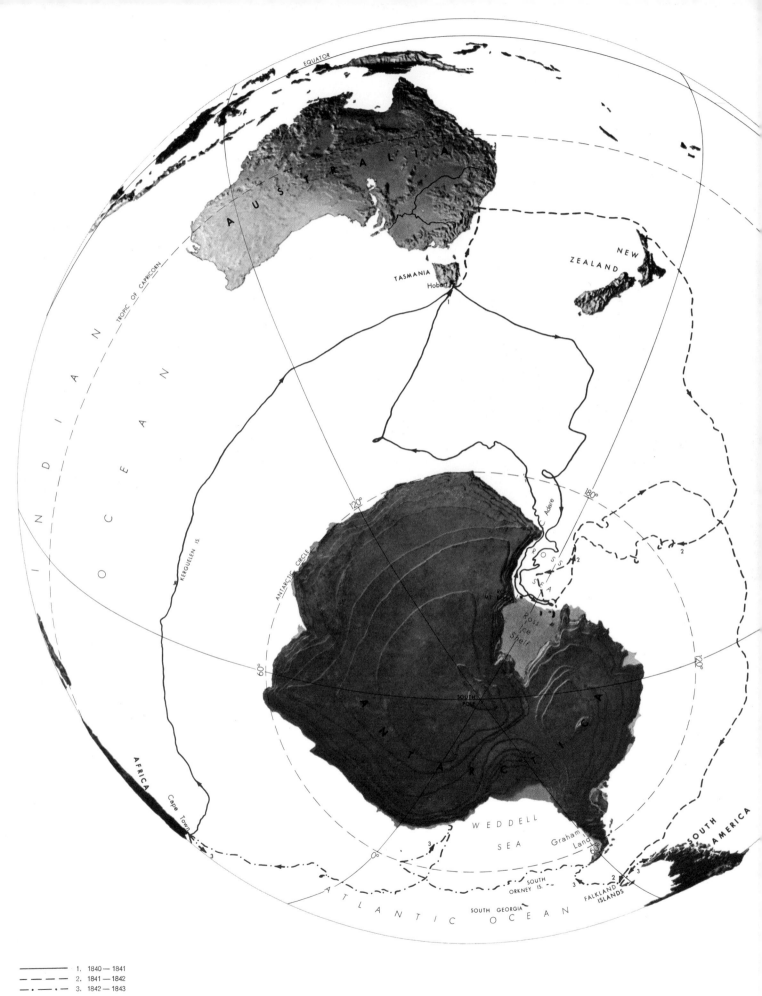

EQUATOR

AUSTRALIA

NEW ZEALAND

TASMANIA
Hobart

I N D I A N   O C E A N

TROPIC OF CAPRICORN

KERGUELEN IS.

AFRICA

Cape Town

120°

ANTARCTIC CIRCLE

60°

C. Adare

R O S S

S E A

Ross
Ice
Shelf

180°

120°

SOUTH
POLE

A N T A R C T I C A

0°

60°

W E D D E L L

S E A

Graham
Land

SOUTH
AMERICA

SOUTH
ORKNEY IS.

SOUTH GEORGIA

FALKLAND
ISLANDS

A T L A N T I C   O C E A N

1. 1840 — 1841
2. 1841 — 1842
3. 1842 — 1843

Fridtjof Nansen
Pioneer of the Arctic

Fridtjof Nansen, perhaps the boldest of explorers of the Arctic, was several times a great man: oceanographer, zoologist, artist, king maker, Nobel Peace Prize winner, humanitarian. He was also a polar revolutionary whose ideas, in the face of extreme skepticism of most experts, led to two of the greatest polar journeys ever undertaken.

In his exploration of the Arctic Ocean, Nansen's special achievement hinged on his bold theory of an ocean current that would drift a ship across the heart of that ice-strewn sea. The vision in Nansen's idea is comparable to Magellan's belief that he would find a way through to the Pacific, at a time when no one knew the limits of South America. To test his theory, Nansen built a special ship, the *Fram*, and deliberately allowed her to be frozen in the Arctic ice off the northeast coast of Siberia, in hope of drifting across the Arctic Basin – in comfort and safety.

Born on October 10, 1861, just outside Oslo, Nansen was a descendant of the seventeenth-century Danish explorer, Hans Nansen. As a boy Nansen loved outdoor life and adventure. He also had a first-rate scientific mind.

Zoology was his first love, and at the age of about twenty-one he seized the opportunity of a voyage in a Norwegian sealer, the *Viking*, to study the anatomy of the seal. For Nansen the most exciting and significant part of the voyage – which was to help shape his future as an explorer – was his sight of Greenland, then, as today, a land gripped in an ice age.

On his return to Norway, Nansen continued his scientific work,

Nansen was to gaze many times out over Arctic twilight scenes such as this one photographed in the late fall. Hoarfrost crystals can be seen forming on the snow surface.

but he was determined to visit Greenland again and become the first man to cross it. With five companions, including two Lapps, he sailed from Iceland on June 4, 1888 in the sealer *Jason*. On July 28, after many days of fatiguing, grim battle with the pack ice off the coast, they reached the mainland, and on August 10 they set out on their main journey across the icecap. As they had worked their way north along the coast to Umivik, from where they were to start their overland journey, they had seen icebergs that were strikingly beautiful. Nansen describes one with ". . . hollowed grottoes so large that a small ship could readily have ridden within their shelter . . . [with] marvelous effects and tints of blue, . . . the whole formed a floating fairy palace, built of sapphires, about the sides of which brooks ran and cascades fell."

After preliminary reconnaissance they fought their way past huge crevasses and onto the main ice sheet, hauling sledges as they went. It was a testing journey. Each night, as the temperature plunged into the minus 40s, frostbite threatened them. Even when the sun shone, frozen mist seemed to form a halo around it. Storms of wind and snow plagued them, and as they penetrated deeper into the heart of Greenland, Nansen began to worry about completing the journey so late in the season. At last, on September 19, they saw land ahead – a towering range of mountains. With the wind behind them they drove rapidly on, literally sailing their sledges over the ice. On reaching Godthaab, Nansen became the first to cross the Greenland icecap. Unfortunately, the expedition was too late to catch the ship back to Europe, so they were forced to spend the winter in western Greenland until the following May when Nansen sailed home and was given a tremendous welcome.

In 1884, Nansen read of the disaster of the American ship *Jeannette*, which sank in 1881 off the coast of Siberia. Her captain was Lieutenant Commander George Washington De Long. Three years after his ship sank and De Long had lost his life, a few pieces of equipment and a pair of oilskin breeches were found frozen in the ice on the southwest coast of Greenland. A Norwegian scholar, Professor Mohn, "conjectured that they must have drifted on a floe right across the Polar Sea." When Nansen heard of this he could see only one explanation – they must have drifted in the pack right across the Arctic, emerging in the ice belt on the east coast of Greenland, having traveled south around Cape Farewell (as the ice in fact moves), and landing up at Julianehaab. Driftwood used by the Greenland Eskimos gave Nansen still more evidence. It could come only from the Siberian rivers that emptied into the Arctic Ocean. All this led him to conclude "that a current flows at some point between the Pole and Franz Josef Land from the Siberian Arctic sea to the east coast of Greenland."

Nansen now hit on the remarkable plan of freezing a ship into the ice and letting it be carried all the way across the sea. Unlike other explorers, he reckoned that, properly designed, such a ship could take him in comfort and safety, and might even carry him to the North Pole itself. But true scientist that he was, his intention was not just to reach the North Pole, but to investigate the whole unknown region.

Many of the experts were against him, especially the pundits of the British Royal Geographical Society, but Nansen managed to get the support he needed from the Norwegian government and

Nansen, in expedition dress, photographed outside Frederick Jackson's hut, June 17, 1896.

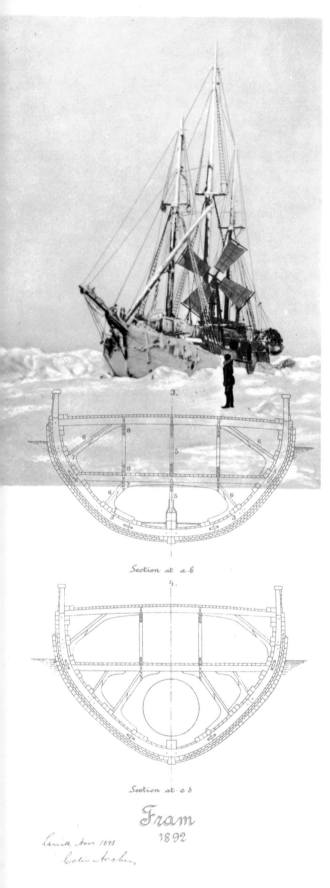

Section at a b

Section at c d

Fram
1892

Larvik Nov 1898
Colin Archer

Firmly but safely locked in the ice, the Fram *awaits the spring thaw of 1895 at lat. 84° N. Below is a section through the* Fram, *showing the construction plan designed to make her withstand ice pressure.*

private contributors, and in the end the Royal Geographical Society granted him three hundred pounds. The success of this expedition would depend almost entirely on the stoutness of the ship, so the *Fram*, later to become world-famous, was specially built to withstand great ice pressure.

Into the *Fram* went all the expert knowledge of Norwegian sealers and whalers. The hull had that special rounded form which provides the best shape for work in ice. Although such a round hull makes cruising uncomfortable in a rough sea, there is nothing for the ice to grip, and the effect of the floes coming together is to push the ship up higher and higher, almost out of the water.

The *Fram* obviously had to be small and very maneuverable, but even so she was a fair size for a polar ship with a gross tonnage of 402. The dimensions of the *Fram* were 128 feet long overall and 113 feet at the water line, while the extreme breadth was thirty-six feet. At full load the draft was fifteen feet. The keel was sunk into the planking so that it projected only a short distance below the bottom, which was flat. The builders took every opportunity to strengthen danger points; the stem piece, for instance, was made of three oak beams with a thickness of four feet altogether. The stern was specially strengthened and the rudder and propeller most carefully set to reduce the danger of ice damage.

The frames were built of two separate layers of oak, and the spaces between were filled with pitch and sawdust to keep the hull watertight, even if the planking were damaged. There was a further internal lining some eight inches thick, while the outer planking was constructed in three layers: first an oak sheathing three inches thick, followed by other layers so that the total thickness of the *Fram's* sides was between twenty-four and twenty-eight inches of watertight wood. In addition there were all sorts of cross stays and supporting beams to give strength against outside pressure.

The same care was given to every other aspect of the design of the ship. The rigging was specially designed, simple and strong, and she was rigged as a three-masted fore-and-aft schooner. The crow's nest was 102 feet above the water line – a matter of extreme importance for navigation where so much would depend on being able to detect leads and gaps in the pack ice. She had a specially designed three-cylinder engine, and the propellers were made of cast iron. In calm weather she could make six or seven knots.

Great care was also given to making the *Fram* livable, for she was to be a moving base, possibly for several years. One of the troubles that many polar explorers have met is the tendency for condensation to form and freeze on the inside of the cabin; if it melts, living in the confined quarters can be quite uncomfortable. Nansen's careful planning took this into account – even when a fire was lighted in the saloon there was no trace of moisture on the walls. The ship was also fitted with an electric generating plant to be powered either by the engine or by a windmill. And as a final touch, the saloon was decorated with pictures of familiar Norwegian scenes and had a library and harmonium. Nansen planned to carry enough scientific equipment and food to last for five years.

On Midsummer Day (June 24) in 1893, Nansen sailed with a crew of twelve Norwegians, each with special qualifications. Most important of these was Otto Sverdrup, who had accompanied Nansen across Greenland. He was a highly experienced sea captain who was later to make his own reputation as a Polar explorer. The *Fram* slipped out of the harbor in Oslo and they set a course across the Barents Sea. Four days later they sighted Novaya Zemlya, north of the Urals, and in two more days they found themselves in the grips of ice. Here was the *Fram*'s first chance to show her mettle. "She twists and turns like a ball on a platter," Nansen wrote, ". . . the ship swings round, and wriggles her way forward among the floes without touching if there is an opening only just wide enough to slip through, and where there is none she drives full tilt at the ice . . . runs sloping bows up on it, treads it under and bursts the floes asunder . . . even when she goes full speed at a floe, not a creak, not a sound, is to be heard in her."

Steadily the *Fram* pushed eastward. From time to time the crew ventured ashore to hunt reindeer or polar bear. Nansen wrote: "There was that strange Arctic hush and misty light over everything, that greenish-white light caused by the reflection from the ice being cast high into the air . . . against masses of vapor the dark land offering a wonderful contrast."

In one place they encountered that extraordinary phenomenon of dead water. This occurs when the ship makes a large undersea wave in the boundary layer between a layer of fresh water resting on a layer of salty water. Because the water on top of the undersea wave moves backward, the progress of a low-powered ship is deadened. Nansen found that while the water on the surface was fresh enough to drink, the water entering the bottom cock of the engine room was too salty to be used for the boiler.

Ice and the hazards of a badly charted route added to their difficulties. They were, in fact, following the famous Northeast Passage, first completed by Baron Nordenskjöld in his famous ship *Vega* fourteen years before. But at last they found their way through the Taimyr Strait, and Cape Chelyuskin lay ahead, jutting far to the north. They rounded the cape and continued into the open water beyond. On September 18 they were in lat. 75°30′ N. and Nansen decided to head for the northern ice. On they sailed, mile after mile through open sea, and on Wednesday the twentieth they faced the main ice pack barrier. Nansen wrote: "I have had a rough awakening from my dreams. As I was sitting at 11 A.M. looking at the map and thinking that my cup would soon be full — we had almost reached 78° — there was a sudden luff and I rushed out Ahead of us lay the edge of the ice, long and compact, shining through the fog." It was at this position that Nansen decided to allow the *Fram* to be frozen in, so they settled down to make preparations for life in winter quarters. His September twenty-fifth diary entry read: "Freezing in faster and faster! Beautiful still weather; 13 degrees of frost last night. Winter is coming . . . ."

Now Nansen's faith was to be tested. The ship was bedded in a good berth and they had to wait for the current to take them on their journey. As the temperature continued to drop they carried on their scientific work — taking soundings and dredging for plankton.

Soon they had their first real encounter with the kind of ice that can crush a ship as if it were a matchbox. "First you hear a sound like the thundering rumble of an earthquake far away on the great waste," Nansen wrote, "then you hear it in several places, always coming nearer and nearer. The silent ice world re-echoes with thunders; nature's giants are awakening to the battle. The ice

Nansen's men took meteorological readings every four hours day and night. Here, Scott-Hansen and Nordahl pose by the observatory, with its thermometer housing protected by a wind screen. Below: A scientist on a recent Arctic expedition prepares to lower a Nansen bottle. Designed by Nansen, the device samples water at chosen depths, records its temperature.

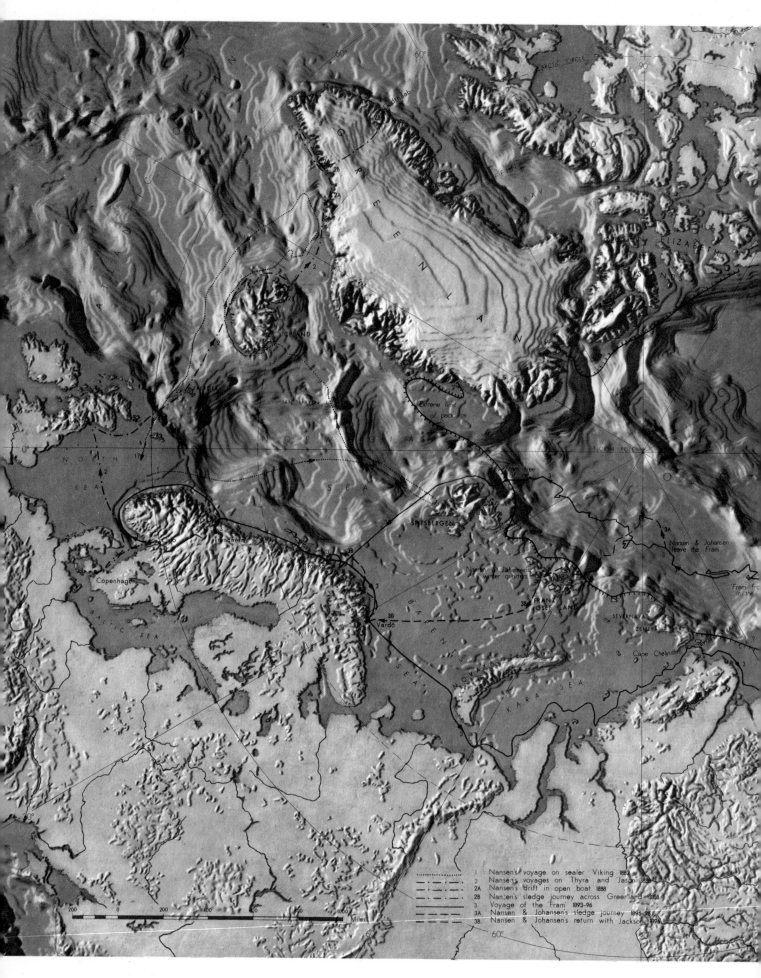

Extreme limit of pack ice

NORTH POLE

Fram free

Nansen & Johansen
leave the Fram

Fram fro
in the

Nansen & Johansen's
winter quarters

FRANZ
JOSEF LAND

SEVERNAYA
ZEMLYA

Cape Chelyuskin

NOVAYA ZEMLYA

KARA SEA

BARENTS SEA

Vardø

Tromsø

Trondheim

Copenhagen

Oslo

BALTIC SEA

NORTH SEA

JAN MAYEN

ICELAND

NORWEGIAN SEA

GREENLAND

SPITSBERGEN

ARCTIC CIRCLE

1   Nansen's voyage on sealer 'Viking' 1882
2   Nansen's voyages on 'Thyra' and 'Jason' 1888
2A   Nansen's drift in open boat 1888
2B   Nansen's sledge journey across Greenland 1888
3   Voyage of the 'Fram' 1893-96
3A   Nansen & Johansen's sledge journey 1895-96
3B   Nansen & Johansen's return with Jackson 1896

200   0   200   400   600   800   1000
                                        Miles

60

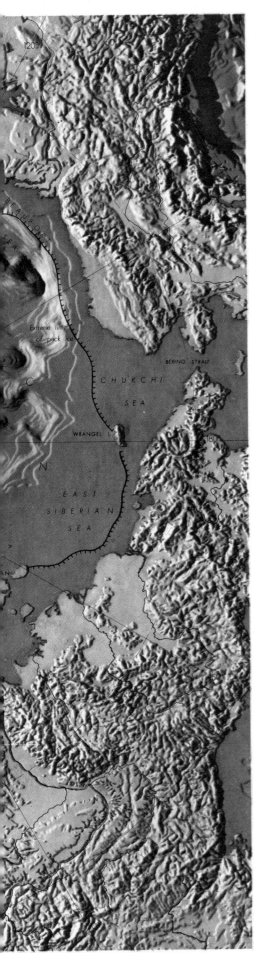

cracks on every side of you, and begins to pile itself up, and all of a sudden you too find yourself in the midst of the struggle. There are howlings and thunderings round you; you feel the ice trembling, and hear it rumbling under your feet; there is no peace anywhere. In the semi-darkness you can see it piling and tossing itself up into high ridges nearer and nearer you – floes 10, 12, 15 feet thick, broken and flung on the top of each other as if they were featherweights. They are quite near you now, and you jump away to save your life. But the ice splits in front of you, a black gulf opens and water streams up. You turn in another direction, but there through the dark you can just see a new ridge of moving ice blocks coming towards you. You try another direction, but there it is the same."

By the end of November they had made little advance, and Nansen began questioning the correctness of his theory about a Polar current that would carry the *Fram* across the Arctic Ocean. "My spirits," he wrote, "are like a pendulum. . . . It is no good trying to take the thing philosophically. . . ."

By the new year of 1894 the ship had drifted beyond the edge of the continental shelf and Nansen had proved that the supposedly shallow Polar sea was, in fact, of tremendous depth; at one point 2850 fathoms. This made Nansen even more doubtful about his current, but he felt that the Siberian driftwood could not lie: ". . . the way it went we must go."

Winter passed. The sun came back and daylight again lit them. The sun circled the heavens and there was no relief from the continuous day. Snow turned to slush, pools of water formed on the floes, and there was even a freshwater lake where members of the expedition practiced sailing. They even wondered if the ice might open enough for them to sail northward. On Norway's national day, May 17, they held a special procession and a mock band marched round the *Fram*. During these days of doubt, Nansen began to develop a plan which he had long had in mind: to leave the ship with one companion and try to sledge to the North Pole. By this time he was pretty well convinced that the ship itself would never drift to the Pole.

As winter came again, storms increased, and the aurora borealis flung its shining curtain of waving, changing light across the ice. Another Christmas and Nansen completed his preparations for his dash to the Pole, but not before the *Fram* was nearly crushed. On January 3 a huge pressure ridge advanced on the ship. Expecting the worst, all hands slept lightly, ready to abandon her. A few days later the ice came crashing on board; then it subsided but again increased its pressure, and snow and ice hurled itself across the deck. The following day the *Fram* was listing nearly seven degrees, but she withstood the attack and remained firm through the danger period.

Nansen now chose Frederick Johansen as his companion to the Pole, leaving the experienced Sverdrup to command the *Fram* and bring her through into open water. But where? he wondered. In the eighteen months since they had been frozen in the pack, they had drifted slowly in a northwest direction over a direct distance of about six hundred miles. The *Fram* was now past lat. 84°N. and was within 360 miles of the Pole.

This map shows the three voyages of Nansen described in this chapter: in the Viking*; voyage to Greenland; voyage in the* Fram.

Nansen and Johansen now set off into the icy wilderness on March 14, 1895, leaving the *Fram* to her fate, and seeking their own. There could be no return, for the moving pack would make it impossible for them to retrace their footsteps to the safety of the *Fram*. Gradually the *Fram* slipped from sight as Nansen and Johansen struggled over the jumble of ice — two men attempting to guide three dog-drawn sledges, an awkward arrangement as they soon discovered. Although occasionally they met smooth ice, much of it was rough and ridged, and there were occasional patches of open water, although it was only March. Soon they had to kill the first of their dogs to feed the others. As they pressed north they fell into a daily routine: hard work during the day, then camp, putting up their tent and crawling into their sleeping bags with their clothes frozen and stiff.

As if their daily hardships were not enough, each time Nansen plotted their position he found that they had not made the progress north he had hoped for. The current must be taking them *away* from the Pole, he thought. A discouraged Nansen soon realized that it would be impossible for them to reach the Pole itself, but they had gone farther north than any man, and on April 8 an observation showed they had reached lat. 86° 13′ 36″ N., only 226 miles from the Pole. After a ceremonial "banquet" to celebrate this, Nansen and Johansen directed their march back — not to the *Fram*, but to Franz Josef Land. Where, Nansen wondered, was the *Fram*?

The weather began to get warmer, and their going was temporarily better. They had the occasional good day, and on one they covered twenty-five miles. But before long, blizzards blocked their path, and lanes of open water with loose brash ice floating in it slowed them down. At one point they found a large piece of Siberian larch stuck in the ice and on it they carved their initials and latitude, 85° 30′ N.

By the end of May they were seriously worried about their provisions. Although they knew their latitude was 82° 30′ N., and they should be near land, their longitude was a source for anxiety because their chronometer watches had run down. Caught amid a maze of open channels, by June they found it almost impossible to move, yet they fought on through slush and melting snow. Soon there were only five dogs left. On June 12 Nansen wrote: "[The situation] is getting worse and worse. Yesterday we did nothing, hardly advanced more than a mile. Wretched snow, uneven ice, lanes and villainous weather." Yet they were cheered by the sight of a water sky in the south. On June 14 they were completely stopped and their supplies were getting short. Finally, as they launched their kayaks Nansen noticed a large bearded seal. Quickly he hurled his ready harpoon into the back of the animal which, moments earlier, Johansen had shot and wounded. Nansen wrote: "Halfpast nine A.M., after a good breakfast of seal's-flesh, seal liver, blubber and soup. Here we lie dreaming dreams of brightness; life is all sunshine again. What a little incident is necessary to change the whole aspect of affairs!"

At least urgency was gone for they had plenty of food and fuel, so much that Nansen decided to camp and await events. His diary at this time is full of the delights of seal and how to cook it, how to make blood cakes with sugar, etc. Slowly they drifted south, but oh how slowly. June passed and they realized that during the

Artist as well as explorer, Nansen did many drawings (like this of the aurora borealis) during his Arctic expedition.

whole month they had scarcely advanced. On July 22 they left "Longing Camp," forcing their way over huge pressure ridges, and at last they had their first glimpse of land — land they had dreamed about. Nansen wrote: "At last the marvel has come to pass — land, land, after we had almost given up our belief in it! After nearly two years, we again see something rising above that never-ending white line on the horizon yonder — a white line which for countless ages has stretched over this lonely sea, and which for millenniums to come shall stretch in the same way. We are leaving it, and leaving no trace behind us; for the track of our little caravan across the endless plains has long ago disappeared."

Nansen made this sketch of himself and Johansen during their winter confinement in a stone hut on Franz Josef Land. They slept on stone benches with a bearskin beneath them and one blanket to cover them.

But they were not yet out of trouble. Rain, mist, grinding ice still blocked their way. On August 6 they reluctantly shot their two surviving dogs and launched their kayaks, enjoying the waves splashing against the sides. For two months they had not seen the surface of the sea. As the wind grew stronger they rigged a sail and glided easily before the wind. They paddled along the coast, pushing their kayaks over the floes until, on August 14, their feet again touched solid land.

Day by day it became more apparent that there was no chance of their getting back to civilization before the winter, so on August 28 they landed again and looked for a winter camp site. They had no materials or supplies, except the rocks around them and what little they had been able to bring in their kayaks, yet they were determined to build a permanent winter hut. For tools they used their cut-off sledge runners and a spade made from a walrus' shoulder blade tied to a broken ski pole.

Their stone hut was anything but satisfactory: it was six feet long and ten feet wide. On separate benches of stone they slept with only a blanket over them and bear skins under them. When the long Arctic night set in they spent their Christmas in their snowy, rocky den, "feasting" on the few precious sledge rations and lighted by a homemade lamp fueled with oil from blubber. They had nothing to read except part of a nautical almanac. And so they spent their winter — grimy and dirty with oil, dreaming of shops and new, clean, woolen clothing. During most of the winter they managed to sleep for many hours (sometimes twenty out of twenty-four), and occasionally on fine nights they went out walking by the light of the moon. For nearly nine months Nansen and Johansen lived in solitude in the frozen winter of Franz Josef Land.

It was not until May 19 that they decided to leave. After setting out and traveling about eighty miles over ice they reached water, at which point they put their kayaks in the sea again and prepared to move. Then disaster threatened. The kayaks were moored insecurely to the ice and drifted away. Nansen quickly tore off his clothes and dived into the icy water after them. As the current continued to carry them offshore it became a race for life itself. At last Nansen reached the kayaks, managed to scramble into one of them and started to paddle back to the floe. Even though he was exhausted and nearly frozen, on seeing two birds bobbing on the water he drew his gun and shot them. Johansen thought that he must have gone mad, until he remembered that their rations were dangerously short. Afterwards Johansen admitted that the race for the kayaks was the worst time he had lived through.

Then came one of the most remarkable encounters in the history

Pressure ridges, mountainlike walls of ice on the move, were an almost constant threat to the Fram. This one was recently photographed in the Canadian Arctic.

This photograph shows the historic meeting between Nansen and the British explorer Frederick Jackson in Franz Josef Land, June 17, 1896. The Jackson-Harmsworth expedition to Franz Josef Land had been in preparation before the Fram set out.

of exploration, comparable to the meeting of Stanley and Livingstone. On June 17 Nansen thought he heard a dog barking. Was it possible, he wondered, that they were in the vicinity of the English expedition to Franz Josef Land, led by Frederick Jackson, which they knew had been in preparation before the *Fram* had set out? Nansen set out to reconnoiter. In front of him he saw tracks – but possibly they were fox or wolf tracks. Again he heard barking and wondered if he were dreaming. Then he heard a shout. He yelled in return and then he saw a figure of a man: "We approached one another and I waved my hat. He did the same. I heard him speak to the dog, and I listened. It was English, and as I drew nearer I thought I recognized Mr. Jackson. . . . I raised my hat; we extended a hand to one another with a hearty 'How do you do?'" . . . On one side the civilized European in an English check suit and high rubber water-boots, well shaved, well groomed, bringing with him a perfume of scented soap, perceptible to the wild man's sharpened senses; on the other side the wild man, clad in dirty rags, black with oil and soot, with long, uncombed hair and shaggy beard.

"Jackson: 'I'm immensely glad to see you.'

"'Thank you; I also.'

"'Have you a ship here?'

"'No; my ship is not here.'

"'How many are there of you?'

"'I have one companion at the ice edge.'

"As we talked, we had begun to go in towards land. I took it for granted that he had recognized me, or at any rate understood who it was that was hidden behind this savage exterior, not thinking that a total stranger would be received so heartily. Suddenly he stopped, looked me full in the face, and said quickly:

"'Aren't you Nansen?'

"'Yes, I am.'

"'By Jove! I *am* glad to see you!'

"'Where have you come from now?' he asked.

"'I left the *Fram* in 84°N. latitude, after having drifted for two years, and I reached the 86° parallel, where we had to turn and make for Franz Josef Land. We were, however, obliged to stop for the winter somewhere north of here, and now are on our route to Spitsbergen.'

"'I congratulate you most heartily. You have made a good trip of it, and I am awfully glad to be the first person to congratulate you on your return.' Once more he seized my hand, and shook it heartily."

Soon after this famous meeting, Nansen and Johansen were on their way home. They put into Vardö, and Nansen reported to the government:

I HAVE THE PLEASURE OF ANNOUNCING TO YOU AND TO THE NORWEGIAN GOVERNMENT THAT THE EXPEDITION HAS CARRIED OUT ITS PLAN, HAS TRAVERSED THE UNKNOWN POLAR SEA FROM NORTH OF THE NEW SIBERIAN ISLANDS, AND HAS EXPLORED THE REGION NORTH OF FRANZ JOSEF LAND AS FAR AS 86° 14′ N. LAT. NO LAND WAS SEEN NORTH OF 82°.

LIEUTENANT JOHANSEN AND I LEFT THE FRAM AND THE OTHER MEMBERS OF THE EXPEDITION ON MARCH 14TH, 1895, IN 84°N. LAT. AND 102° 27′ E. LONG. WE WENT NORTHWARD TO EXPLORE

THE SEA NORTH OF THE FRAM'S COURSE, AND THEN CAME SOUTH
TO FRANZ JOSEF LAND, WHENCE THE WINDWARD HAS NOW
BROUGHT US. I EXPECT THE FRAM TO RETURN THIS YEAR.

FRIDTJOF NANSEN

About a week later the following telegram was delivered to
Nansen:

FRAM ARRIVED IN GOOD CONDITION. ALL WELL ON BOARD.
SHALL START AT ONCE FOR TROMSO. WELCOME HOME.

OTTO SVERDRUP

Nansen was overwhelmed with joy when with everyone cheer-
ing he sailed out to meet the *Fram*. There is little to add. The rest
of the story of the *Fram* was a repetition of the previous years. Her
drift was capricious, but she moved steadily north, and even
reached a latitude of 85° 57′ N., the farthest point that any ship had
been until Anderson and the *Nautilus* dived under the ice. Winter
passed, and then in May they began to prepare to emerge from the
ice. With the aid of ice picks, gunpowder, and lances they helped to
break the *Fram* from her cold matrix. Not until June 27 did the
ice slacken enough so that she was clear. Finally on August 13,
1896, the *Fram* emerged and rocked triumphantly on the ocean.

Nansen did this woodcut showing the Fram
beneath a ribbonlike curtain of the
aurora borealis during the Arctic night.

The *Nautilus*
Under the North Pole

Commander William R. Anderson.

The Nautilus *and her crew are welcomed as they arrive at Portland Bill, England, after completing the historic first voyage beneath the North Pole.*

The last of our sea explorers, Commander William R. Anderson, U.S.N., is very different from those we have already described. Although his responsibilities and the skill with which he carried them out were of the highest order, it was essentially as a leader of a technological team that Anderson's remarkable voyage in the nuclear submarine *Nautilus* under the Pole was achieved. Yet in a way the voyage was still in the great tradition of naval exploration. Like Cook and Ross, Anderson was dispatched by his country, although he was supported a good deal more generously than explorers of the past.

Earlier explorers traveled the seas to open up new lands, chart reefs and islands, and define the coasts of continents, but Anderson in the *Nautilus* explored vast regions under the ice and thus provided a new dimension to sea exploration. The ice that stopped Captain Cook to the north of the Bering Strait was successfully circumnavigated – or more precisely, undernavigated – by the nuclear-powered *Nautilus*.

The idea of using a submarine to explore under the ice of the North Pole was not new. Sir George Hubert Wilkins in 1931 had attempted it, but his bold venture came to nothing. While we now know that the idea was sound, the technical resources at Wilkins' command were not enough. What Jules Verne imagined to be possible in the way of underwater travel in the *Nautilus* of his imagination was to be achieved in reality – but not until the development of controlled nuclear power.

The history of Anderson's voyage began when Rear (now Vice) Admiral Hyman G. Rickover was first fired with the idea of a nuclear submarine. But the problems inherent in such a revolutionary scheme were formidable. One was to make a reactor compact and reliable enough to fit inside a ship. At the time, the reactors at Oak Ridge, Tennessee were about the size of two city blocks. Another problem was the development of a safe heat transfer unit that would drive a steam-propulsion system. Rickover's dream: a submarine that could stay submerged indefinitely because its fires were nuclear, not chemical, and so did not depend on outside air; and a craft which would run on a few pounds of fuel as opposed to tens of thousands of gallons of Diesel oil. And so the *Nautilus* was born. Its performance, compared with conventional submarines, was remarkable.

Commander Anderson, a devoted submariner, had served during World War II. A married man with children, he was hand-picked to command this important vessel of the United States Navy. When in 1957 he took command he was fairly certain that one day soon he would be going to the North Pole – but he was far less certain about what he would find when it came time for him to nose his way beneath the ice.

The *Nautilus* was tailor-made for such a venture. Unlike earlier expeditions – Nansen's in the *Fram*, for example – it would be possible for the crew of the *Nautilus* to glide in warmth and comfort beneath the irregular surface of the ice, coming up if necessary in various gaps that appear from time to time. On the other hand it is difficult to navigate in high latitudes. Magnetic compass needles swing erratically when they are near the Magnetic Pole. When I was in Greenland our compasses pointed southwest. Gyrocompasses are much more reliable, but even they can lose their stability. Although it would be possible, in theory, for the submarine to surface to discover its position from astronomical observations, or from wireless signals, what if there were no convenient hole in the ice when one was needed?

Fitted with the most up-to-date gyrocompass, the Mark 19, the *Nautilus* sailed on August 19, 1957, under conditions of high security, bound for the ice pack between Greenland and Spitsbergen. Commander Anderson's orders from Rear Admiral Charles W. Wilkins read: "At discretion proceed under the ice to the vicinity of 83°N. latitude and return." This meant a journey of 240 miles under ice. On August 27, when they were in the vicinity of Iceland, Commander Anderson addressed his crew: "Men. This is the Captain. This is going to be one hell of an interesting cruise from now on, particularly starting about Saturday. I hope there is no one on board who thinks it will be grim or in any way unsafe. If I thought for one moment we might even halfway jeopardize this magnificent ship, or her magnificent crew, I would turn around and head for port right now." The Executive Officer later replied for the crew: "Captain, they are as ready as anyone could ever be. They will go anywhere with you."

On its way to the pack ice, the ship developed some difficulties. For example, the CO_2 scrubber, which keeps the carbon dioxide to a non-toxic level, was not working too well. But generally life was comfortable, much more comfortable than on the average submarine. There was a huge mess room, excellent food, a large library of films and books, a Coca-Cola machine, and even a jukebox. As Commander Anderson said, "This, I thought, is the way to explore the Arctic!"

After one or two trial dives under the ice to test the equipment, Anderson was convinced that all was well. At 8 P.M. September 1, the *Nautilus* nosed under the ice and set a course due north. Through the periscope Anderson could see the ice. He wrote: "I turned the

Captain Nemo takes a sun shot aboard the Nautilus of Jules Verne's imagination. There are remarkable similarities between Captain Nemo's Nautilus and that of Commander Anderson. The length of the real Nautilus is 320 feet compared with 282 feet for Nemo's submarine; diameter of 28 feet (real Nautilus) compared with 26 feet. Each ship was equipped with an extensive library, and Nemo's Nautilus was powered by electricity generated from sea water, which enabled it to remain submerged for long periods.

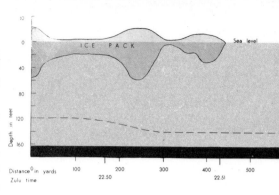

field of the periscope up, bringing my eye, through magnification, within a few feet of the underside of the floes, which appeared to be scudding overhead like grey clouds. It was a fascinating but eerie experience."

On the first trial trip under the ice the *Nautilus* tried to surface in a pool but crashed into solid ice overhead (a block of ice floating in the pool) and the periscope was smashed. When they surfaced, the crew managed to repair the periscope by means of stainless steel welding. It took fifteen hours to do the job in a gale force wind.

With equipment now working satisfactorily, Anderson decided to make his probe deep into the heart of the Arctic Ocean, hoping that it might be possible to reach the Pole 660 miles away – in a return journey of four or five days. When Les Kelly, commander of the escort submarine *Trigger* standing by, radioed Anderson and asked how far north he intended going, Anderson cagily replied: "We might get close enough to talk with Saint Nick." On the ship sped, its navigation equipment working well, then suddenly after they had passed the eighty-fifth parallel and were approaching the eighty-sixth, Anderson was told that both gyrocompasses had gone crazy. Restarting a gyrocompass is a difficult and technical job. On the other hand, to navigate with magnetic compasses in such high latitudes might have started what Anderson calls "the dreaded game of longitude roulette," and the ship might have traveled almost in circles and then emerged against the wrong shore. None the less they pushed on until they had passed lat. 87°N., farther north than had ever been attained by a ship – even Nansen's *Fram*. At this point Anderson decided to turn back to the edge of the ice to avoid undue risk.

The navigators, averaging out the constant to-and-fro swinging of the magnetic compass, gradually pulled the ship around in what they thought was the right direction. But soon they found that they *had* been victims of longitude roulette. Where the water should be leading into deep, open seas, it was beginning to shallow. They had almost run into the ice-logged coast of northern Greenland. A day later they emerged from the pack and made contact with the *Trigger*, that had been waiting for them. After one more short trip to make an ascent into an open pool, the *Nautilus* left for a NATO exercise. En route she clocked her sixty-thousandth submerged mile – equal to Verne's twenty thousand leagues under the sea.

While *Nautilus* was carrying out her operational and training duties, a spectacular voyage across the Arctic Ocean under the ice was being planned for her. The plan was for the *Nautilus* to start the voyage in the Pacific, thread her way through the Bering Strait, navigate under the Arctic ice and the Pole, and emerge in the Atlantic. But the *Nautilus* got off to a bad start. First there was an irritating salt water leak in one of the steam condensers, then fire broke out in the engine room, forcing them to surface to clear the smoke. After it was extinguished, Anderson thought of what could have happened if *Nautilus* had been deep under the ice.

On June 9, 1958, *Nautilus* sailed for the ice pack with her identifying numerals blocked out. Commander Anderson announced to the crew: "All hands. This is the Captain speaking. Our destination for this trip is Portland, England, via the North Pole." After navigating carefully through the treacherous waters of the Aleutians, *Nautilus* passed through the Bering Sea and then through

On June 17, 1958, an hour before midnight the nuclear submarine Nautilus *had one of her most narrow escapes beneath the ice. Only 25 feet above her was the bottom of a gigantic block of ice, while only 20 feet below her was the ocean floor. The chart shows the bottom profile of ice beneath which the* Nautilus *passed during a period of about 15 minutes. Depth of water is shown in feet; distance (horizontal scale) is shown in yards.*

Cross section of the Nautilus.

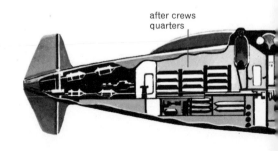

after crews quarters

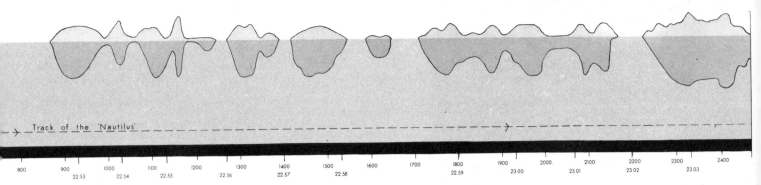

800   900   1000   1100   1200   1300   1400   1500   1600   1700   1800   1900   2000   2100   2200   2300   2400

22.53   22.54   22.55   22.56   22.57   22.58   22.59   23.00   23.01   23.02   23.03

the ice-choked Bering Strait, which leads into the Chukchi Sea. On the left lay Siberia, on the right, islands and the Alaskan coast. Soon their electronic equipment picked up ice; they passed under a huge block that extended thirty feet below the surface. This ice was rafted, that is to say, layers jammed one on top of another as they pressed against the land. The sea was dangerously shallow: only forty-five feet of water beneath them to the ocean floor and about twenty-five feet above them to the ice. This way was closed.

Anderson next tried to find a way through on the eastern side of the Bering Strait. This they did with no difficulty and entered the Chukchi Sea, but at 11 o'clock on the night of June 17 they were faced with a crisis. Anderson was called from his cabin and told that *Nautilus* had just passed under ice sixty-three feet thick. Quickly he ordered a swing to the left and a dive to within twenty feet of the ocean floor. "Our sonar revealed that the gigantic block under which we hovered was over a mile wide," Anderson wrote. "Not in many years had I felt so uneasy in a submarine. Obviously, it was urgent that we move away from that ice .... As we crept into our turn, the recording pen [which was tracing the profile of ice above] wavered downward. All of us – Rex Fowray, who was operating the equipment; Bill Lalor, who was co-ordinating and checking on the ship's course, speed, and depth, together with sonar reports; and myself – stared transfixed. Then slowly the pen receded. We all breathed more easily. We had cleared the monstrous hunk by twenty-five feet."

No sooner had they recovered from that ordeal than their sonar began to show even deadlier ice just ahead. The *Nautilus* crept forward, and downward again came the ice. "I waited for, and

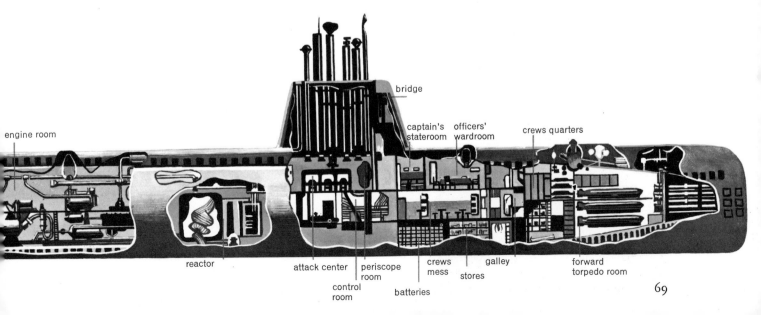

engine room   bridge   captain's stateroom   officers' wardroom   crews quarters

reactor   attack center   periscope room   crews mess   galley   forward torpedo room   control room   batteries   stores

A radarscope view from inside the nuclear submarine Skate (below) of the southern tip of South America. This instrument, called a plan position indicator, records an instantaneous picture of the land within a limited range.

honestly expected, the shudder and jar of steel against solid ice. The recording pen was so close to the reference line which indicated the top of our sail [the superstructure] that they were, for what seemed like hours, almost one and the same .... In pure agony we stood rigidly at our stations. No man moved or spoke. Then suddenly the pen, which had been virtually stationary, slowly moved upward. The gap between the ice and *Nautilus* was widening. We had made it! We had cleared — by an incredible five feet — a mass of ice big enough to supply a hundred-pound block to every man, woman and child in the United States."

Operation "Sunshine," as it was called, had failed. The way to the Arctic Basin was blocked. Reluctantly Anderson announced to the crew his decision to turn back; it came on his thirty-seventh birthday. Painfully *Nautilus* set a course for Pearl Harbor and on June 18 made a vertical ascent to transmit its report of failure for relay to Washington. Anderson flew back to the Pentagon to discuss the next stage in Operation "Sunshine." They decided to make another attempt in July, but this time a thorough ice reconnaissance survey was to be made with the aid of long-range Naval aircraft based in Alaska. Meanwhile new equipment was installed in the *Nautilus*. In addition to her inertial guidance navigation system, a special closed-circuit television set was fitted so that a constant visual picture of the ice could be given. More favorable ice reports were now coming in, as was to be expected. It was clearly an error to have tried so early in the year, as other explorers such as Nansen had found.

On July 23 *Nautilus* slipped into the deep water off Oahu and headed north for Yunaska Pass in the Aleutians. Their daily newspaper continued to amuse them, the movies were good, and life was generally comfortable on board. Commander Anderson wrote: "Our reactor, the powerful source of energy that drove us, gave us light, cooked for us, and shaved us, performed silently and majestically. Watch-standers scanned networks of instruments, each of which had a vital story to tell about how our magnificent ship was performing. Ours was a world of supreme faith — faith in instruments, faith in the laws of physics, faith in each other and in Him who guided our destiny in the unknown seas ahead."

On July 26 they reached the Aleutians, cautiously rose to periscope depth to take bearings, then dived and penetrated into the Bering Sea. That evening the North Pole Celebration Committee met to discuss prizes for the best title for those who had been to the North Pole submerged. On they drove into the Chukchi Sea without difficulty except for an irritating short circuit. The *Nautilus* had covered 2900 miles in six days at an average speed of 19.6 knots — a record run. By midnight of the twenty-ninth they began to pick up scattered ice, then came the pack, which grew denser, parts of it nearly coal black from the dirt it had picked up. Some floes Anderson estimated to project 120 feet below the surface. Cautiously he felt his way along "pinging for deep water" which would lead them into the Barrow Sea Valley (off Point Barrow), but each new and apparent opening was blocked. At one time, when they were cruising along the surface, a man returning from watch reported that it was raining up there. One member of the expedition was surprised and said that rain was extremely rare in the Arctic, which is, in fact, not quite true. Rain falls widely through-

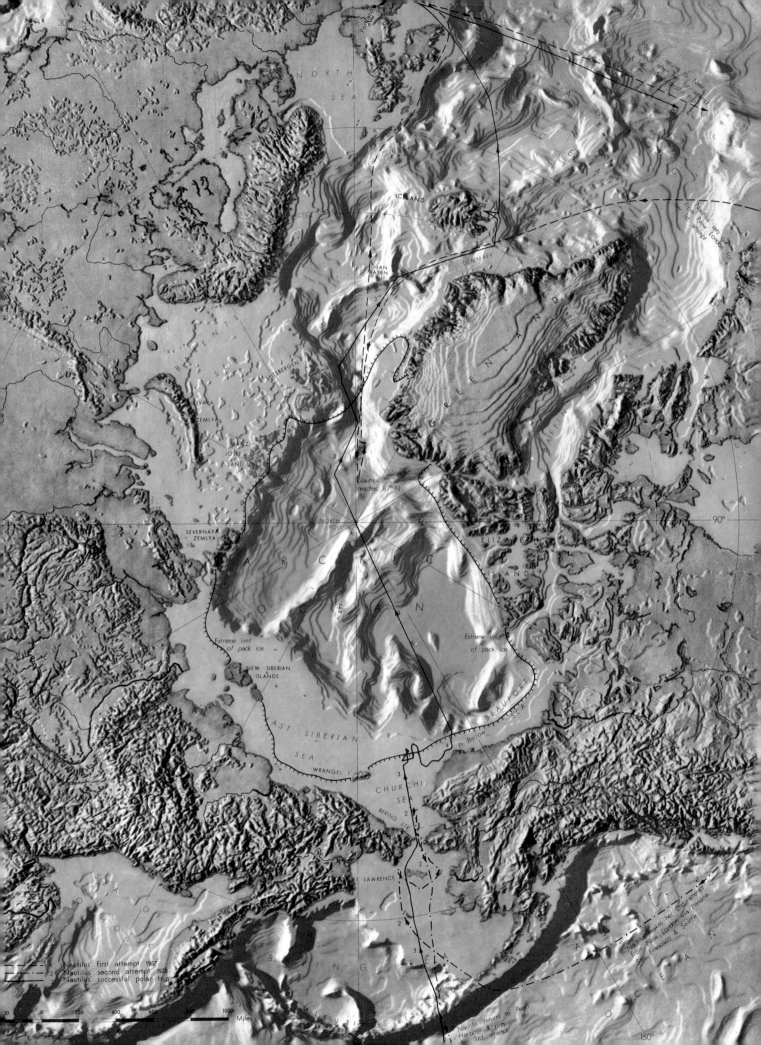

NORTH
SEA

ATLANTIC

ICELAND

JAN
MAYEN

DENMARK STRAIT

BARENTS
SEA

SPITSBERGEN

G R E E N L A N D

OCEAN

NOVAYA
ZEMLYA

BAFFIN

FRANZ
JOSEF
LAND

Nautilus
reaches 87° N

90°

SEVERNAYA
ZEMLYA

NORTH
POLE

ELIZABETH

A R C T I C

ISLANDS

O C E A N

Extreme limit
of pack ice

Extreme limit
of pack ice

NEW SIBERIAN
ISLANDS

BEAUFORT

E A S T   S I B E R I A N

SEA

SEA

Pt. Barrow

WRANGEL I.

20°

CHUKCHI
SEA

BERING STR.

ST. LAWRENCE

Nautilus sets out
from New London
for her 3rd attempt

60°

Nautilus returns to New
London after her 1st
unsuccessful trip

30°

Nautilus returns to Pearl
Harbor & prepares for
3rd attempt

Nautilus makes her 2nd attempt
from New London via Panama,
San Francisco & Seattle

P A C I F I C   O C E A N

150°

BERING
SEA

ALEUTIAN ISLANDS

————— Nautilus first attempt 1957
—·—·— 2 Nautilus second attempt 1958
——————— 3 Nautilus successful polar trip

0   200   400   600   800   1000
Miles

out the Arctic in summer. Anderson wondered: "Was this rare Arctic rain pelting *Nautilus* an ill omen?"

North of Point Franklin they found themselves round the edge of the pack and headed into their deep-water gateway of the Barrow Sea Valley. "As we planed below the surface, I said this to myself: 'This is it. Let's go, go, go.' Through the periscope I caught a last glimpse of the sky. It was a lovely clear morning with a full moon. The sun was rising, and there was a gentle southerly breeze."

Increasing speed to eighteen knots, they were soon deep under the true Polar pack. Less than eleven hundred miles ahead lay the North Pole; and eight hundred miles beyond that the opposite edge of the pack. Now the way was clear. *Nautilus* drove on, increasing her speed to twenty knots. At times they sighted pressure ridges far deeper than anyone had ever anticipated, projecting down to one hundred and 125 feet. They saw peaks rising from the deep, 1670 fathoms, of ocean. In one place the water suddenly shoaled from 2100 fathoms to less than five hundred. As Anderson watched this unknown underwater world slip by he "camped alongside the fathometer for several hours, intently watching the rugged terrain as it unfolded beneath us. I saw incredibly steep cliffs – undersea ranges—rise thousands of feet above the ocean floor. Several times I ordered speed slackened, then resumed, as a promontory leveled off or descended as rapidly as it had risen. The shape of these undersea mountains appeared phenomenally rugged, and as grotesque as the craters of the moon."

At lat. 83° 20′N. they passed the Pole of Inaccessibility, the geographical center of the ice pack and the most inaccessible point in the Arctic. A feeling of suspense and anticipation communicated itself throughout the crew; also, a feeling of admiration and trust in this great, mobile computer called *Nautilus*. Few could sleep, or wanted to, and many were saying silent prayers for the success of their mission. All stood transfixed, monitoring the marvel of electronic instruments that flashed, beeped, clicked, and hummed.

Unable to sleep, Anderson kept frequent watch through the periscope. Jokes were cracked, and there was a general feeling of lightheartedness on board, despite the tension. About this time one crew member proposed that on reaching the Pole the rudder might be put hard over so that they could make twenty-five circles, "thus becoming the first ship in history to circle the Earth non-stop twenty-five times." The ship was running perfectly. Even so, the. torpedo tubes were kept ready in case they had to blast a hole through the ice for a sudden ascent.

At 10 A.M. on August 3, they slipped across the eighty-seventh parallel, and glided on in comfort. Above them was the Polar ice, and above that Arctic winds battering and grinding the ice. But inside the *Nautilus* all was snug and warm. As they approached the Pole the crew gathered in the mess and attack center. Then after sixty-two hours under the ice came Anderson's announcement, full of drama, of the attainment of the Pole:

"All hands – this is the Captain speaking . . . . In a few moments *Nautilus* will realize a goal long a dream of mankind – the attainment by ship of the North Geographic Pole . . . . The distance of the Pole is now precisely four-tenths of a mile. As we approach, let us pause in silence dedicated with our thanks for the blessings that have been ours during this remarkable voyage – our prayers for

After his reception in Washington, Commander Anderson was flown to England and lowered aboard the Nautilus by helicopter before the submarine entered Portland Harbor.

◀ Map shows the three attempts of the Nautilus to navigate beneath the ice of the Arctic Ocean. On August 3, 1958, she passed directly beneath the ice at the North Pole.

lasting world peace, and in solemn tribute to those who have pre-ceded us, whether in victory or defeat." Silence. Then, "Stand by. Ten ... Eight ... Six ... Four ... Three ... Two ... One. MARK! August 3, 1958. Time 2315. For the United States and the United States Navy, the North Pole."

Cheers echoed throughout the ship. When Commander Anderson looked to the inertial navigator and its guide, Tom Curtis said: "As a matter of fact, Captain, you might say we came so close we pierced the Pole."

Before joining the Polar party in the crew's mess, Anderson reflected on their moment under the Pole: *Nautilus* had achieved the long-sought Passage, a navigable route for merchant nuclear submarines, a route that could save 4900 miles on a voyage from Japan to Europe. The temperature of the water was 32.4°F. The depth was 2235 fathoms, deeper than reported by Ivan Papanin in 1937 and by Admiral Peary in 1909. The ice directly beneath the Pole extended twenty-five feet beneath the surface.

In the mess a special North Pole cake had been prepared and the winning name for the competition was "Panopo," standing for "Pacific to the Atlantic via the North Pole." There was also a costumed visit from Santa Claus, who berated *Nautilus* for invading his domain out of season.

The rest of the run – to complete the transpolar voyage into the Atlantic – seemed easy. The next immediate job was to find a hole in the ice to send the news to the world, the signal being "*Nautilus* 90 North." But the ice was too thick overhead. As they moved into the area they had covered on their previous trip they found the depth did not match, and a feeling of uneasiness flowed through the ship. The fathometer was showing 2400 fathoms, much deeper than they had expected, and a giant ice floe twelve miles across was visible. They also discovered that the temperature was getting colder, not warmer. Had they, at this crucial moment, fallen into the terrible game of longitude roulette? And could they be heading back toward the Pole? Just then they found themselves under a patch of clear water. On surfacing there were tense moments before the navigators were able to confirm from astronomical obser-vations that they were where they thought they were – northeast of Greenland. After a transit of 1830 miles and ninety-six hours under the ice they were only a mile off their dead reckoning course!

Nautilus now tried to send its news to Washington: "Any U.S. Navy radio station. This is an unidentified station with two opera-tional immediate messages." No reply. And then Japan answered ... and other stations. The three-word message "*Nautilus* 90 North" was sent and *Nautilus* moved on out into the ocean – mission accomplished.

At a secret rendezvous off Reykjavik a helicopter momentarily hovered over *Nautilus* then took Anderson to a waiting aircraft which flew him to Washington, where the news of the history-making voyage would be released to the world. Anderson was greeted by President Eisenhower, was awarded the Legion of Merit, and was given a Presidential Unit Citation – the first in peacetime – for the *Nautilus*. But perhaps more dramatic, and more apt, was Anderson's presentation of a chunk of Polar ice to Admiral Rick-over, who made the voyage possible by his devotion to the idea of nuclear submarines.

Life in the Sea

Maurice Burton

A near endless variety of life abounds in the sea, from its shimmering surface to its greatest depths. The spectacular rose-petal bubble shell, a mollusc (above), is found on the Great Barrier Reef, Australia. About an inch long, it never withdraws its colorful mantle into its shell. (Japanese print is by Kuniyoshi, c. 1833.)

Many invertebrates found in the sea – the jellyfish, for one – are absent from the land. The Portuguese man-of-war is a "community" of specialized polyps: some for feeding, others for reproduction, and others form stinging tentacles that paralyze prey. All are attached to the floating bladder, which was the original larva from which the polyps budded.

There are probably two million different kinds of plants and animals in the world, at least. Yet, although two thirds of our planet's surface is covered by the oceans, far fewer species of living things dwell in the sea than on land or in the air. Of the roughly one million species of insects, for instance, only half a dozen are truly marine. And the more highly developed and larger plants live almost exclusively on the land, leaving only seaweeds and the microscopic plants of the plankton in the seas. There are no marine ferns or mosses, no subaquatic trees.

Marine biology – the science devoted to plants and animals that live in the sea – ought, therefore, to be easier to study than the rest of biology. But there are good reasons why this is not so. The most obvious is that man himself is a land animal. Even as children, we become familiar with the living things around us and learn about them almost unconsciously. Throughout our lives we can continue to investigate many land plants and animals without special effort. We can more readily appreciate their way of life because they breathe the air we breathe and because they respond to night and day, to heat and cold, to the changing seasons, much as we do. Even when they live in a far different environment from our own, we can visit and study them easily; or they can be brought from distant lands to a local botanical or zoological garden. And those that are not available to us locally we can see in films and photographs.

The sea is different. It is an alien world whose mysteries can be probed only slowly and painstakingly. Hence our knowledge of life in the sea has come late in the records of human history, and we still have a great deal to learn. Another obstacle is that sea plants and animals do not, for the most part, resemble those found on land. Although there is a certain amount of overlapping, the marine part of the living world is the more primitive and therefore the less easy for us to understand because we do not always have familiar standards for comparison.

This point is made clear if we consider the two great subkingdoms of the animal world: the vertebrates (animals with backbones) and the invertebrates (without backbones). If we ignore the overwhelmingly large number of species of fish, we can regard the vertebrates as mainly land animals that include those most familiar to us – the mammals, birds, and reptiles. Only a few of the remaining vertebrates – for instance, whales, seals, sea birds, sea snakes – inhabit the oceans. The *typically* marine animal, then, again ignoring the fishes, is an invertebrate.

Several classes of invertebrates, like the sponges, sea anemones, jellyfishes, and starfishes are wholly absent from the land, and very few of their members live in rivers or lakes. Others, such as worms and molluscs, are preponderantly marine, though they have a number of relatives living on land. There remains the largest and most highly evolved group, which can be conveniently described as the higher invertebrates. They are the Arthropoda, or jointed-legged animals, that include crustaceans, insects, spiders, millipedes, and centipedes. Except for a handful of species, the last four of these are entirely terrestrial or live in fresh water. Together they number more than a million species – over half the total of known species of living organisms.

Because of the numerical superiority of the land-living arthro-

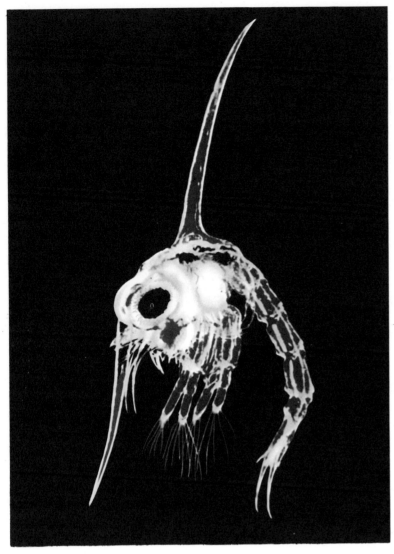

The crustaceans, having skeletons on the outside of their bodies, include lobsters, shrimps, and crabs. Shown here is the larva of a velvet swimming crab (magnified many times). At this stage in its life cycle it forms one of the many varieties of plankton, the basic food source in the sea.

pods, and because most of us are familiar with them from our early dawning of consciousness, they tend to overshadow their marine relatives, such as the crustaceans and copepods. All of us are acquainted with crabs, lobsters, and shrimps, but to most of us the copepods are as unfamiliar as Chinese script; yet our harvests of the sea, by which so much of our civilization is sustained, depend on copepods. These seemingly insignificant and unfamiliar crustaceans are one of the chief mainstays in the total economy of that two thirds of the world's surface covered with salt water.

Just as an understanding of the copepods eludes most of us, their essential value in the economy of the sea eluded marine biologists until fairly recently. Although fishes have been known and exploited for millennia, the basic principles of their existence — in this instance their food — were wrapped in mystery until the nineteenth century. Spectacular discoveries in many areas of marine biology have been made over the years, but always they have come about slowly, and usually through the persistent efforts of obscure workers. An attempt to follow the history of marine biology is like a journey through a labyrinth, the most important signposts of which are obscured by moss.

Consider, for instance, one of the supreme examples of this state of affairs. Paradoxically it concerns a fish most of us think of as a fresh-water fish, although it spends the first part of its life in the

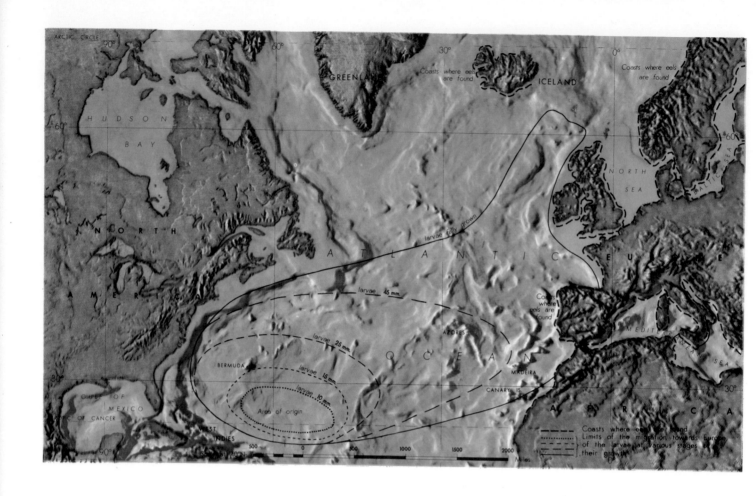

Coasts where eels are found
Limits of the migration towards Europe of the larvae at various stages of their growth

Eels of Europe and eastern North America hatch from eggs laid in the Sargasso Sea (below). The larval eels take three years to make the long journey east to the coastal rivers of Europe where they mature. When adult, the eels return to the Sargasso Sea, lay their eggs, and die.

sea and returns to the sea to die – the eel. The eel must have been eaten by very early men in many parts of the world. It is one of the few fishes capable of traveling overland and of lying on the banks of rivers and lakes to bask in the sun. During migration millions fill the rivers. Since it cannot fail to attract attention, we can reasonably suppose that men have been eating eels for five, ten, fifteen or more thousand years.

Even so, the mystery of the eel was not solved – if it can even now be said to have been solved – until a few decades ago. What we now know is that in autumn the adult eels in the rivers of Europe make their way to the sea and cross the Atlantic to the region of the Sargasso Sea where they spawn and die. The eggs later hatch and the larval eels make their way back to the coasts of Europe. Taking three years for the journey, they arrive in the spring, at which time they change into elvers, make their way up the rivers, and spend several years feeding and growing, then repeat the cycle. The eels of eastern North America do the same thing, except that the larvae take only a year to reach the coast from the Sargasso Sea. A similar story can be told for the eels of eastern and southeast Asia and for those of Australia and New Zealand, but in no case do any of them make so long a journey as the European eel.

There is a statue in Copenhagen of Johannes Schmidt, the man who finally unraveled the mystery of eel migrations. But there remain many obscure milestones on the path leading to his achievement. The search began in 350 B.C., when Aristotle declared that mature eels migrate to the sea and disappear. It seems likely, too, that he knew about the ascent of the elvers from the sea into fresh water, and that he realized these were the young eels. Aristotle's ideas were soon discarded, though. As late as the seventeenth century people believed that eels came out of the sea to mate with snakes, or that they rubbed themselves against rocks and their shreds of skin turned into young eels. Such legends emphasize how puzzled people were about the sex and breeding habits of the eel.

In 1684 a Tuscan scholar, Francesco Redi, put forward the theory that eels spawned in the sea, but it was not until 1777 that Professor C. Mondini, of the University of Bologna, dissected an eel and discovered the ovary in it. In 1856 a German naturalist, Johan Jacob Kaup, caught a small fish in the Strait of Messina and named it *Leptocephalus brevirostris*. He did not know that he had found an eel larva. In 1874 a Polish naturalist, Simone de Syrski, identified a male eel by its testes, and in 1896 two Italian naturalists, Giovanni Battista Grassi and Salvatore Calandruccio, watched a so-called Leptocephalus "change" into an eel. Finally, in 1904, began the culminating discoveries of Denmark's Johannes Schmidt.

Schmidt began his study of the eel by chance. He was aboard a Danish research ship, the *Thor*, in the North Atlantic to investigate the eggs and larvae of cod, herring, and other food fishes when a Leptocephalus was brought up in the trawl off the Faeroes. Did eels, then, spawn out in the Atlantic? Determined to get the full answer, he began a long search through first one part of the Atlantic, then

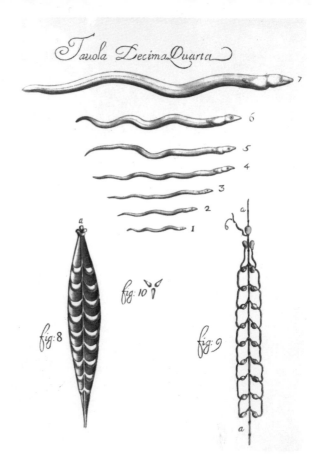

An illustration from Francesco Redi's treatise on eels.

This sixth-century B.C. vase, found at Vulci, Italy, shows a Greek diver about to enter the sea, probably in search of sponges, which were then in common use.

This modern Greek sponge seller displays his wares as did his ancestors more than twenty centuries ago. Of the 2500 species of sponges, only a half dozen or so are suitable for household use. Once regarded as a plant, sponges actually are the dried skeletons of a primitive marine animal.

another. It was not until 1922 that he completed the job of plotting the migrations of European eels and discovering their spawning ground. Thus he finally solved a problem that had occupied scholars for more than two thousand years.

Like the eel, sponges have been fished for well over two thousand years. Evidence of their use goes so far back that we can assume they were familiar household articles in the earliest Mediterranean civilizations. They have been of such value to trade, art, and medicine (for their iodine content) that one scholar has suggested a possible link between the rise and fall of civilizations and the number of sponges used. Even today, however, there remains a degree of uncertainty about the exact nature of this marine organism whose dried skeleton has proved so useful to man throughout the centuries.

First of all, there has always been some confusion over the use of the word "sponge." There are at least 2500 species of sponges and they are found on the ocean floor in all seas, from pole to pole, and at all depths. But only a half dozen or so of the 2500 species can be used in your bath, and these are concentrated mainly in the Mediterranean and around the Bahamas and Florida. What *is* the household sponge? Aristotle correctly guessed that it was the skeleton of an animal, but his research was again ignored by later generations. Between the fourth century B.C. and the eighteenth century A.D. sponges were variously held to be plants, the homes of marine worms, the work of "some kind of sea insect," or solidified sea foam. Not until 1786 was their animal nature again stated, this time by an Englishman, John Ellis, after he had noticed jets of water coming out of the round holes of a living sponge that he had placed in a bowl of sea water. As late as 1841 at least one well-known naturalist was still arguing that they were plants.

It is easy to understand why there was so much disagreement about the nature of sponges. Apart from the unicellular animals, they are the lowest on the animal scale. A typically marine invertebrate, the like of which is not found on land, the sponge is also one of the most peculiar animals in that it remains fixed throughout life, except in its larval stage. Here we have another marked difference between life on land and life in the sea. The bottom of the sea is populated not only by animals that crawl or burrow but by many that are fixed, plantlike, on the sea bed. Some zoologists now agree that we should regard sponges not as animals but as animal-like, that we should think of them as belonging to a separate subkingdom of the animal kingdom (the Parazoa).

The reasons why sponges should probably be set aside from the main stream of animal life make a fascinating study for the specialist. The body of a sponge is not made up of tissues composed of layers of cells in the usual way, but of a network in which individual cells have special functions. This network is crisscrossed by a labyrinth of fine tubes marked at intervals by pumping chambers. The economy of a sponge is very simple. The pumping chambers draw streams of water in through fine pores in the skin, pores that are invisible to the naked eye. This stream brings in food and oxygen, and after flowing through the body it is pumped out through larger openings on the surface, carrying waste products along with it. Because the incurrent pores are so tiny, the sponge can draw only fine particles inside itself. Thus, since the food of at least some sponges consists of bacteria and very small specks of dead animals and vegetable remains, they play a scavenger role in the economy of the sea.

Although some sponges are annuals, others seem to qualify for a place among the immortals. Few animals feed on this group of sponges, and the wounds caused by those that do are readily repaired. If a crab pulls a sponge to pieces, each fragment can grow into a new sponge. A piece of sponge pressed through fine silk can be separated so that all its cells lie individually at the bottom of a glass dish. But within two to three days the individual cells will have joined to form small masses of cells, each able to grow into a new sponge. In addition, two nearby sponges may grow toward each other and, when they touch, join to form one huge sponge.

The stories of the eel and the sponge are very much the same in that they show that our understanding of living creatures in the sea does not come about spontaneously and suddenly. Our learning process is a painfully slow one, and the efforts of dozens or, more often, hundreds of researchers ranging over an equal number of years are usually required before we come to an understanding of how even the simplest organism lives. And the search is endless.

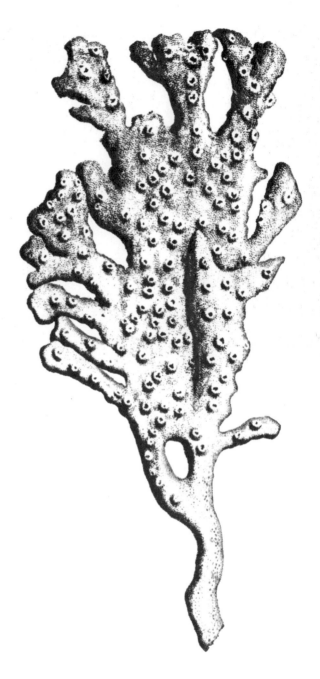

In 1765 the biologist John Ellis proved that sponges were not dead structures by observing their inhalent and exhalent currents. This one, which he found off the coast of southern England, he called Spongea palmata. Apart from the single cell animals, sponges are the lowest on the animal scale.

Creatures of the Sea

Among the wide variety of coelenterates are solitary cup polyps (shown above, twice life size). In aggregates of millions they help form coral reefs like this one on the Barrier Reef. Each animal lives attached and independently captures food with its tentacles.

One of the biologist's first tasks is to put the two million or so living species into some sort of order. In short, he must classify them. Although our immediate concern is to review life in the sea and to determine how it is linked with our own destinies, no such discussion is possible without some notion of how marine life is classified.

First, all living things are either plant or animal. Where sea plants are concerned this presents no problems. All true sea plants belong to one group, the Algae, and they are of two main kinds: seaweeds and single-celled plants. But more about plants later. Animals are more varied and more complicated. As we have seen, they can be divided into vertebrates and invertebrates; and the invertebrates can be divided quite arbitrarily into higher invertebrates and lower invertebrates. Most of the many kinds of lower invertebrates are sea creatures. Let us look at one branch of these animals, the so-called Coelenterata.

This name derives from two Greek words: *koilos* (hollow) and *enteron* (intestine). The Coelenterata, then, are hollow-stomached animals. But can there be a stomach that is not hollow? What is meant is that the coelenterates are animals that are *all* stomach except for a few accessories. The sea anemone is a good example. It is nothing but a bag with an opening (the mouth) surrounded by a ring of tentacles. The wall of this bag is made up of two layers of cells — an inner or digestive layer and an outer or limiting layer. The outer layer is, so to speak, the skin. Between the inner and outer layers is a layer of jellylike substance. There is also a network of nerve cells, and apart from this network the sea anemone has no further nervous structure, neither brain nor sense organs. Its tentacles are sensitive to flavors, though; when they detect the presence of food they grab the substance and cram it into the mouth, and the undigested remains are later ejected through the mouth.

Life, then, appears to be a simple affair for the sea anemone, but

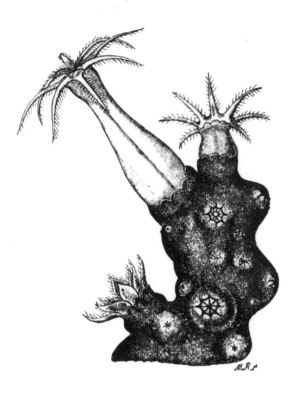

what of the other types of coelenterates: the jellyfishes, corals, sea firs (or hydroids), and sea pens? To look at, these animals represent a very mixed group. They range from the stony coral to the saucer-size jellyfish, which, when stranded on the shore, disintegrates under the sun's rays into a patch of dried jelly. They also range from the small mosslike growths known as sea firs to giant jellyfishes that measure more than seven feet across, with tentacles 120 feet long. Whereas the jelly layer in a sea anemone is thin, it forms about 95 per cent of the total bulk of the jellyfish. Apart from their great range in size, another difference among the coelenterates is that the sea anemone and jellyfish are individual animals (known as polyps), whereas a stony coral may be a colony of hundreds or thousands of polyps weighing half a ton, all joined and working as one to build a common skeleton.

One reason why the coelenterates are so varied in appearance is that, like plants, they have an infinite capacity for budding. The sea fir starts as a larva that settles on a rock, then the larva turns into a polyp on a stem. A bud appears on the stem and grows into a second polyp, and on its stem another bud appears and forms a third polyp, and so on. This continuous process of budding forms a complex of stems and branches up to a foot high, crowded with polyps.

Stony corals do much the same, except that each polyp lays down a stony cup for itself, and the result is a huge stony mass like the brain coral. Even jellyfishes pass through a similar stage when the larva grows into an elongated polyp seated on a rock. The polyp buds off small saucer-shaped jellyfishes, or medusae, each of which swims away and grows into a mature jellyfish.

Perhaps the most remarkable example of budding is seen in the siphonophores, of which the Portuguese man-of-war is the most familiar. Its larva grows into a hollow sack having one tentacle beside the mouth opening. It then produces additional buds that develop into specialized polyps – some for feeding, others for

The sea anemone, also a coelenterate, is a carnivorous animal low on the evolutionary scale. Tentacles, which are sensitive to flavors and so detect food, surround the opening to the stomach. This opening is also used to eject waste. Left: an early engraving of open and partly open coral polyps.

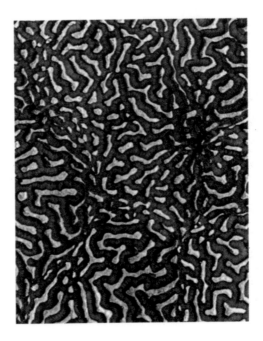

Unlike the solitary cup polyp, the polyps forming the "brain" coral share a great cluster of cups, resulting in the boulderlike formations that are the true reef builders.

This young jellyfish, a coelenterate, is
only a half inch wide. As it matures, the
space between its tentacles fills up and the
adult bell-shaped creature takes form.

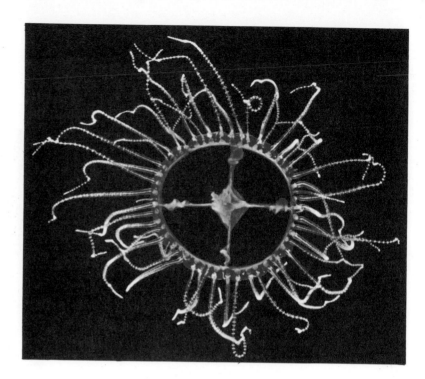

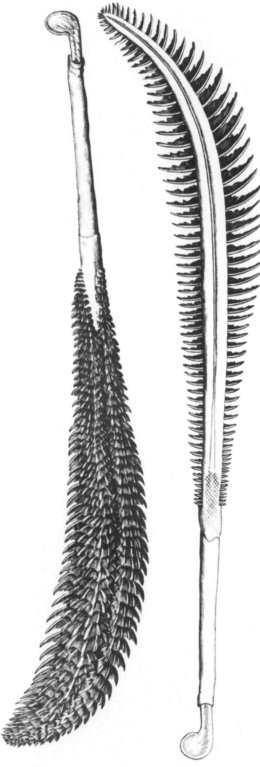

The sea pen, another coelenterate, is a
collection of polyps arranged in featherlike
fashion on a stem rooted in the ooze.
When brought to the surface, some
glow with a pale blue light.

reproduction, and a third group forms the stinging tentacles. The
original larva forms the bladder that floats on the surface and serves
as a carrier of the stinging, feeding, and reproduction polyps hanging from its underside.

Whatever their diversity in appearance, all the coelenterates have
certain things in common. Each is a bag with a hollow stomach,
the wall of which is two-layered with a jelly layer between. And no
matter what their size or make-up, they can be easily identified by
an outstanding feature they all have in common: Their tentacles
are armed with stinging cells. These animals sting like nettles, and
their stings – like those of the land plant – work on the principle
of the hypodermic syringe.

The sponges and the coelenterates form two large groups of
lower invertebrates that inhabit the seas. (The biologist's term for
any such branch of the animal kingdom is *phylum*.) A third and
somewhat more advanced group includes the familiar starfish (or
sea star), the less familiar sea urchin, and the almost unknown (to
the layman) brittle star, sea cucumber, and sea lily. These animals
have not only a stomach but also an intestine, and the waste from
the food that enters their mouths leaves by a second, specialized
opening.

Another advance in the structure of this group of animals is
their three-layered body wall. The third layer marks a big step
forward from the two-layered sea anemone. The outer layer still
forms the skin and the inner layer lines the digestive tube; but the
middle layer gives rise to a system of muscles. As a result, the
starfish can move about at will, and it can use its arms to exert a
great enough pull to force open a mussel or clam. Although this
group – like the coelenterates – is without a brain, each animal in
the group has a ring of nerve cells around its mouth and a nerve
cord running through each arm.

The starfish, sea urchin, and others related to them are grouped
under the phylum Echinodermata, or spiny skins. Again the name
is something less than accurate since many of the "spiny skins" are

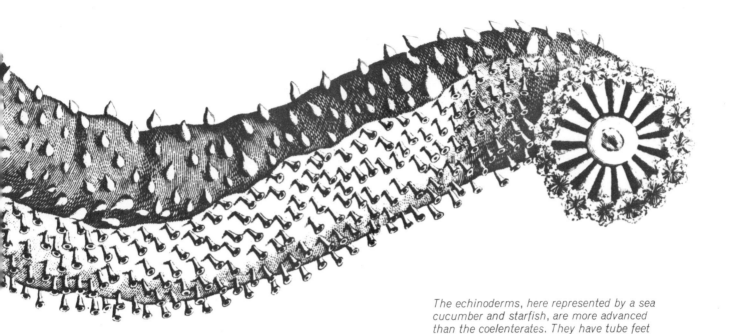

The echinoderms, here represented by a sea cucumber and starfish, are more advanced than the coelenterates. They have tube feet for moving about, a three-layered body wall, an intestine, and a specialized opening for the ejection of waste.

either quite smooth or roughened without being spiny. If the name echinoderm can be considered vaguely descriptive, it is because all members of this phylum but one – the sea cucumber – have their skin strengthened by nodules or continuous plates of lime. These nodules do sometimes form low spines on the surface; and the box of limy plates that encloses the body of all sea urchins is in some species armed with spines.

Can we single out one characteristic that all echinoderms have in common and that at the same time distinguishes them from all other groups – their tube feet, say? The answer is no, which once more points up the difficulty of framing precise rules in biology. We cannot even say that, taken as a whole, these animals have progressed a great deal further than the Porifera (sponges) and the Coelenterata in having muscles that give them freedom of movement. The sea lilies, for example, remain fixed on stalks once they pass the larval stage. As their name suggests, they are flowerlike, but they so closely resemble a starfish turned upside down and set at the top of a stalk that there can be no doubt about their family ties.

Moving about, especially the active movement we call locomotion, demands legs or feet or some equivalent. Every starfish has hundreds of feet. In a groove along the underside of each arm are hundreds of suckers, each sucker at the end of a short tube, and all the tubes connected with other tubes inside the body. This entire system of tubes is filled with fluid, and the fluid, together with the muscles, enables the starfish to pull itself along over the sea bed. The movements of the tube feet and the inflow and outflow of the fluid that makes them rigid are controlled by a complex system of nerve fibers laid out like the wires in a telephone exchange, with a nerve running to each tube foot from the main system.

The echinoderms have acquired a new importance in the eyes of the biologist within the last twenty-five years or so, for they seem to represent a forward leap in evolution. For a long time now we have taken for granted that life began in the sea. We think that the first living things were simple single-celled plants, and that they

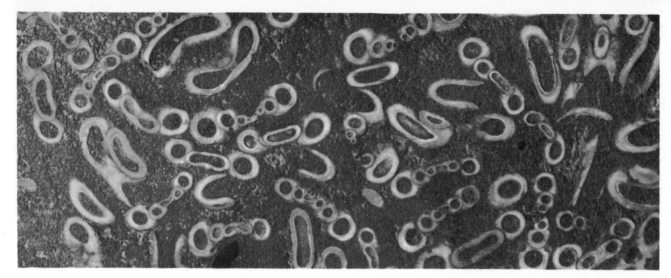

This fossil of marine bristle worm tubes was found on the beach at Sidmouth, England, and dates back to the Mesozoic era. The worms (Serpulidae) were true segmented worms.

The peacock worm, a marine bristle worm, builds a protective tube around its body and anchors itself to coral or sand. Feather-like gills enable the animal to breathe and serve as food collectors. When alarmed, the animal withdraws into its tube.

came into existence in the shallow seas some 1500 million years ago. But we can do little more than guess what actually took place, although it is a fair guess that plants were the first on the scene, because only plants can make food out of non-living materials. Still guessing, it seems reasonable to suppose that some plants lost their ability to make their own food and began to feed on other, simpler plants. As time passed groups of cells came to live together, and the first simple seaweeds, sponges, and coelenterates came into being. They moved about very little and their food requirements were not complex. The ages sped past with little or no change, until muscle fibers appeared in some of these creatures and they began to stretch their arms, not merely to reach for food but to move out in search of it.

An animal can get from one place to another in a variety of ways. It may crawl, walk, or swim, doing any of these in one of several ways. Jellyfishes can swim, but not strongly enough to counter the currents, so they mainly drift about. Sponges are mostly fixed, but some kinds can drag themselves laboriously and very slowly over the surface of rocks. Sea anemones remain fixed for long periods, but they also can move slowly over the rocks, and a few can inflate their "hollow stomachs," let go of the rock, and float away.

But none of these is locomotion in the real sense. Starfishes can do better, but even their efficiency is limited by their body plan – they are built on a radiate plan, meaning that they are without a head end and a tail end that would structure them for efficient locomotion. Little progress could be made, therefore, until such an animal came on the scene. Let us now turn to another great group of invertebrates – the worms.

Anything small, elongated, and creeping is called a worm, but the precise term for the marine animal in this group is "bristle worm." A typical bristle worm has a mouth with a pair of stout jaws at the head end of a long cylindrical body divided into a number of segments. On each segment is a pair of parapodia – outgrowths of skin used for breathing – supporting one or more bristles. With the aid of the bristles the worm can creep over the sea bed, burrow in sand, or swim through the water.

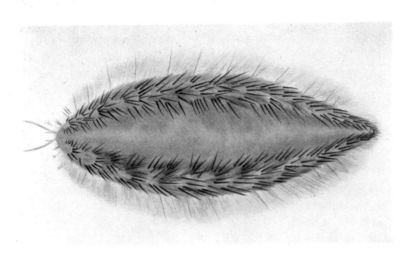

W. C. McIntosh, the nineteenth-century biologist, did these drawings of marine worms. The seamouse (above) grows to a length of about four inches and has an armor of stiff spines and scaly plates. The brightly colored Napthys cacca (right) is about life size.

Many bristle worms build and live in tubes of sand grains, mucus, or carbonate of lime. These tube dwellers seldom move about much. They wait for their food to drift by and catch it by means of bristles arranged around their heads. Like the sponges, they feed on small particles of animal or vegetable matter, but instead of filtering water through their body they trap the fragments directly from the water. Other marine bristle worms, as active as the tube dwellers are static, hunt their prey. They move along quickly, either crawling along the bottom or swimming through the water, and seize their victim with their strong jaws. Although the habits of the various marine worms differ, they all have segmented bodies, longitudinal and transverse muscles that enable them to stretch out and to contract, and a nervous system with the beginnings of a brain as well as a stout nerve cord running the length of the body. Thus the worm is highly specialized compared with the radiated invertebrates.

Once animals had developed a segmented body, a head end, a hind end, organs of locomotion, and a specialized nervous system (including a concentration of nerve cells at one end of the main nerve cord), the way was open to rapid evolutionary progress. So long as they were constructed on a radial plan and had to live either fixed to the sea bed or at best crawling slowly over it, they evolved very slowly. A study of fossils shows that the radiated animals have made relatively few advances since the beginning of the fossil record some 500 million years ago. From the ancestral bristle worms, however, there burgeoned out a great variety of types, most of which are included today in two phyla – Mollusca and Arthropoda.

Though these two groups developed along radically different lines, we can trace the genealogies of both all the way down to a bristle worm. Within each phylum some classes have made little progress, or have even dropped back in the evolutionary race, while others have forged ahead to become highly developed. Among the molluscs it is the sea-dwelling octopus and squid that have reached the highest point. Among the arthropods it is the land-living insects and spiders; but their relatives left behind in the seas – the crustaceans – have also been left behind in an evolutionary sense.

The word "mollusc" can be interpreted to mean soft-bodied,

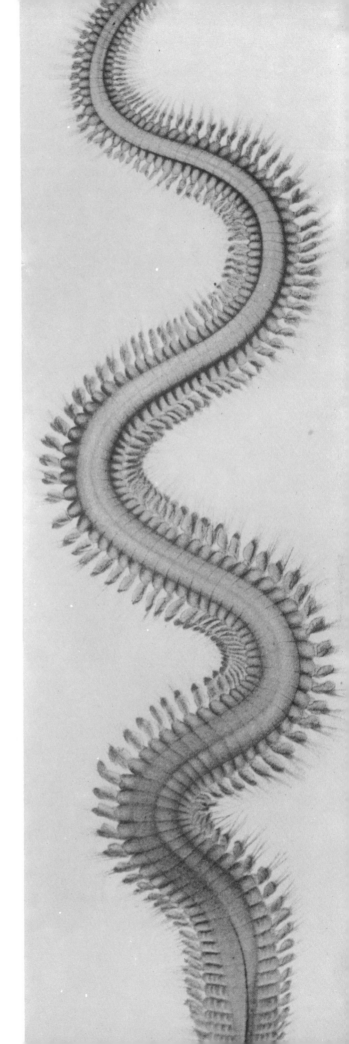

since its Latin root is *mollis* (soft). Obviously, there are plenty of animals with even softer bodies than those of molluscs. What is actually implied in the name is that the molluscs have a soft body that contrasts with the hardness of the shells in which they live. Typically the shell is of carbonate of lime and conforms pretty much to one of two patterns. On the one hand we have the bivalves (hinged shells), such as clams and oysters; on the other, the univalves (spiral shells), such as snails and slugs. But there are several modifications of these two basic patterns: The shell may be lost altogether, it may be reduced in size or altered in shape, or it may be laid down inside instead of outside the body. So classification of the molluscs cannot be based wholly on the appearance of the shell.

There are, in fact, five classes of molluscs. In one, the Amphineura, belong the chitons or coat-of-mail shells. These range in length from half an inch to ten inches, and all have a flat muscular foot and carry on their backs eight overlapping crescent-shaped plates that represent the shell and suggest some kind of segmentation. As the most primitive of molluscs, the chitons are close to the bristle worm. The next class, the Scaphopoda, is little known and comprises the tusk shells, whose shells resemble elephant tusks. Next come the Gastropoda (snails and slugs on land, whelks and sea snails in the oceans). Like the chitons they have a muscular foot and, usually, a spiral shell. But some, like the limpets, have a conical shell, and others, like the sea slugs, have none at all. Then comes the most numerous class, called Pelecypoda, consisting of the bivalves of which the most popular examples are oysters, mussels, and clams. Finally, there are the Cephalopoda, those remarkable invertebrates including the octopus, squid, and cuttle. Some of these have lost their shell entirely, others carry only the relics of a shell inside their body. Yet the related nautilus has a well-grown spiral shell. The cephalopods are far more active than the four other classes of molluscs. Speedy hunters, they hold their prey in their arms, which are lined with suckers, and eat it with their parrotlike beaks. Most remarkable of all, perhaps, is the eye of the cephalopods, which is as highly developed as that of many higher vertebrates.

So much for the lower invertebrate sea dwellers. As for the higher invertebrates, we have already noted that they are mostly land creatures. Called arthropods because of their jointed legs, only one big class – the Crustacea – plus fifty or so types of insect inhabit the oceans. The crustaceans have jointed bodies as well as jointed legs, the body being clothed in a chitinous (horny) cuticle which may or may not be reinforced with lime salts. This cuticle is soft at the junctions between the segments – a softness that enables the lobster, for example, to flex its tail. On the head of every crustacean are two pairs of antennae; and nearly every segment of the body has one pair of legs for swimming or walking.

Of the five subclasses of crustaceans the first includes the fairy shrimps and the water fleas that live in fresh or brackish water. These are tiny creatures, as are the ostracods, whose distinguishing mark is a bivalve shell formed by the cuticle. The third subclass, the copepods, has a typically spindle-shaped body with a forked tail, several pairs of swimming legs, and two pairs of antennae, one of which is noticeably the longer. The fourth subclass, the barnacles, needs no introduction. The ones many of us know best are the

Because giant squids can attain a length of fifty feet or more, they have earned their reputation as "sea monsters." A ten-armed cephalopod, the squid, like the octopus, is a mollusc that has lost its outer shell during the course of evolution.

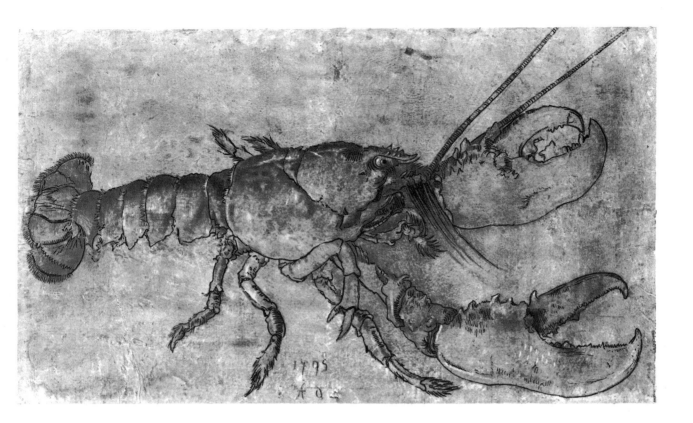

stalked barnacles that grow on ships' hulls or floating timbers. But the most familiar and most numerous are the smaller acorn barnacles (stalkless barnacles), small conical turrets of limy plates that in their millions coat the rocks between tide marks.

The fifth, which includes crabs, lobsters, prawns, and shrimps, is even more familiar. The animals making up this group are called loosely the decapod or ten-legged crustaceans because of their five pairs of legs, one pair or more of which serve also as claws. But there are also a variable number of swimming legs tucked under the abdomen, which in shrimps, lobsters, and prawns is commonly called the "tail." These decapod crustaceans range from tiny shrimps swimming freely in the plankton, or burrowing in the sand, to the many kinds of lobsters and crabs of great and small size. The giant crab of Japan has a body one foot across, its legs spanning six feet. Many shrimps and prawns are luminous, particularly those living in the depth of the oceans. And it is here, too, that the legs of the decapod crustaceans are long in proportion to their body. Their legs serve as stilts that keep the animal's body from settling into the soft ooze coating the bottom.

The rest of the sea's visible animal inhabitants, apart from some rather puzzling animals known as prochordates, are vertebrates: fishes, a few reptiles (notably turtles and sea snakes), sea birds, whales, seals, and sea cows. This completes the catalogue of marine animals, except for the Protozoa, the single-celled animals of microscopic size. But to discuss them here would destroy the sequence of our story. Our understanding of microscopic creatures of the sea has come late in the history of marine biology. The animals we have dealt with so far are all readily visible to the naked eye and have been known by man for centuries. Before biologists could explore the microscopic marine world, certain technological breakthroughs had to be made.

Among the larger of the decapod crustaceans is the lobster, which has been a favorite food for many centuries. As this drawing made in 1495 by Albrecht Dürer shows, the lobster has a segmented body and segmented legs, as do all crustaceans.

When they reach maturity stalked barnacles of this type attach themselves to ships and floating timber. The more common acorn barnacles are stalkless and are found in the millions coating the rocks between tide lines. All barnacles are crustaceans.

Like the mussel and oyster, the octopus is a mollusc (meaning soft bodied). But its class (Cephalopoda) is higher on the evolutionary scale. Like other cephalopods, the octopus has an eye as highly developed as that of many land vertebrates.

In 1236 a shipwrecked sailor started this form of mussel culture in Brittany. The young mussels are placed on the bottom rack where they are bathed by tidal water. As they grow older, and are able to stay out of water longer, they are moved to successively higher levels. After a year or so on the higher levels the mature mussels are ready for marketing.

Like certain other molluscs, the oyster and mussel (pelecypods) produce pearls when a grain of sand or some other foreign body is embedded in their soft body. To protect itself from the irritation the animal secretes layer upon layer of nacre, "mother-of-pearl."

Chitons, sometimes called coat-of-mail shells, are probably one of the most primitive types of mollusc. They are sea slugs covered with scaly plates arranged like armor plating.

 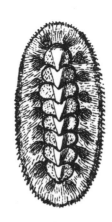

Deceptively like its relative the giant clam from this view, this species of a much smaller clam (about six inches long), found on the Barrier Reef, displays a brilliantly colored mantle. Like the oyster and mussel, the clam is a bivalve mollusc.

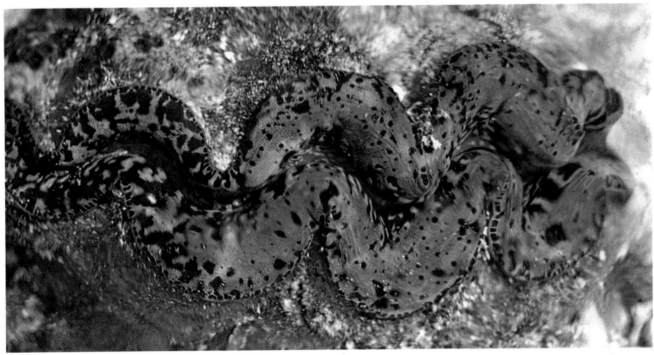

Among the larger crustaceans is this species of hermit crab that lives on Australia's Barrier Reef. Like other hermit crabs, this one has found a home within the empty shell of another animal (usually a gastropod).

Among the smaller crustaceans are the copepods, the main food of herring. Ranging in size from a pinhead to a quarter of an inch, copepods feed on the microscopic diatoms found among the plankton population.

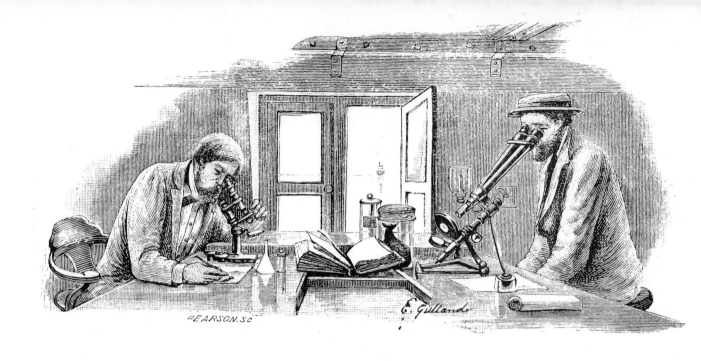

The Discovery of Plankton

Today most of us know the word "plankton," even though we may not be able to give a precise meaning of the word. Like so many current biological terms, it is a comparatively new word, but, more important, knowledge of plankton – those free-floating plants and animals – goes back no further than 1828. In that year, a British Army surgeon and amateur naturalist named J. Vaughan Thompson, who was studying the early stages of crab life, hit on a novel method of catching specimens: He attached a jar to the rear end of a small conical net of fine gauze which he then towed through the water. As water flowed into the mouth of the net and out through its meshes, tiny bits of sea life were caught on the gauze and washed back into the jar. At the end of a run the jar contained a concentration of the microscopic life floating in the surface waters of the sea.

The invention of the tow net meant that biologists could now catch a form of life that had hitherto escaped them. There is no doubt that the conical net with its built-in jar revolutionized the study of marine biology. Yet Thompson is seldom given credit for his work; a German naturalist, Johannes Müller, who did not begin to use a tow net until 1844, is generally credited with its invention. Out of Thompson's first use of the net came an interesting side discovery: He found that barnacles, which had been classified with the molluscs because of their limy shells, were, in fact, crustaceans. Their larvae were free-swimming nauplii closely resembling the larvae of crabs.

An important offshoot of the use of the tow net was the formation of new concepts in the ecological grouping of marine animals. Most mid-nineteenth-century biologists followed the lead of Ernst Haeckel, a famous German zoologist, by dividing all marine life into two groups: the "nekton" (swimming organisms) and the "benthos" (those living on the bottom of the sea). Toward the end of the century the word "plankton" was coined to identify a third group (those that drift with the currents).

The knowledge that the surface waters of the sea contained vast quantities of microscopic organisms – and the realization of their importance in the economy of the sea – did not become apparent

Top: Scientists aboard the Challenger *(1872–76) examine plankton specimens in the ship's laboratory.*

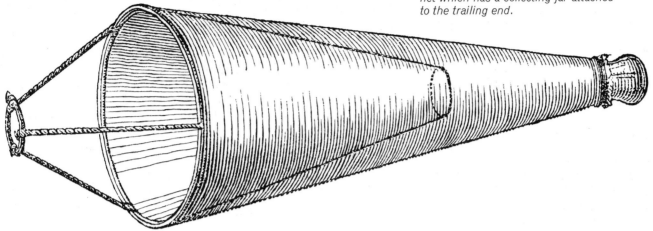

With the tow net, marine biologists were able to collect microscopic plants and animals from any depth. An inner net traps the specimens within the larger net which has a collecting jar attached to the trailing end.

immediately. Both were hastened by discoveries in other fields. One such discovery was that a simple sounding line could be used to bring up samples of the bottom, as was done by Captain Phipps on Cook's second voyage. As late as the early nineteenth century there were those who maintained that it was unlikely that life would be found below 300 fathoms. Then, in 1845, J. M. Brooke, a young midshipman in the U.S. Navy, hit on the idea of fixing a hollow tube device (in this case a quill) to the sounding lead whenever it was used for its ordinary purpose. He easily managed to get mud and ooze from depths of 1000 fathoms or more, and to report to the world that the mud contained microscopic shells.

Had the inhabitants of the shells lived on the bottom, or had the shells fallen to the bottom after the death of the animals? Today it is hard to understand that such a question could have seemed debatable, but it was debated until findings made possible by the tow net settled the question.

With the nineteenth century's advances in techniques, it at last became possible to work out the life histories of many marine animals. This had enormous importance for the fisheries research programs that were soon to play a vital part in increasing the world's food supplies. Once the researchers could understand the food chains upon which life in the sea depends, they could make good use of their knowledge. Furthermore, the identification of animals brought up in tow nets was soon to make it apparent that the currents in the ocean could be plotted and their movements determined by a scientific study of plankton. And another important idea began to emerge: that there is an orderly distribution of plants and animals in the sea, just as there is on land. So the marine biologist, who until 1845 had been satisfied with merely listing and describing the sea dwellers, now began to map out their habitats with precision.

The earliest tow nets were simply let down into the sea, towed through the water for a while, then hauled to the surface, where the contents of the bucket were examined. This method had a big drawback. To bring to the surface a net that had been towed horizontally at a depth of 100 fathoms meant hauling it up vertically

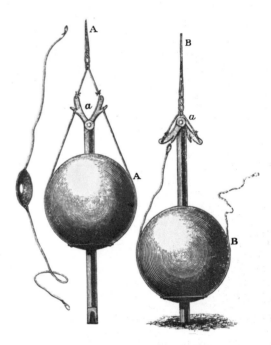

Brooke's cannon-ball core sampler. The ball's weight drove the hollow rod firmly into the sea bed. Reduced tension on the line released the ball, permitting the rod to be withdrawn.

Map on the following pages shows by colors distribution of sediments over the sea floor. "Terrigenous" deposits are generally coarse and derive from the land. In contrast, fine "pelagic" deposits are found in the deep sea and derive largely from the skeletal remains of marine creatures. (See key to map.)

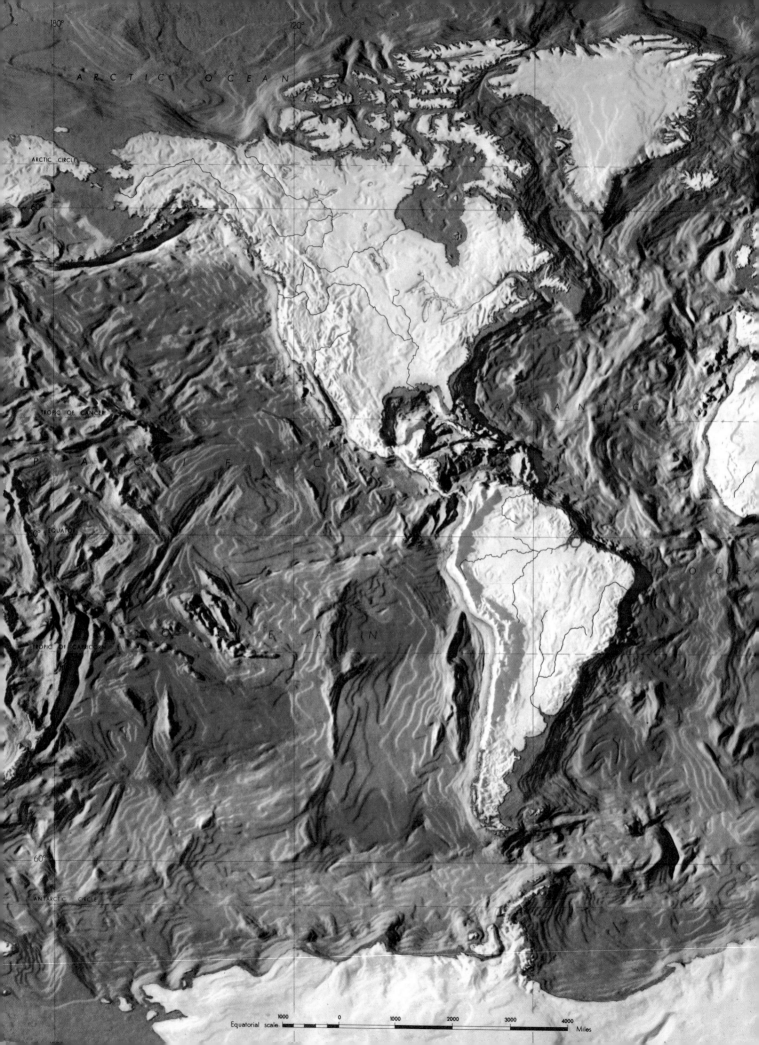

ARCTIC OCEAN

ARCTIC CIRCLE

60°

TROPIC OF CANCER

P A C I F I C

EQUATOR

O C E A N

TROPIC OF CAPRICORN

A T L A N T I C

O C E

60°

ANTARCTIC CIRCLE

180°   120°

1000   0   1000   2000   3000   4000
Equatorial scale   Miles

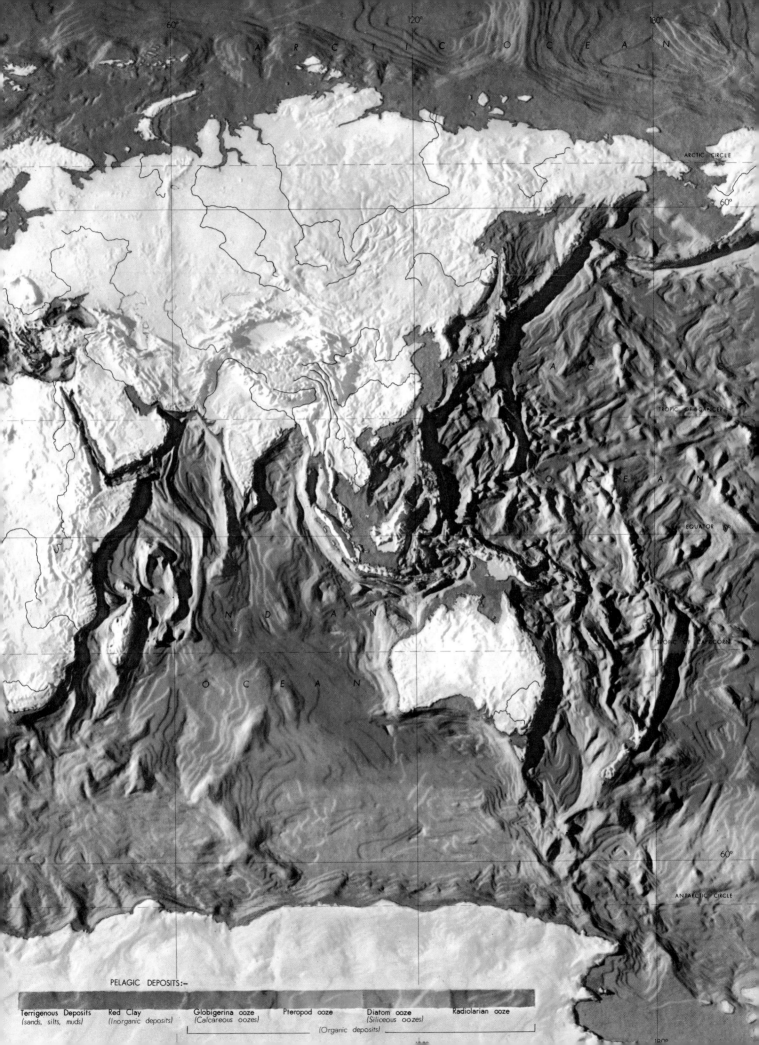

PELAGIC DEPOSITS:-

| Terrigenous Deposits (sands, silts, muds) | Red Clay (Inorganic deposits) | Globigerina ooze (Calcareous oozes) | Pteropod ooze | Diatom ooze (Siliceous oozes) | Radiolarian ooze |

(Organic deposits)

This engraving made in the 1800s shows several shells of microscopic animals forming part of the plankton. It was not until the tow net was developed in 1828 that biologists became aware of the staggering amount of planktonic life.

in such a way that when it was surfaced there was no means of telling whether the plants and animals in the bucket had been picked up at 100 fathoms or two inches from the surface. To overcome this difficulty, researchers eventually found a device for closing the net at any desired depth before they brought it up. As a further refinement they attached several tow nets to a single hawser so that different depths could be fished simultaneously.

With such equipment the distribution of plankton in depth as well as horizontally has been plotted over wide areas. The results show a zoning that corresponds roughly to the temperature of the water. They also show that although planktonic plants and animals drift passively with the currents, many make daily vertical migrations, coming toward the surface by night and sinking to some depth by day in order to avoid the bright light.

The plankton population is not the same everywhere, nor is the population static in one place throughout the year. In the shallow seas, near land, the plankton includes many larvae of animals that, when adult, live fixed to the bottom. Over deep water only the larvae of swimming adults or of planktonic animals are found, and these are different from those found in shallow waters. So a distinc-

This engraving shows how a deep-sea dredge used aboard the Challenger was lowered by stages to the bottom. A weight traveled down the line by stages (G, G', G'') so that when the dredge struck bottom it would be positioned to scoop up samples.

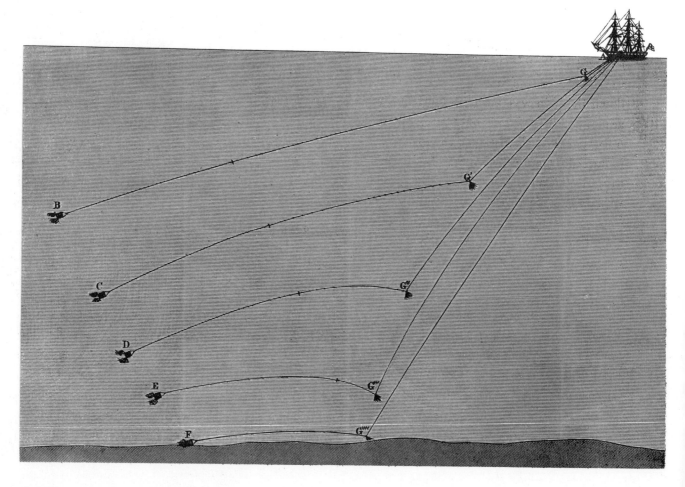

tion can be made between the neritic (coastal) and oceanic (blue-water) plankton. On a map, the 100-fathom line, which is also the edge of the continental shelf, forms an approximate – not a sharp – dividing line between the two types.

No lines of demarcation are more important to the life of plankton than those that mark changes in temperature. Even small differences in heat and cold may spell the difference between life and death for these tiny creatures. (They are also influenced by the amount of salt in the water, and this varies perceptibly from one part of the sea to another.) Since water temperature changes with the depth, certain kinds of plankton live at one level in one part of the ocean, at another level in another part. For instance, some species that are found in both the Arctic and Antarctic oceans are also found in temperate and tropical latitudes at depths where the water temperatures are the same as in shallow polar waters. But animals that are characteristic of the Gulf Stream cannot survive in either deep water or in cold surface waters. Whenever, as sometimes happens, warm and cold currents change their course, the effects on plankton can be disastrous. They can also be disastrous to the sea creatures we know best – the fishes.

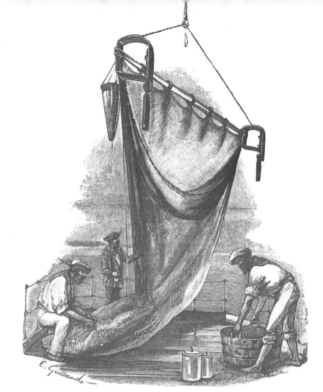

This beam trawl, used aboard the Challenger, *collected specimens from any desired depth. Iron clamps kept the mouth of the bag open. A small cotton bag lining the bottom of the large net trapped minute organisms.*

Plankton, the basic food in the sea, is composed of microscopic floating plants and animals. Enlarged many times, this photograph shows the translucent shells of a velvet swimming crab larva (left), a copepod (right), a megalopa (top), and a squat lobster larva (bottom).

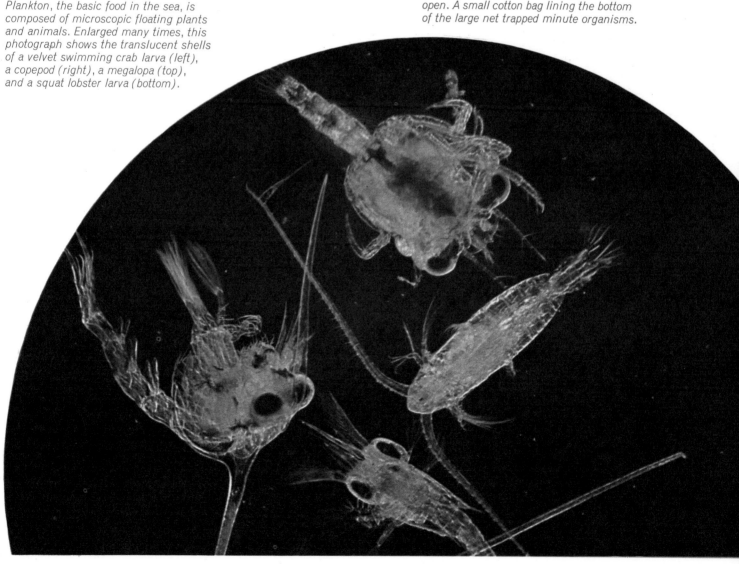

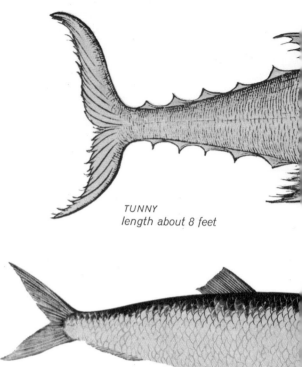

TUNNY
length about 8 feet

HERRING
length about 9 inches

The Movement of Fishes

Two tons of fish – cod, haddock, halibut, and skate – are dumped onto the deck of a British trawler fishing in the Barents Sea. The temperature of the water, its salt content, and the migration habits of fish are all important factors that determine the distribution of fish. The more the commercial fisherman knows about them, the better his long-term catch will be.

Fishes are about as much tied to temperature as is plankton. The different kinds of sardine, for example, are limited in both Southern and Northern hemispheres to waters between 12°C. and 20°C. Dangerous sharks, found all the year round in tropical seas between latitudes 21°N. and 21°S., are likely to do some traveling during the hot summer months. With a rise in the temperature of the water, they have been known to attack swimmers as far north or south of the Equator as 42°.

Temperature is only one of the factors that determine the range over which a species may be distributed. There are many others, and the more the fisherman knows about them, the better his long-term catch will be. Because we know that the sardine makes a breeding migration from the southern end of the Bay of Biscay to the English Channel and then returns south, the sardine fishery sensibly moves with the fish. Similarly, men have learned that the so-called Mediterranean tunny makes its home in the Atlantic, to the west of Spain and Portugal, as well as in the Mediterranean. (There is also a subspecies – the tuna – on the American side of the North Atlantic.) The tunny spawns off the Azores, off Gibraltar, and in the western Mediterranean along the coasts of Sardinia, Sicily, and Tunisia.

After the spawning migrations, large numbers of the tunny move north. They pass to the west of the British Isles, round the north

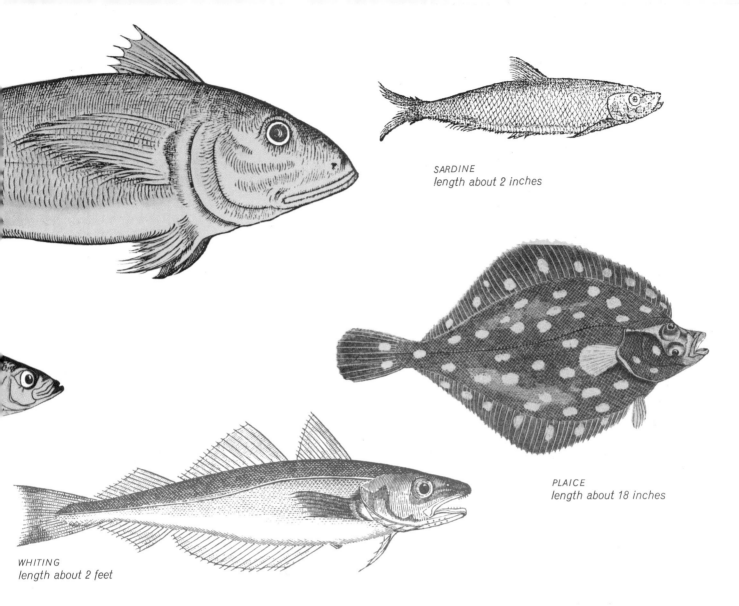

SARDINE
length about 2 inches

PLAICE
length about 18 inches

WHITING
length about 2 feet

of Scotland, then cross over to Norway, where they are often harpooned or continue down into the North Sea. Why do they take the long way round to Norway instead of using the English Channel? One explanation is that these migrations have been going on since the days, more than 10,000 years ago, when the British Isles were linked to the continent and there was no English Channel. The tunny may still be following the traditional route, though a short cut has been possible for thousands of years. Another explanation is that this is the way the plankton drifts, carried by the Gulf Stream, or North Atlantic Current, which curls round the north of Scotland and does not flow up the English Channel.

In general, our knowledge of the migrations of fishes has been accumulated slowly, as the result of meticulous, planned observation. In some cases, however, we have learned much through accident. For example, "accidental tagging" has taught us a lot about the tunny's habits. As these fish move from one part of the sea to another, fishermen tempt them with baited hooks that vary in different localities. Sometimes a fish may bite and escape with the hook still in its mouth. When it is later caught, the type of hook can be identified and so the tunny's travels can be plotted. One tunny that had been harpooned off Norway escaped with the head of the harpoon still buried in its flesh. It was later caught off Tunis in the Mediterranean.

The principal food fishes of Europe and North America are shown here: SARDINE: closely related to the herring and nearly as important commercially, sardines are caught mainly in the eastern Atlantic and Mediterranean. PLAICE: these flatfish are bottom dwellers related to the European flounder and the American summer flounder. As they mature, one eye migrates to the right side of the head. TUNNY: these fish are found mainly in warm seas. Among them is the tuna, the popular game fish weighing up to 1000 pounds. Tunny are a particularly important food source in Spain and Portugal. WHITING: like haddock and hake, the whiting is a member of the cod family and is distinguished by its delicate flavor. HERRING: an important food fish throughout most of the world, herring are found in cold waters and live fairly near the shore. They are represented by about 200 different species.

Scottish herring girls, migrant laborers work their way south from port to port along with the trawlers which follow the seasonal movements of the herring shoals. Their job is to clean and pack the catches for marketing. They work their way from Scotland down the east coast of England.

Mackerel have a different migration pattern. At the end of October they leave the surface waters, swim toward the bottom, and concentrate in troughs on the sea bed. Toward the end of December they start to spread out over the sea bed, feeding on such small animals as shrimps, worms, and little fishes found near the bottom. Early in the following year they return to the surface waters and start their spawning migrations, which take them in large shoals to the south of Ireland. In the early summer the female lays up to half a million eggs, which also appear to be of "migratory" habits. For about two days they float at the surface, then they gradually sink halfway to the bottom and remain suspended there for a few more days. Eventually they settle to the bottom and the young mackerel hatch.

Mackerel are among the fastest and most graceful swimmers in the sea. They grow to about eighteen inches, inhabit the northern latitudes, and travel in vast shoals. From about February to October they live in the surface waters and for the remainder of the year live near the bottom.

Not all fishes migrate. The herring, for example, breeds in cold coastal waters of relatively low salinity, where the temperature is less than 14°C. and the salinity less than 3.5 per cent. Fishermen used to think that there were annual mass migrations of herring from north to south in search of these favorable conditions. What actually happens is that the warm and highly salty water of the

By the fifteenth century many of the merchants of Hamburg, one of the Hanseatic towns, had grown rich on the herring industry. The mass movement of herrings has determined the siting of villages and towns in Scotland, England, Newfoundland, Alaska, Japan, and Siberia.

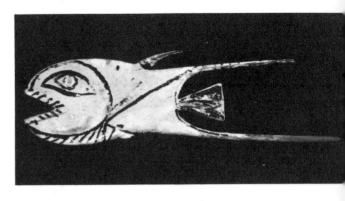

Fish symbols have long been important in religion. This one, carved of wood, is used by the Melanesians of New Ireland.

船鶩魚

子折双

Gulf Stream moves across the Atlantic during the summer, and as it reaches the coasts of France, the British Isles, and the Low Countries, Scandinavia, and Iceland, the herring are forced to retire to the deep waters of the continental slope. Later in the year, as the water of the Gulf Stream withdraws, leaving colder and less salty water at the surface, the herrings come up and spawn. This happens first in the north off Iceland, which is where the fishing begins, and it is not until January that the withdrawal of the Gulf Stream is felt on the coasts of Brittany. So although the fishing fleets follow the shoals from north to south, they do not follow the same shoal. In one area after another the local populations of herring come to the surface, thus giving a false impression of a north-south movement.

The Chinese and Japanese have devised many ingenious ways of catching fish, including nets that scoop fish out of the water. They also train cormorants to fish for them. Each bird wears a ring around its neck so that it cannot swallow its catch.

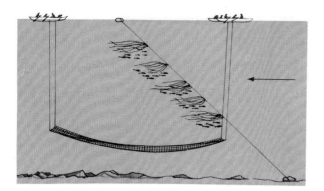

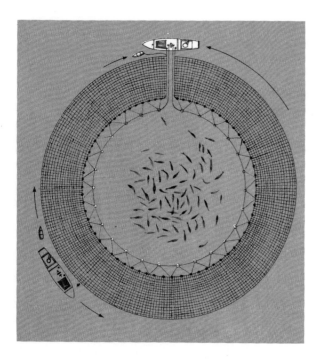

The diagram at bottom shows the "purse seine" net method of fishing. As it moves in a circular path the boat unwinds a long net until the circle is closed. While the rim of the net is kept on the surface by floats, the bottom part is allowed to sink. Fish within the net are trapped when a "purse string" line draws the bottom of the net closed. This method is commonly used in North American waters. A different method, the "madi valai," is common along the Madras coast of India. Four boats hold a net suspended horizontally below the surface. A long line with masses of weed is then lowered above the net, and when enough fish have been attracted by the weed the net is quickly drawn to the surface.

This behavior of the herring was confirmed when marine biologists discovered that local populations of herring differ from one another in their average number of vertebrae, their rate of growth, and age of sexual maturation. If there were widespread migrations, interbreeding would result in a mixture of such characteristics. The fact that there are local races seems to prove that the only migration of a given local population is a limited one from deep waters to coastal waters and back again. A similar story can be told of the cod: Because local races have recognizable characteristics, the expert can take a particular specimen of cod and say which part of the world it came from.

A better understanding of the breeding and migration habits of fishes means a better life for mankind. From the earliest times fish must have been a staple article of men's diet. Through the ages we have been concerned with devising easier and more efficient fishing methods. Primitive man probably caught fishes by hand, flipping them out of the water as bears and other mammals do. Later they were speared or trapped in simple wicker baskets, the forerunners of the cages and fish weirs still in use in many places. In the Japanese province of Gifu cormorant fishing survives to this day. Torches from the fisherman's boat attract the fish at night, then the birds, which are on leashes held by the fisherman, are allowed to go after the fish. A ring around the bird's throat prevents it from swallowing its catch. In due course, the hook and line and the net came to be invented; and today we have electric fishing and the detection of shoals by radar or by echo sounder.

Fishes, fishing, and fisheries have been closely linked with the advances in civilization. Björnson has put forward the view that wherever a shoal of herring has touched the coast of Norway, there the villages have sprung up. The siting of villages and towns, in relation to the mass movement of herrings, can be seen also in Scotland and eastern England, in Newfoundland, Alaska, Japan, and Siberia. The wealth of the merchants of the Hanseatic towns of Lübeck, Bremen, and Hamburg was founded largely on revenues

Fisheries biologists can record the depths and distribution of fish with the "shark recorder", an echo sounder towed behind a boat. It produces an echogram (left) which shows a shoal of fish near the bottom. Some fish in deep water, at the left of the echogram, are moving toward the surface.

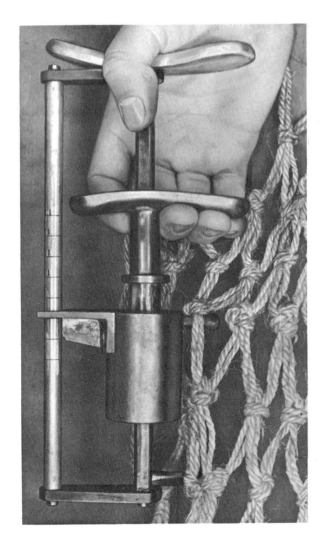

A small (legally undersize) plaice escapes from the net and has an opportunity to breed. Fish conservation depends largely on regulating the mesh size of nets, which can be measured by a gauge (right).

from the herring fisheries. Their fortunes declined somewhat when, in the fifteenth century, the local herrings altered course to run down the coast of Holland instead of along the German coasts. But there were other, and more important reasons for the decline. During the fifteenth century there were improvements in offshore fishing boats and in methods of preserving herring. This enabled Dutch fisheries – and later English fisheries – to compete with the Hanseatic inshore fisheries; hence to a large extent the decline was a relative one.

Modern science is increasingly interested in conserving the supply of fishes. Man's inroads when harvesting the sea have led to the need for vast programs of research into new methods of conserving the world's fisheries. In the closing years of the nineteenth century an idea was born – an idea that was to make possible a working co-operation between scientist and fisherman the world over.

The hope was that there might be a way to judge the age of fishes by the markings on their scales. A widespread study of this concept has made it possible for modern man to apply the principle of age determination to all marketable fish. At first biologists discovered a linkage between the size of herring and the number of rings on their scales. Then a Norwegian, Einer Lea, did some pioneer research on the scales themselves. He and his followers studied them minutely, split them into layers for an examination of their internal structure, cut them into thin sections, and examined them microscopically until it was established beyond doubt that there is a definite relationship between the growth of a scale and the growth of the fish.

The annual rings on the herring proved trustworthy, as did those of some other food fishes, such as the salmon. In others the scales proved unreliable for a variety of reasons. But it was found that the otoliths – small calcareous concretions in the ears – serve as well, since they also show annual rings. Age determination by the otoliths is now used extensively for such fishes as plaice.

This work ushered in an age of scientific management of the world's fisheries, first in Europe, then elsewhere. For a long time, however, many thoughtful men had realized that *something* must be done to maintain the dwindling supply of food fishes. One of the chief causes of depletion in the stocks of the ocean's food fishes has been the destruction of small fishes, which are taken from the sea before their time and are thus prevented from breeding. The work on age determination is vitally important in dealing with this problem, and so is the work that has been done on determining the best nets, sizes of mesh, and fishing seasons.

Although the most familiar crops of the sea are fish, there are other important harvests, among them seals; and it is from the sealing industry that we have learned an important lesson in conservation. With the exception of the Alaskan fur seal, the score or more of different kinds of seals are far less numerous today than they used to be. In all parts of the world they have been severely reduced in numbers, and in some places, as with the West Indian monk seal, they have been brought to the brink of extinction.

This happens to any group of animals for one of two reasons, or both: Either the animals are a nuisance to man or they are of great use. Seals have suffered persecution, especially in modern

Because the breeding grounds of the fur seal have long been known, the animals have long been subject to slaughter by the sealers who indiscriminately killed nursing mothers and pups. Deprived of its mother, a pup (the one shown here is two weeks old) cannot fend for itself and may perish.

times, because they were supposed to be depleting the fisheries. The trouble may be only temporary, or it may be due to causes other than predation by seals, but the mere fact that seals are nearby leads to their becoming the scapegoats. The outcry against seals has been particularly strong in recent years against the fur seals of the northeast Pacific, where they are accused of depleting the salmon.

The results of this persecution by the canning industry, however, is small by comparison with the sealers themselves, who killed nursing mothers and young, and simply left mortally injured animals to die in the sea. There was, therefore, a proportionately high wastage compared with the total harvest of skins.

Seals, like other animals, are bound by tradition and by their physical requirements. In spite of their complete adaptation to life in the water, which theoretically should give them great freedom of movement and therefore an escape from persecution, they still cling to traditional beaches for breeding, and their distribution also seems to be limited by temperature. The limit of distribution for the monk seals of the Mediterranean and eastern Atlantic corresponds to the winter isotherm of 20° C.

The fact that human communities have been able to survive in the Arctic was due largely to the presence of seals. Crantz, in his *History of Greenland* (1767) describes the uses made of the seal harvest: "The flesh supplies [the Greenlanders] with their principal, most palatable, and substantial food. The fat furnishes them with oil for their lamps and fires; they use it also with their food; and barter it for other necessaries with the factor. They find the fibres of the sinews better for sewing with than thread or silk. Of the skins of the entrails they make their windows, curtains for their tents, and shirts; and part of the bladders they use in fishing, as buoys or floats to their harpoons. Of the bones they formerly made

Today there are strict controls governing the number of fur seals killed. Above is a large herd on the beach of one of the Pribilof Islands in the Bering Sea.

Seals and walrus have long provided the Eskimo with his basic needs. From the tusks and bones he made tools; other parts of the body provided him with fuel, clothing, food, his kayak, and house furnishings.

105

all those instruments and working-tools that are now supplied to them by the introduction of iron. Even the blood is not lost; for they boil that, with other ingredients, as soup. Of the skins they form clothing, coverings for their beds, houses and boats, and thongs and straps of every description. To be able to take seals is the height of the Greenlanders' desires and pride; and to this labor, which is in truth an arduous one, they are trained from their childhood. By this they support themselves; by this they render themselves agreeable to each other, and become beneficial members of the community."

Primitive communities like the Greenlanders' do no more than skim the surplus from the seal populations. Somehow or another, modern civilizations have to learn to emulate the ways of primitive communities: to take what they need without impairing the sources of supply. This is what we mean by conservation. And conservation must be based on scientific knowledge. Some impression of the prodigious numbers of the world populations of seals can be gained from the history of one species alone – the Alaskan fur seal. And it so happens that this seal has given us an object lesson in conservation.

The main base of the Alaskan fur seal is the Pribilof Islands in the Bering Sea. When first discovered in 1786, the islands were the breeding base for millions of fur seals, but owing to exploitation by Russian and American sealers, this population was reduced to a mere 200,000 by 1911. By international agreement the islands were then put under strict control and the annual catch of seals limited. By 1927 the population had risen again to a million or so. Now the population is in excess of 3,000,000 and the number of skins taken is 50,000 each year. Even with that ample harvest the population continues to rise, hence the complaints from the salmon canners.

This spectacular result has been achieved by a scientific study of the habits of the seals. In the autumn the seals spread out across the two thousand miles of the North Pacific to feed. With the return of spring they begin to head for certain passages in the Aleutian Islands and continue on for another hundred miles to the fogbound Pribilofs. The breeding colonies are begun by the bulls, which arrive first, claim their territories, and await the arrival of the cows, for whom they fight, gathering them into harems of thirty to forty. Within a day or two of arrival each cow gives birth to a single pup conceived during the previous year. After this they mate with the bull, who during the breeding season does not leave the harem to feed. The cows go out to sea to feed and after an absence of days return to suckle their young. Meanwhile bachelor males two to three years old and not capable of forming harems live apart on what are called "bachelor beaches." When the breeding is ended the bulls return to sea until the next season. In October and November, when the pups are old enough to make the journey, they and the cows follow the bulls the two thousand miles south to their winter quarters.

While the harems are still dominated by their respective master bulls, the immature bulls are constantly challenging their right to the harems. The old bulls charge across their territories with no regard for the cows or the pups, and this, together with casualties from the actual fights, results in a heavy mortality. Once this was understood, it was an easy matter to see that the harvest of skins

The principles of seal conservation have also been applied to sea elephants, which were once abundant on many islands such as South Georgia in the South Atlantic. At one time they were reduced everywhere, but are now increasing again.

should be taken only from the bachelors. By weeding them out there were fewer casualties, especially among the pups, and the numbers killed for commercial purposes were more than offset by the saving of life by reducing the number of fights. So were saved the immense breeding colonies of the Pribilof seals, one of the natural wonders of the world.

Once this principle had been established it could be applied elsewhere, because the breeding behavior of seals follows much the same pattern whatever the species. The numbers in the harems may differ with different species, and there are other variations in behavior besides, but the principle used in this conservation with exploitation – a perfect example of having your cake while eating it – has been applied to other species, notably to the southern sea elephant. This animal was once abundant on the many islands in the sub-Antarctic, but commercial killing had all but wiped the sea elephant out on some islands and reduced them everywhere to dangerously low levels. The numbers are now everywhere on the increase. For fishes, conservation depends on a knowledge of the food supplies available for the different species, as well as their breeding habits. Mackerel, for example, depend at one stage of their lives on shrimps, worms, and small fishes. But these in turn must depend on smaller organisms, whether very small animals or plants.

But it is not enough merely to study the food of fishes to ensure good harvests from the sea. We must also take into account physical aspects of the sea itself. Temperature, for instance, can play a very important role. A striking example of this is in the story of the tilefish. The particular species in question grows to a length of two feet and lives beneath the Gulf Stream along the seaboard of North America at depths of forty-five to a hundred fathoms, where the temperature is from 8°C. to 12°C. In 1882 the warm water was displaced by an unusually strong wedge of cold water from the Labrador Current coming down from the north. That same year a ship's captain looked out across Delaware Bay one early morning and saw mile after mile of dead and dying tilefish – the estimated death toll was six times the total annual catch of all fish in the United States. The drop in temperature of the water had done its deadly work; for all time, some people thought. The tilefish was not quite extinct, although thirty-five years were to elapse before they were caught again in large numbers.

Almost as deadly as the influx of cold water, and in many ways more spectacular, are the so-called "red tides." They are caused by abnormally high concentrations of microscopic plant-animals, dinoflagellates, most of which are less than one thousandth of an inch across. These plant-animals are usually present in the plankton in smaller numbers than the diatoms. They differ from the diatoms by having an outer casing of cellulose (instead of silica) or no casing at all. In the warmer waters a "tide" occurs when the diatoms become less plentiful and their place is taken by vast numbers of dinoflagellates. When this happens the sea may be colored red for miles. Such growths have given the Red Sea its name. When, as happened in 1947 off the west coast of Florida, their numbers rise there may be fifty million or more to each pint of sea water. The sea becomes slimy to the touch and highly poisonous to fish. The red tide off Florida in 1947 killed upward of fifty million fish.

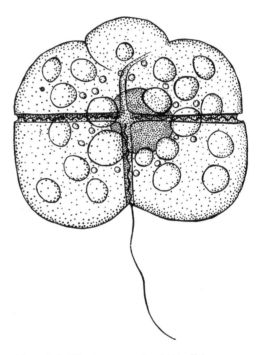

Mass fish kills known as "red tides" have been known since biblical times. Some are caused by abnormally high concentrations of a dinoflagellate called Gymnodinium brevis (magnified about 1700 times). During a red tide millions of dead and dying fish are washed up onto the beaches. Exactly how they are killed is still not known.

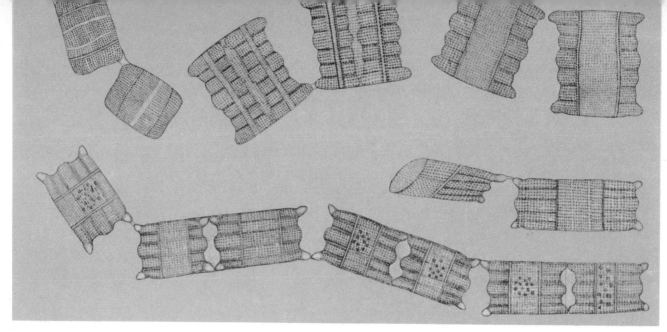

The Great Chain of Life

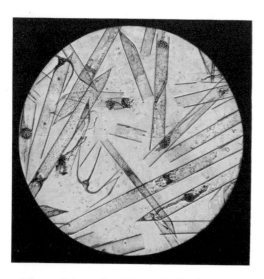

Where diatoms flourish, so do the fish. As a basic food source for the plankton, diatoms form rich pastures for fish. Those shown on this page are magnified about 420 times. They grow attached to rocks and seaweed and form chains. All diatoms live in the upper layers of the sea and are kept afloat by the shape of their delicate skeletons, which are made of silica.

Logically our discussion of life in the sea ought to have begun with the plants. They form the pastures of green food on which all animal life must depend, either directly or indirectly. But there are two reasons why we did not begin with the plants. First, the seaweeds, which are a familiar and much-studied senior member of the ocean's plant kingdom, are relatively unimportant to life in the sea. The second reason is that little was known about the floating microscopic green plants (that part of the plankton known as phytoplankton), which are the basic food source for the bulk of marine animal life, until after the invention of the tow net.

The enormous importance of the phytoplankton to the economy of the sea cannot be too strongly stressed. The phytoplankton forms the base of nearly all the food chains. It is vitally important to all the harvests of the sea, whether these be the food fisheries, sponge fisheries, whaling, or sealing.

Plants alone can manufacture food from such inorganic chemicals as the minerals and gases. But they can do this only in the presence of light, and light can penetrate water only to a limited extent. So for all practical purposes the vegetation of the sea does not go below forty fathoms — which represents only a thin skin over the oceans. Throughout that skin, in every part of the oceans, float vast quantities of phytoplankton. The seaweeds, on the other hand, are found only on a narrow fringe bordering the land masses. One major exception, of course, is found in the floating seaweeds of the Sargasso Sea; but in comparison with the phytoplankton, the seaweeds are too sparse to have much effect on the economy of the sea.

This does not mean that man has made no use of them. Seaweeds were once an important source of iodine. In many places where the soil is barren seaweeds have been carted and spread over the fields for use as fertilizer. Some have been used as food. For centuries, too, the Japanese have been extracting agar-agar from seaweeds; the product is widely used in medicine, in bacteriological work, for the making of jellies and emulsions.

By the end of the eighteenth century many thousands of tons of soda were being extracted from the brown seaweeds. With the development of cheaper sources of soda in the early nineteenth century, the industry died out; but after 1811, when iodine was discovered, there was a small revival in the processing of kelps.

Although a ton of dry weed yields only four pounds of iodine, the kelps long remained the only source of this important element. Then iodine was found in the niter of Chile. So the kelps were once again neglected – except in places like Japan where they are still valued as food and processed for the extraction of agar.

The phytoplankton is made up of four main constituents: the diatoms, peridinians, coccolithophores, and smaller members of these and other algal classes which together make up the so-called "nanoplankton." Diatoms are of many shapes, and they range in size from one three thousandths to one thirtieth of an inch. The larger ones are solitary while the smaller ones tend to live in chains. All float in the upper layers of the sea in much the same way as minute particles of dust are suspended in the air, and you can see them dancing in a sunbeam. The protoplasm of their bodies is enclosed in a lovely shell of highly ornamented silica, but the ornamentation is not so much a thing of beauty as a means of helping the organisms remain afloat. In bodies so small, the slightest irregularity of the surface structure provides enough friction with the water to arrest any downward movement due to gravity.

The peridinians are about the same size as the diatoms, but they have distinctive shapes. Their shells are made of cellulose and they have two flagella, one of which is extended, while the other lies in a groove around the equator of the shell. The flagellum in the groove keeps the peridinian spinning around, while the free flagellum, by a whipping action, drives it through the water.

Coccolithophores are much smaller than the diatoms and peridinians. Seldom more than one five hundredth of an inch in diameter, they have a single flagellum and their surfaces are protected by small disks of lime. Like the diatoms and peridinians, they contain green chlorophyll, multiply rapidly by simple fission, and often contain a small droplet of oil – a food reserve that some biologists believe may represent the source of the worlds's supply of petroleum. The primary function of the oil droplet is to help buoy up the plant, but when it dies it sinks down to the floor of the ocean. Century after century the slow accumulation of these oil droplets under the sediments may be transformed into our reserves of oil.

The fourth type of phytoplankton, the nanoplankton, is so small that fine-mesh (600 meshes per inch) tow nets are required to collect the creatures. But most work done on nanoplankton to date has been performed by growing cultures in the laboratory.

There is one more form of plankton plant life: the bacteria. These differ from the rest in that they are concerned not with the nourishment but with the breakdown and decay of their fellow sea creatures. The bacteria are highly important because they help to reduce all organic remains into phosphates and nitrates, which in turn serve to feed the other four types of phytoplankton and so complete the cycle of life. These dissolved salts accumulate in the water at the bottom of the oceans and are brought up to the surface waters by the currents. Where they upwell, as in the Peru and Benguela currents, the phytoplankton flourish. And where the phytoplankton flourish, so do the animals feeding on them. Thus the rich supplies of guano from seafowls off the Peruvian coasts, and – to a less spectacular degree – the great fishery stocks wherever they occur. Quite simply, the cycle of life is as follows: Dissolved salts and light from the sun provide food for the phytoplankton; the

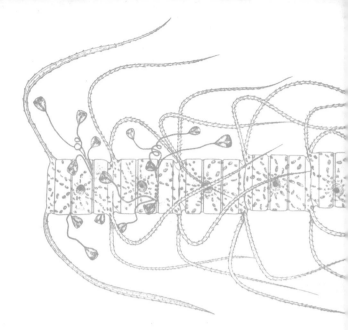

The cellular structure of a chain type of diatom that lives in tropical and subtropical seas is shown in the engraving above. At the end of each individual cell in the chain is a pair of horns which help give the chain buoyancy. Below: a photograph of a variety of diatoms (enlarged twenty-five times) shows some in chain form, others as individuals.

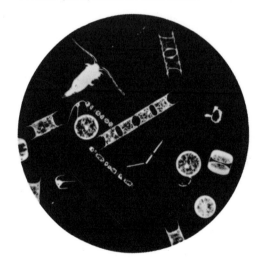

The whale, the largest living animal, feeds on plankton as do creatures only a small fraction of its size. A blue whale in its life eats about 10,000 tons of euphausians, a shrimplike plankton which grows to two inches in length. Called "krill" by whalers, euphausians in this quantity in turn require about one million tons of phytoplankton. (Print of the stranded whale is by the Japanese artist Kuniyoshi.)

phytoplankton is eaten by the smallest floating animals (the zooplankton); these in turn feed the larger animals; when the larger animals die, their organic remains are broken down to phosphates and nitrates by the bacteria.

The animals of the plankton are much less numerous, though more varied, than the plants. Just as a very rough estimate, you might expect to find about 20,000 plants, against only 120 animals, in a cubic foot of sea water. Something like that proportion must be maintained in order to maintain the balance of life in the oceans. When one of the zooplankton eats a quantity of phytoplankton only 10 per cent of the material consumed is converted into flesh. The rest is "lost" as waste or energy. The larger animals that feed on the zooplankton also conserve only 10 per cent of their food as flesh, and so on along the scale.

The enormous number of organisms in the sea cannot be set forth in figures. But to get some idea of the multitudes, consider the required amount of food for one blue whale weighing about 100 tons. To maintain such a weight it must consume in its lifetime 100 times 100 tons of euphausians, its sole food. Euphausians are shrimplike zooplankton up to two inches long, so the number

of them in 10,000 tons is astronomical; and we must multiply that fantastic figure yet again by 100 to determine the number of phytoplankton that must be consumed by the euphausian supply of only one among the tens of thousands of blue whales. Furthermore, the euphausians (or krill, as whalers call them) are eaten by other kinds of whales and several other animals.

The incalculable number of euphausians is exceeded by the number of copepods, which are also shrimplike but less than a quarter of an inch long. These animals filter the smaller forms of phytoplankton by means of special bristles that make a more effective strainer than any man-made net. In turn the copepods are eaten by jellyfishes, by arrow worms, by the young of many species of fishes, and by the adult herring and mackerel.

Fisheries research cannot afford, then, to be parochial. It may be necessary for one scientist or a group of scientists to concentrate on one localized problem or on a limited area of the sea. In the long run, though, we must take account of knowledge gained from the length and breadth of the ocean – the flow of nutrients, the physiology and movements of the plankton, the sources of food for commercial fishes, their breeding and migrating habits, and so on.

The rocky shores of most coasts abound with seaweeds, important as a source of food for creatures of the sea and important to man commercially. Different varieties of weed are found in different 'zones' along the shore. In general, the weed found highest on the shore is a bright green species. Along the middle shore are varieties of brown weed and the lowest, sublittoral, zone contains red types of weed which are not exposed to the air for long periods of time.

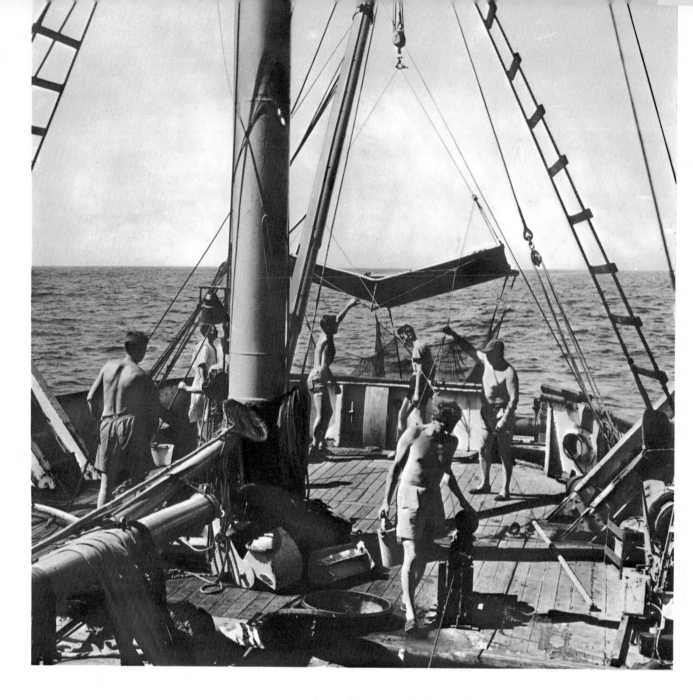

Marine Biology as a Science

Marine biology's greatest stimulus was the ocean-going research ship. It enabled a systematic collection and recording of plant and animal specimens over all of the oceans and seas. Scientists aboard Britain's Discovery II are here seen hauling a midwater trawl onto the afterdeck.

As we have seen in the exploration chapter of this book, and as we will see in the last chapter, man's knowledge of the oceans has come slowly. The marine biology branch of oceanography is no exception. Over the years biologists of the seas have depended on three general techniques for building up knowledge: the work of marine biological stations; research done by ocean-going expeditions; and attempts to explore the oceans directly in depth. These three lines of development were drawn up almost simultaneously in several different countries during the nineteenth century, and they are all being followed today.

The story of marine biological stations may be said to have begun with Philip Henry Gosse, an English naturalist born in 1810. He had been chiefly interested in birds until, some time after 1840, his health broke down and he went to Devon to recuperate. There he spent much of his time on the shore and soon found himself writing books on marine zoology. More of a crusader than an author, he also began to organize parties that set out on specimen-

By the mid-nineteenth century interest in marine biology was attracting week-end enthusiasts to the shores. William Dyce painted his family collecting specimens in Kent.

collecting expeditions. His son has described one such party: "At the head of the procession, like Apollo conducting the Muses, my father strides ahead in an immense loose black coat and fisherman's boots, with a collecting basket in one hand, a staff or prod in the other. Then follow gentlemen of every age, all seeming spectacled and old to me, and many ladies in the balloon costume of 1855, with shawls falling to a point from between their shoulders to the edge of their flounced petticoats, each wearing a mushroom hat with streamers."

Gosse also popularized the keeping of marine aquaria in the home; he even published instructions on the best ways of obtaining salt water and stocking an aquarium. It was Gosse who encouraged the construction of large public aquaria, including the one at the London Zoo in 1853. His efforts were largely responsible for an almost phenomenal rise of British interest in marine zoology, and the logical outcome of his crusade should have been the founding of a marine biological station. Although he came very near to doing so, the credit must be shared by two other men – an American and a German.

The first, Louis Agassiz, was born in 1807 in a small Swiss village. After taking a degree in medicine he turned to the study of fishes and in due course was invited to Boston to lecture. He was so successful that he settled in America, accepting the new chair of natural history at Harvard. His enthusiasm for marine biology, stimulated by trips aboard U. S. Coast Survey vessels in 1847, grew to a point where he finally asked the Massachusetts legislature for funds to establish "a seaside marine laboratory." This appeal failed, but news of it reached the ears of a wealthy merchant, John Anderson, who offered Agassiz the island of Penikese in Buzzards

Alexander Agassiz watches a deep-sea trawl being hauled over the side of the Albatross, one of the steamers he chartered to carry out oceanographic research.

Edward Forbes, the British naturalist and professor at London and Edinburgh universities, achieved recognition in all the natural sciences.

Bay and fifty thousand dollars to convert existing buildings on the island into a laboratory. This happened in 1873, but Agassiz died before the close of the year and the laboratory died with him.

Meanwhile, Agassiz's work was being paralleled by that of Anton Dohrn, a German born in 1840, who was to succeed permanently where Gosse had failed and Agassiz had tasted only temporary success. Dohrn's early studies in marine zoology at Messina, in Italy, inspired him with the idea of establishing a marine biological station that would have an international character. Eventually he chose Naples for the site and appealed to the German government for help. As with Agassiz' appeal to the Massachusetts legislature, Dohrn's request got nowhere; but with the assistance of friends, England's Royal Society, plus his own determination and the use of his personal fortune, he managed to tip the scales. The first part of the Stazione Zoologica at Naples was opened in 1873. This time the venture flourished. A second building followed in 1890, a third in 1907; today the Naples Station, directed by Dr. Peter Dohrn, the founder's grandson, is considered the alma mater of scores of marine stations throughout the world.

The biologists, chemists, physicists, and technicians who staff a typical marine station study life along the shore and in the shallow seas; their work, therefore, complements the work done by ocean-going research vessels. Although much of the work carried out by a marine station can be performed in university laboratories situated inland, there are enormous advantages in having permanent laboratories located on the coasts. The permanent marine station allows continuous study of the shore and shallow seas throughout the year; and with one or more vessels attached to it, the station can conduct routine surveys – compiling charts of temperature, salinity, and other properties of the offshore waters. At the same time, particular problems – that affect fisheries, for instance – can be studied within hours of the time they are detected, when time can be very important.

The work done at the more than 500 marine stations scattered over the world varies according to the object for which each station was founded. Some, such as the Fisheries Laboratory of the Ministry of Agriculture, Fisheries, and Food (at Lowestoft, England) and the Shellfish Laboratory of the U. S. Fish and Wildlife Service (at Milford, Connecticut), are more concerned with fishery problems. Others, such as the Plymouth Laboratory of the Marine Biological Association of the United Kindgom, the Seto Marine Biological Laboratory in Japan, and the Woods Hole Marine Biological Laboratory near Cape Cod in the United States, are concerned with more academic studies. But in all the spirit of inquiry is broadly based and every station takes a close interest in the work being done in all the others.

As the founding of marine stations was an inevitable next step from the informal exploration of the shores and shallow seas, ocean-going expeditions inevitably followed the establishment of marine stations.

It was again an Englishman who provided much of the impetus for the nineteenth-century upsurge of interest in such expeditions. In 1843 Edward Forbes, who was a professional lecturer on natural science, suggested that no plant life – and very little animal life – could exist in the sea below 100 fathoms, and that below 300 fathoms

there was an azoic zone where all life disappeared. It seems a bit difficult to understand how Forbes could have maintained such a view, particularly since in 1817 and 1818 Sir James Ross had brought up starfishes and other animals from a depth of 1000 fathoms. The discussions stimulated by Forbes's idea triggered many attempts to test it.

Several expeditions by British Naval ships set out, notably the *Rattlesnake, Bulldog, Lightning*, and *Porcupine*. Each ship had a naturalist on board and all succeeded in bringing up many animals from depths far greater than 300 fathoms. Even so, many scientists stubbornly refused to be convinced that animals could survive at such depths. But in 1860, when the telegraph cable between Sardinia and Bône was raised for repairs, little doubt could remain. The cable was incrusted with thousands of animals – and it was known to have lain on the sea bed at depths up to 1000 fathoms. To settle the matter once and for all, the British organized marine biology's first ocean-going expedition, that of the *Challenger*.

In December 1872 H.M.S. *Challenger*, stripped of her guns, loaded with scientific gear, and with a party of biologists led by Professor C. Wyville Thomson, sailed for a cruise around the world. For three and a half years she went on trawling and dredging, taking samples of the sea bed. In the course of her voyage she covered 68,890 nautical miles, and on her return the mountain of specimens and data she had collected were studied by leading scientists of the world. The results, published in a series of massive volumes, marked a turning point in the study of the oceans.

At long last things were beginning to dovetail. On the heels of the *Challenger* expedition cruises by other research ships were beginning to build up a picture of the shore and the shallow seas.

Sir Charles Wyville Thomson was scientific officer on the famous Challenger *expedition.*

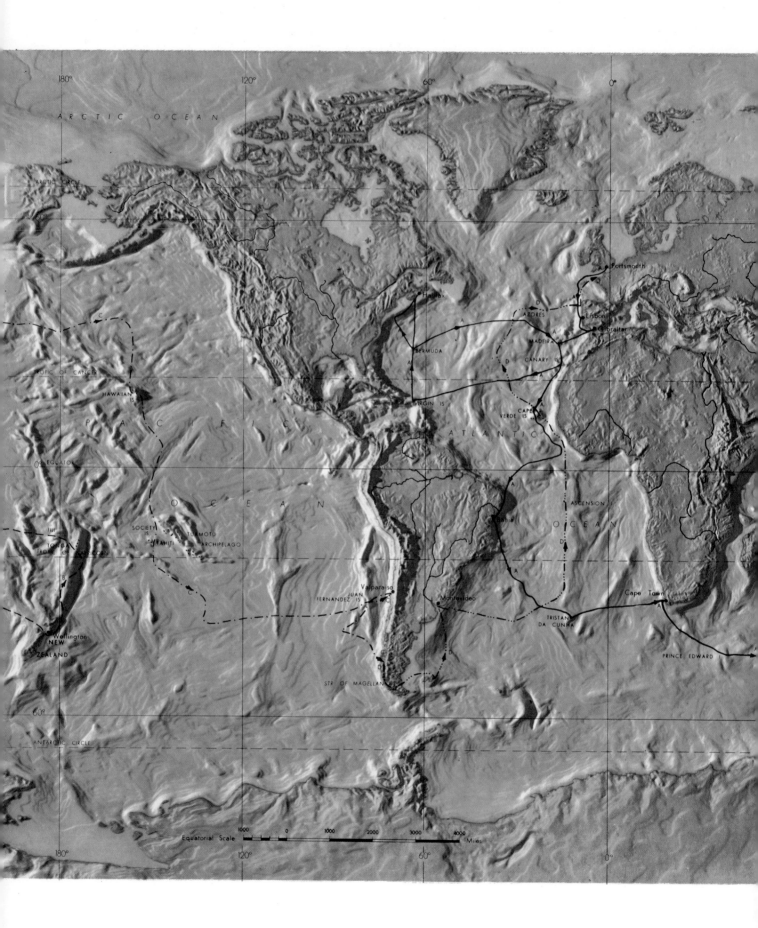

ARCTIC OCEAN

180°   120°   60°   0°

ARCTIC CIRCLE

60°

A · Portsmouth
D
D
Halifax   AZORES   Lisbon
A   Gibraltar
BERMUDA   MADEIRA
A   D   CANARY IS
TROPIC OF CANCER   A
HAWAIIAN   VIRGIN IS
IS   CAPE
PACIFIC   VERDE IS
ATLANTIC
O   C   E   A   N
0° EQUATOR
ASCENSION I
SOCIETY   Bahia   OCEAN
IS   TUAMOTU   D
FIJI   TAHITI   ARCHIPELAGO   A
TONGA
TROPIC OF CAPRICORN   A
B   Valparaiso   Cape Town
JUAN   A
FERNANDEZ IS   C   Montevideo
C   TRISTAN
Wellington   DA CUNHA
NEW   PRINCE EDWARD
ZEALAND   D
STR OF MAGELLAN   D

60°

ANTARCTIC CIRCLE

1000   0   1000   2000   3000   4000
Equatorial Scale
Miles

180°   120°   60°   0°

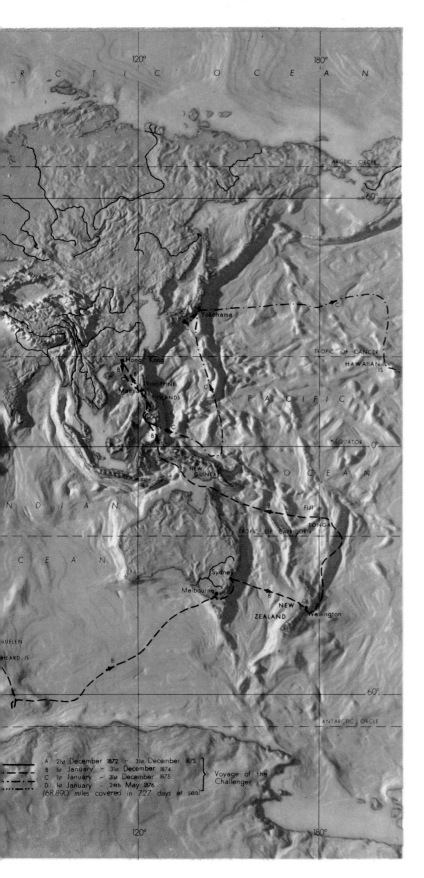

This world map shows the voyage of the Challenger *from the time she set out in 1872 until her return in 1876.*

The Monaco Oceanographic Museum and Laboratory was founded in 1910 by Prince Albert I, a leading pioneer of oceanographic research.

The Naples Zoological Station, established and opened in 1873 by Anton Dohrn, is considered the alma mater of scores of marine stations throughout the world. Its present director is the founder's grandson.

A 21st December 1872 — 31st December 1873
B 1st January — 31st December 1874
C 1st January — 31st December 1875
D 1st January — 24th May 1876
(68,890 miles covered in 727 days at sea)
Voyage of the Challenger

Prince Albert I of Monaco (left) prepares a balloon equipped with automatic instruments designed to record meteorological data at sea. Albert spent much of his life and private fortune on oceanographic research.

Now the oceans were to be surveyed in breadth and depth. One ocean-going expedition followed another, sponsored by one nation after another. The U. S. Coast Survey steamer *Blake* set out in 1877 to explore the Gulf of Mexico and the Caribbean under the leadership of Alexander Agassiz, son of Louis. As a mining engineer, he had made a substantial fortune, and it was he who paid off the debts of his father's abortive marine station. Now, turning to oceanography, he made an important change in method. Instead of the stout ropes the *Challenger* had used for deep-sea dredging, Agassiz adapted the steel cables used in mining, making a great saving in stowing space on board ship and a considerable saving in the time needed for letting down and hauling in the nets. The *Challenger* had taken more than two-and-a-half hours to make a sounding in 2435 fathoms; in contrast the *Blake* took about an hour for a sounding of 2929 fathoms.

From 1880 to 1883 the French research ships *Travailleur* and *Talisman* surveyed the deep waters of the Mediterranean and eastern Atlantic in an attempt to compare the deep-sea fauna found in each. Their results revealed the same kinds of animals in each, but they were more numerous in the Atlantic. In 1882 the U.S.S. *Albatross* was commissioned for oceanographical work by the U. S. Fish and Fisheries Commission. Working in the tropical Pacific, she took more deep-sea fishes in one haul of her dredge than the *Challenger* had collected in her whole cruise. In 1885 Prince Albert of Monaco began a series of cruises in the Mediterranean and North Atlantic, using first the yacht *Hirondelle* and later the *Princess Alice* and *Princess Alice II*. Although his particular interest was in exploring the deep seas, his many expeditions contributed greatly to oceanography as a whole. As a young man he had served in the Spanish

Navy, and his navigating skill as well as his private fortune were soon being devoted to oceanography. The most obvious memorial to his work is the magnificent and world-renowned marine station at Monaco, but equally outstanding is the long series of volumes he published on the collections he made during his many cruises.

In 1889 a German group aboard the *National* surveyed for plankton in the Atlantic. The years 1895-96 saw the Danish *Ingolf* working off Iceland; 1898-99 the German *Valdivia* working in the Atlantic and Indian Oceans; and in 1899 the Dutch *Siboga* investigated the waters of the Dutch East Indies. These last three expeditions exemplify how ocean-going expeditions complement the work of shore stations. Each ship surveyed a particular part of the ocean far beyond the reach of any shore station, and it did so systematically and methodically, just as a shore station studies the shore and shallow seas.

Before these expeditions life in the deep seas had been virtually a closed book. Darwin's theory of evolution had influenced thought to the extent that many scientists tended to believe that life in the deep seas, if any, would consist of animals from earlier geological times. The general idea was that life had begun in the shallow seas and had spread outward into the oceans and onto the land, and that the primitive forms of life had taken refuge in the ocean depths. This theory was strengthened when, in 1866, an unusual animal was brought up from the deep waters of the Lofoten fjords in Norway. It was a living sea lily, closely related to certain remains that had been found in rocks 350 million years old and that were believed to be the remains of a long-extinct species.

Louis Agassiz, for one, had maintained that deep-sea collecting would reveal the presence of "living fossils" – that in the depths of the oceans was a kind of Lost World. But the collections made by the *Challenger* showed that, while deep-sea animals might be different from those living nearer the surface, it was only because they were specialized to life in the great depths. Some, indeed, showed no differences at all. A recent find of a species of worm (Pogonophoran) shows that this animal lives at depths ranging from fifteen fathoms to 6000 fathoms. One sea urchin brought up

Until 1938 the coelacanth, which lived seventy million years ago, was thought to be extinct, but fishermen off Madagascar have been bringing them up in nets for years. The drawing (below) was based on a coelacanth fossil found in English chalk cliffs before the first live coelacanth was studied.

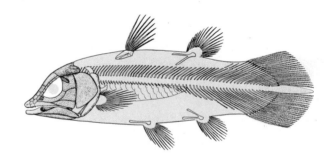

from the depths had a flexible shell and very much resembled sea urchins found in chalk deposits laid down 100 million years ago, but it soon became clear that such rare "living fossils" are also distributed more or less evenly on land, in shallow seas, as well as in the ocean depths. There is no great concentration of them at any one point on land or sea.

What is probably the most spectacular discovery of a living fossil is that of a group of fishes thought to have died out seventy million years ago. In 1938 a trawler fishing off the Chalumna River, near East London, South Africa, took a five-foot-long fish in its nets. Its paired fins did not spring directly from the body, as is usual, but were on fleshy limblike lobes, and it had a supplementary tail. Professor J. L. B. Smith, who examined it, noticed its likeness to the fossils of "extinct" coelacanths. Further investigation, and the discovery of more of these fishes suggests that they live in the mid-waters off Madagascar, where the local fishermen have probably been catching and eating them for years.

Every now and then an ocean-going expedition brings back one or more spectacular finds. While whale fishing around the Azores, Prince Albert of Monaco took an interest in the contents of the sperm whales' stomachs. He was later able to report that they contained the more or less perfect remains of giant squids with "... muscular arms, though much shrunken and contracted, as thick as those of a man and covered with more than a hundred great suckers, each armed with a short claw as powerful as those of a lion or tiger." It is hard to single out any one outstanding specimen discovered by the *Challenger* because almost everything brought back was novel. The *Valdivia* is remembered for its deep-sea squids — small squids with beautiful luminescent organs; and also for the single-rod sponge from the Indian Ocean. The German ship *Meteor*, which went into the South Atlantic during 1925-29, sailed with the intention of trying to extract gold from sea water, but came back instead with valuable information on phytoplankton.

Whatever else any such expedition may accomplish, each comes back with general collections and systematic data about physical conditions of the sea. From the steady accumulation of all these bits of knowledge a good picture of life in the sea is being laboriously built up. However, the picture cannot be entirely satisfactory so long as it must be seen from a shore-based biological laboratory or from the deck of a ship. Inevitably the student of marine life longs to go down and see things at firsthand.

Today the bathyscaphe is our only direct link with the deep bottom of the oceans. Developed over the last fifteen years or so, there have been several models, each succeeding one showing improvements on the last. In 1953 two French naval officers descended in one to more than 2000 fathoms off Dakar, West Africa; and in 1960 came the news that, in an improved model, Jacques Piccard and Lieutenant Donald Walsh of the United States Navy had gone down to more than 6000 fathoms (nearly seven miles) in the Marianas Trench, southwest of Guam in the Pacific. One of the marine biologist's dreams is a bathyscaphe-type vehicle capable of roaming over the sea bottom at any depth, making photographs, sound recordings, and collecting samples at will. Such a device would be an enormous aid to our present techniques of studying life in the sea.

On the opposite page, a sixteenth-century Indian painting shows Alexander being lowered to the sea bed in his glass diving bell. Since his time oceanographers have devised many ways of exploring the sea bottom by direct means. Cousteau's plunging saucer, shown on this page, is a free-swimming device capable of carrying two people to a depth of about a thousand feet. Future and improved versions of this craft should enable oceanographers to carry out many research activities that today must be controlled from the surface.

Sunken Cities

and Forgotten Wrecks

N. C. Flemming

*Submergence of coasts and rising sea level
have drowned dozens of proud harbors
that graced the shores of the Mediterranean
in ancient times. This Roman painting may
be of Pozzuoli, the most important trading
port during the time of the Roman Republic.
The Syracuse coin (above) with sea motif
was designed around 412 B.C.*

At the Greek city of Helike, on the shores of the Gulf of Corinth, stood the great temple of Poseidon, god of the sea. According to the historians of ancient Greece, more than 2300 years ago, when a party of invading Achaeans dragged a group of suppliants from the temple and slaughtered them, Poseidon was enraged by this sacrilege and promised revenge. A few days later a terrible earthquake shook Helike. Buildings crashed and crumbled and, according to one account, "the ground rose and fell like molehills come up from the bowels of the earth." Two thousand feet up in the mountains behind Helike, the city of Burra disappeared completely into a chasm. During the evening of the same day, the sea withdrew slightly, but when darkness fell surged forward with such violence that, although Helike was a mile and a half inland, the waters poured over it and covered the city to the tops of the trees. The destruction was complete. By dawn of the next day there was not one inhabitant of the city left alive.

Sailors and fishermen from nearby, rowing over the ruins of the submerged city, could look down on the trees and on the vast bronze statue of Poseidon, still standing beneath the waves and holding a sea horse in his upraised hand. For many years after the disaster ferrymen rowed travelers over the sunken city, pointing out its corroded, weed-covered walls, inch by inch disappearing under layers of fine mud. Fishermen steered clear of the victorious statue of Poseidon, knowing that he would surely tear their nets if they ventured too close. Pliny, the Roman historian, dates the catastrophe at two years before Epaminondas' victory over the Spartans at Leuctra. So it seems likely that the city of Helike was destroyed in 373 B.C.

The city now lies beneath twenty feet of water, and its streets are covered by twenty feet of slime and mud. To excavate Helike's priceless ruins is an underwater archaeologist's dream, but it would be a project that would take many years of complex salvage work and a huge amount of money.

In many parts of the world, in all ages, there have been similar tragedies; and with the help of geologists, the archaeologist can determine their cause. Most changes in the elevation of coasts are very slow, and have been less dramatic than the drowning of Helike. But in places where the change has been rapid, men have been defenseless and have had to flee or die. Where the change has been gradual — in Holland, for instance — great engineering works have prolonged the life of coastal cities. Sometimes it has been simply a matter of dredging channels in a shallowing harbor; other times of raising the height of quays and sea walls to keep the water at bay, as on the Thames estuary. Yet so great are the forces of the sea that human efforts to hold it back have never been more than temporarily successful.

The study of lost cities is inevitably linked with the study of geology and oceanography. To begin with, we want to understand the reason for a given disaster. We know that there are several ways the sea encroaches on the coasts. There may be an absolute change in sea level — known as a eustatic change. This can be brought on by a change in volume of the ocean basins, by excess melting or freezing of the polar and continental icecaps, by a change in the total quantity of water on the earth's surface, or by a change in the temperature of the oceans. On the other hand, the coastal land

A print of Lisbon being rocked by the earthquake of 1755. Dramatic changes in the height of the land relative to the sea can be brought about by violent earthquakes.

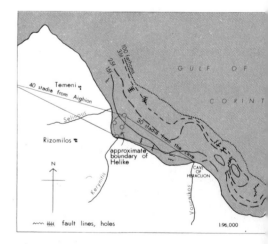

Details of the ocean floor and fissures are shown near the submerged site of the Greek city of Helike which sank into the sea during an earthquake about 373 B.C. Today Helike lies beneath more than forty feet of water and mud.

itself may change its level. This can be brought on by localized landslips, subsidences, or faults, or it may involve slow land movements over hundreds of miles of coast. Over the last twenty years surveys made by the United States Coast and Geodetic Survey show that the coast line from Florida to Massachusetts is sinking at the rate of about .02 feet every year. At this rate, in a thousand years the coast would be twenty feet beneath the sea, but the geological process is not so simple.

Usually it is impossible to distinguish between short-term eustatic changes and true land movements during the same period, because the only measurable quantity is the relative position of land and sea. Over short periods, say a thousand years, the change in level of a given site is usually due to local land movement; it is risky to try to attribute such a change to small eustatic changes. But over longer periods, tens of thousands of years, the eustatic changes mount up so they can be measured. We can, for example, find raised and sunken beaches tens and hundreds of feet above or below the present sea level.

From 14,000 to 4000 B.C., at the end of the last glaciation when the polar icecaps were melting, the sea rose about three hundred feet all over the world. When this happened, water flowed far inland, flooding the coastal river beds and forming long inlets and estuaries. The first great sea voyages that we know of were made soon after the sea had stopped rising; at that time there were many natural harbors, ideal sites for cities. But the cities that sprang up at such sites were menaced by heavy silting, with the result that old coastal towns like Myos, Miletus, Priene, and Utica are today one to twelve miles inland from the sea.

Regions subject to such large-scale sedimentation are very often subject to subsidence, so that any city built on or near a delta — even if it is not threatened by silt — risks being inundated by the sea. This was probably the fate of Fos-sur-Mer near the Rhône, Carthage near the Medjerda, and the small island of Pharos off the Nile delta. Although there certainly have been absolute changes in sea level since 400 B.C., it is extremely difficult to measure them, simply because we cannot be certain about land movements. Consequently we must attribute many of the submerged cities of the Mediterranean to local earth movements or earthquakes. Helike obviously disappeared in an earthquake; Epidaurus probably did; and Apollonia, the port of Cyrene, possibly did. Because our knowledge of absolute sea level changes and land movements is so confused, the analysis of present positions of ancient sites is of real value to the geologist and oceanographer.

Man's feeble ability to combat the ponderous and inevitable movements of the coast line in the past has been matched by his helplessness in the face of capricious storms of the open sea. The ocean bed of the Mediterranean is littered with the wreckage of ships. Through five thousand years of maritime adventure, war, squalls, rocks, and a variety of other hazards have sent hundreds of ships to the bottom. These too, like sunken cities, contain archaeological treasures that can help us fill in many details of history. While the study of the movements of coastal cities is inevitably linked with geology and oceanography, the study of wrecks is pure archaeology. The essential facts that are interesting about a wreck are its date, cargo, construction, origin and destination, and the reason it sank. Usually we can assess the cargo fairly quickly, which gives us the approximate date of the voyage, and with a bit of luck, the ports of origin and destination.

If the ship is an unknown type, it is extremely difficult to determine just how it was constructed, unless the cargo has covered and preserved the beams, in which case the whole cargo must be excavated. On the other hand, we can sometimes deduce the method of construction by comparing a few key parts with wrecks previously excavated. Complete excavation is such a lengthy and expensive business that only once in ten years or so do we find a wreck worthy of detailed analysis. Each excavated and unexcavated wreck is recorded by archaeologists, who then can build up gradually a picture of volumes of trade over various trade routes.

Discovering sunken cities and wrecks is tedious work. Classical histories, old charts, and archaeological reports must be searched minutely, and whenever possible the researcher should make full use of local sources. Even so, we find most wrecks by chance, and it is a cunning research worker who can find the man who knows the man who actually knows the exact site of a classical wreck.

If a ship with its cargo sank in a shallow harbor, it would either have been salvaged almost immediately, or destroyed to prevent danger to other ships. If a ship was driven onto the shore by a gale, the wreck would soon be pounded to pieces by the crashing surf. Only the ships that struck isolated rocks or were swamped and sank

This third-century B.C. mosaic from Ostia, the port for Rome, shows Sardinian ships being loaded with amphorae. Thousands of amphorae from this period (below) have been recovered from wrecks in the Mediterranean.

These spheroid-type amphorae, probably used for storing oil, were found by Cousteau near the Île de Maire, off Marseilles.

in deep water would be preserved from the destructive forces dominating the surface of the sea.

Although the land archaeologist is concerned with the same kind of material as the underwater archaeologist, a complete wreck and its cargo can still be found only beneath the sea. But even in the motionless depths a wreck is not safe. Soon the weeds grow over it and marine borers begin to eat their way into the wood. After a while the structure is so weakened that the hull collapses like an egg shell beneath the weight of the cargo, the sides fall outward, the cargo settles down onto the keel strip, and the splintered deck is devoured by the borers. Its death agonies are now over, and the corpse can lie unchanged for a thousand years until men come again to disturb the grave.

If by chance the ship settles into very soft mud, and is quickly covered over with sea bottom deposits, the wood will be permanently protected. But few such rewarding wrecks are found, simply because they are so difficult to detect. Occasionally, however, a diver brings up bits of a hull during commercial excavations in places like London and Ostia. But before describing some of the wrecks and lost cities discovered in the Mediterranean, we should first say something about the periods of sea power of various civilizations, the extent of their trade, and the construction of their ships.

Hundreds of ships of classical times foundered on treacherous rocks along the Mediterranean coast. This Admiralty chart shows the sites of several wrecks (circled in red) near the entrance of Toulon Harbor.

Ancient Civilizations

At the height of their power the Egyptians exacted many tributes from the peoples whose lands they ruled. This wall painting shows Nubians bringing gifts of gold to Sebekhotep, who ruled in Thebes around 1420 B.C.

Pre-dynastic petroglyphs in Egypt show large river boats fitted with many oars, and other archaeological finds show that the Egyptians were building sea-going ships for voyages in search of iron, lead, and silver before 3000 B.C. From the Palermo Stone we know that Seneferu (c. 2750 B.C.) built sixty huge ships for an expedition to Syria to obtain cedarwood. Sahure, 2958 – 2946 B.C., sent ships to Punt (probably Somaliland) to fetch frankincense, aromatic gums, ivory, gold, rhinoceros horns, panther skins, and rare woods.

Sporadic trade continued between Egypt and Punt until the time of Rameses III, who reigned from 1198 – 1161 B.C., and who built powerful fleets in the Mediterranean and the Red Sea.

After Rameses III the Egyptian Empire began to decline, and it was about this time that the Phoenicians broke their ties with Egypt. Phoenician sea power expanded dramatically and continued to dominate the Mediterranean until the ninth century B.C. Because of her lack of strength on land, Phoenicia eventually fell under Assyrian rule, although Tyrian sea power was not really broken until the victory of Alexander about 332 B.C.

The decay of Egypt stopped temporarily during the reign of Sheshonk I, 945 – 924 B.C., an energetic Pharaoh who permitted Solomon to trade in the Red Sea from a base at Ezion Gebir, on the Gulf of Aqaba. To obtain ornamental timber, precious stones, and gold for the construction of the Temple, Solomon turned to Tyre for help. He hired Tyrian engineers to build the Temple and arranged for the construction of a Phoenician fleet on the Red Sea to carry the commodities from Ophir. Hiram of Tyre provided the timber from Lebanon, the shipwrights, pilots, and seamen. It is probable that Ophir was on the west coast of India, and that Solomon wanted to trade directly to cut out the Arab middlemen who normally would have had a share in the transaction.

From about 3000 B.C. a distinctive culture, called Minoan after the legendary king Minos, flourished on the island of Crete. The Minoans' prosperity depended largely on sea trade, especially with Egypt and the East, and they seem to have been a highly refined and peaceable people, since none of their palaces was fortified. The great palaces of Knossos and Phaestus were built about 2000 B.C., and in spite of widespread destruction by an earthquake around 1580 B.C., the Minoans' prosperity continued to increase, so that Crete became a world power.

Minoan influence spread to the mainland of Greece, and was absorbed by the Indo-European tribes who arrived there after 2000 B.C. This mainland civilization centered on Mycenae, and some time before 1400 B.C. the Mycenaeans conquered Crete, adopting the late Minoan script known as Linear B. The decipherment of Linear B in 1952 by Michael Ventris has shown that the Mycenaeans spoke an early form of Greek.

Mycenaean traders settled in Rhodes, Cyprus, northern Syria, and the west and southwest coasts of Asia Minor. This is the legendary period of Greek mythology when the gods walked the the earth, and is the period of the Trojan War. Strabo says that the Phoenicians established colonies in Spain shortly after the Trojan War, which was about 1200 B.C., but 900 B.C. is a more likely date for this colonization.

Sometime after 1200 B.C. the bronze-clad Mycenaeans were overthrown by the iron weapons of the Dorians from the North, and as a result of this invasion the Greek tribes – Aeolians, Ionians, and Achaeans – fled to the islands and to Asia Minor. Here the Greeks learned the arts of trade and seafaring from the Phoenicians and Mycenaeans, and by the eighth century Greek was being written in the Phoenician script. Overpopulation of the Greek mainland, and the Greeks' increased nautical know-how, led to a vast emigration movement, the first area of settlement being southern Italy, known as Magna Graecia.

Later colonies were chosen particularly for their harbors and commercial value, and soon the increased wealth of a civilization based on trade enabled the mother cities on the mainland to import food, so the need for emigration ceased. In this period, from the eighth to the sixth century B.C., the Greeks colonized the Black Sea coast, Asia Minor, Libya, Sicily, and parts of France and Spain.

Competition between the Greek cities finally resolved itself into a struggle for power between Athens and Sparta, a struggle described in tragic detail by Thucydides in his history of the Peloponnesian War. It was during this war that the Athenians sent a magnificent fleet to Syracuse, where the long campaign eventually ended in catastrophic defeat in 413 B.C. In 405 B.C. the last Athenian fleet was destroyed at Aegospotami.

Traditionally founded in 753 B.C., Rome in 510 B.C. freed herself from the Etruscan tyrant Tarquinius Superbus. By the beginning of the third century B.C., Rome controlled the whole of central Italy, and was expanding into Magna Graecia. By 270 B.C. all of Italy was united. Just before Rome freed herself from Etruscan rule, Carthage, a Phoenician colony, had won its freedom from Tyre (about 600 B.C.), and soon established control over Phoenician colonies in the western Mediterranean. This brought Carthage into conflict with Rome in Sicily when the Romans expelled the Carthaginian garrison of Messana. The Carthaginians were a great seagoing mercantile people in true Phoenician style. In order to challenge their supremacy the Romans had to build a fleet of 160 ships, almost overnight. After three protracted wars – the Punic Wars – during which Rome herself almost bled to death, Carthage was razed to the ground in 146 B.C., and Rome was mistress of the Mediterranean. The sequence of power in the Mediterranean lands, then, was Egyptian, Minoan, Mycenaean, Phoenician, Greek, Carthaginian, and Roman.

This map of the Mediterranean shows in different colors (see key) the spheres of influence of ancient civilizations, beginning with Egypt around 5000 B.C. and ending in Roman times about A.D. 100. The Roman sphere extended beyond all others of earlier times.

The Phoenicians were the first to venture far afield in search of trade. Here they bring tributes of monkeys, animals highly prized by the King of Assyria (c. 885 B.C.).

Section of the François Vase (c. 570 B.C.) showing Theseus, legendary Greek hero who killed the Minotaur, coming ashore after his voyage from Crete.

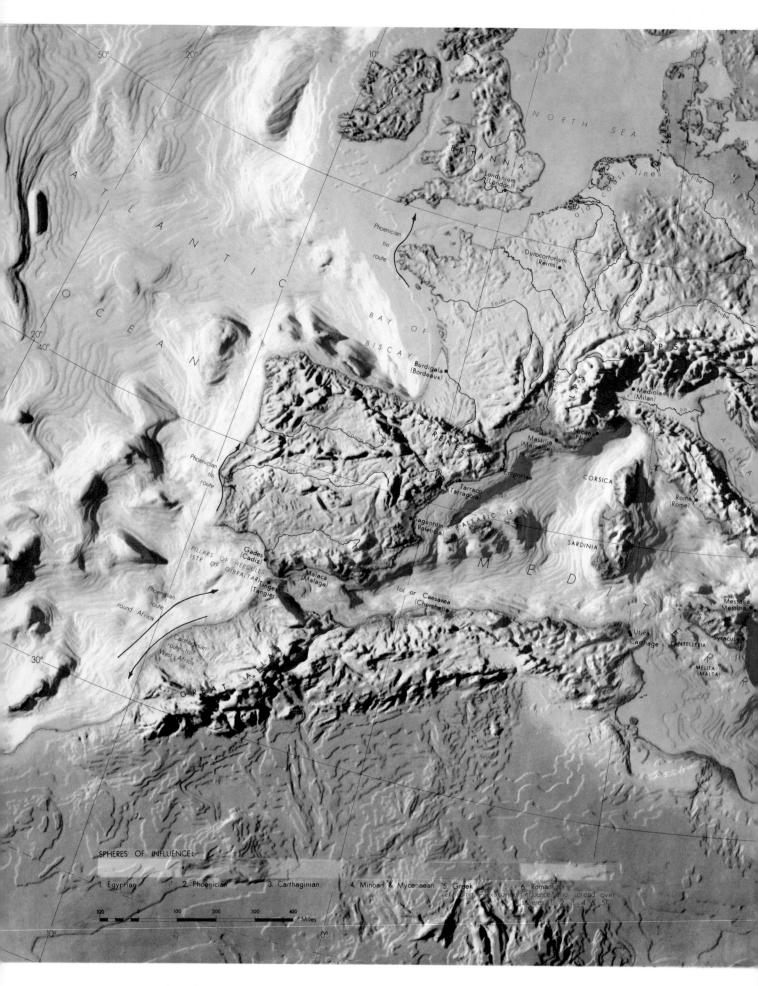

ATLANTIC OCEAN

NORTH SEA

BRITANNIA

Londinium
(London)

Old coast lines

Elbe

Phoenician
tin
route

Durocortorium
(Reims)

Loire

Rhine

BAY OF
BISCAY

Burdigala
(Bordeaux)

PYRENEES

Douro

Rhône

A L P S

Mediolanum
(Milan)

Po

Phoenician
tin
route

Tagus

Emporiae

Massilia
(Marseilles)

Nicaea
(Nice)

CORSICA

ADRIA

Tarraco
(Tarragona)

Saguntum
(Valencia)

BALEARIC IS.

SARDINIA

Roma
(Rome)

Gades
(Cadiz)

PILLARS OF HERCULES
(STR. OF GIBRALTAR)

Tingas
(Tangier)

Malaca
(Malaga)

M E D I T E R

Iol or Caesarea
(Cherchel)

Phoenician
route
round Africa

Carthaginian
route to
West Africa

GREAT ATLAS

Utica
Carthage

PANTELLERIA

Messana
(Messina)

Syracuse

SICILY

R A N E

MELITA
(MALTA)

SPHERES OF INFLUENCE:

1. Egyptian   2. Phoenician   3. Carthaginian   4. Minoan & Mycenaean 5. Greek   6. Roman
(excluding Alexandrian influence also spread over
spheres 1, 2, 3, 4 & 5)

100   100   200   300   400
                                          Miles

50°   20°   10°   0°   10°

40°

20°

30°

10°

0°

130

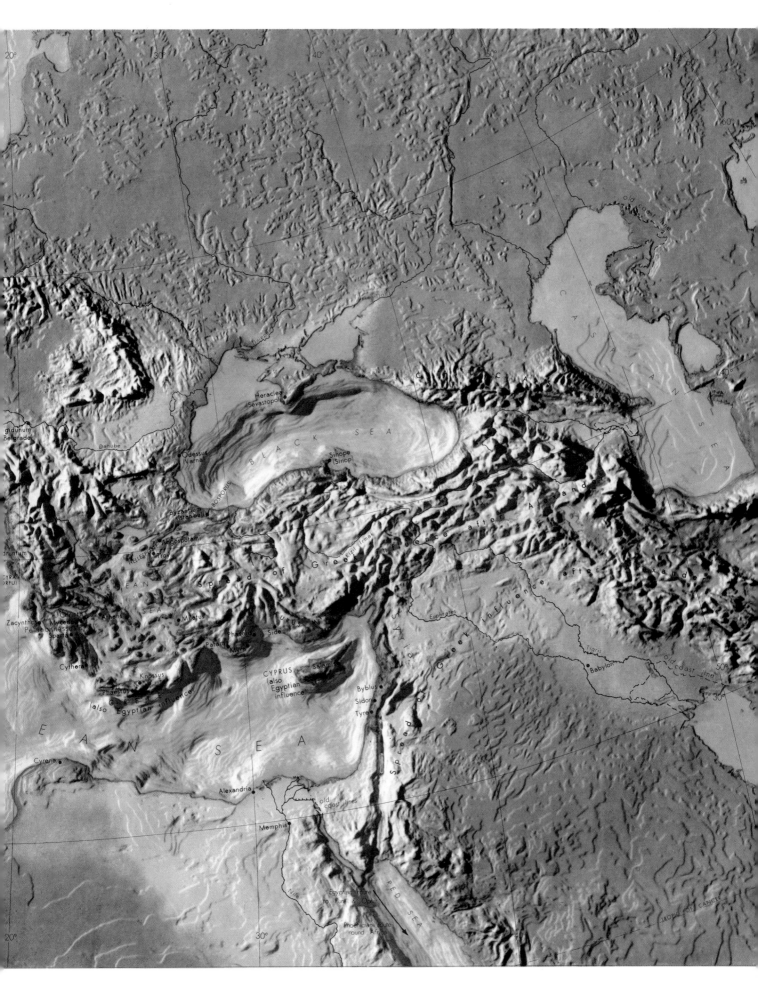

20°   30°   40°

gidunum
Belgrade?

Danube

Odessus
(Varna)

Heraclea
(Sevastopol)

BLACK SEA

Sinope
(Sinop)

C A S P I A N

Byzantium
(Istanbul)

BOSPORUS

Aegospotami

HELLESPONT Troy

druntum

S p r e a d o f G r e e k influence after Alexand

Kizil Irmak

CYRA
ORFU)

AEGEAN

SEA

Corinth Athens

Zacynthos
Peloponnessus
Mycenae
Sparta

Cythera

Knossos

Phaestus

GREECE
(also Egyptian influence)

Miletus

TAURUS MTS

Phaselis Side
Patara Myra

CYPRUS
(also
Egyptian
influence)

Salamis

Euphrates

Tigris

Babylon

G r e k influence after Alexand

old coast line

old coast line

S p r e a d

Byblus

Sidon

Tyre

S p r e a d o f

E A N   S E A

Cyrene

Alexandria

old
coast lines

Memphis

Nile

Egyptian route
to Punt & Ophir

R E D   S E A

Phoenician route
round Africa

TROPIC OF CANCER

20°   30°

Ships and Navigation

Phoenician ship stamped on a coin of Sidon.

This Egyptian model of a boat is dated about 2000 B.C. Models like this one, from which we gain some idea of Egyptian boat construction, were placed in tombs to provide the deceased with passage into the next world.

It seems that the Egyptians must be given credit for inventing the sail some time well before 3000 B.C., possibly as early as 6000 B.C. It may have developed from the custom of hanging a shield from a pole in a small boat during religious ceremonies, but we have no way of being certain of this.

The first sails were square rigged, stretched between two booms, and hoisted on a mast near the bow—the distance of the mast from the bow was equal to only sixteen per cent of the length of the boat. This is an extremely inefficient position for a mast, since it allows a ship to sail only directly before the wind. From paintings and pottery we can trace the gradual repositioning of the mast nearer the center of the ship, the most efficient position. This adjustment took place gradually, probably based on trial and error, from 3200 to 1600 B.C.

The ships of Queen Hatshepsut around 1500 B.C. were probably a hundred feet long, with a beam of twenty-five feet, and were capable of carrying eighty tons of cargo. The mast was amidships, and the bows could probably be pointed as much as eighty degrees off the wind. The fact that a ship will point eighty degrees off the wind does not mean that it will sail in that direction, since it will drift to leeward. The spoon-shaped hulls of the Egyptians were particularly bad in this respect, and their best course was probably less than seventy degrees off the wind.

Because of their lack of timber, and since most of their navigation was confined largely to the Nile, the Egyptians did not develop good seagoing hulls. There was no frame, and the planks, which were imported from Syria, were four inches thick, set edge to edge and keyed together with dowels and dovetails. There were, however, a few crossbeams at the level of the gunwale strake. Most of the sea sailing of this period was done by the Minoans, but we know nothing about their ships, and nothing about those of the Mycenaeans.

The Phoenicians were certainly building ships with frames before 1000 B.C. This enabled them to make longer, sleeker vessels with more rigid hulls. Their warships, fitted with iron beaks, were powered by oars in battle and by sail when cruising. Their cargo ships were broader and heavier and were sailed at all times in order to save the cargo space which would be occupied by batteries of rowers.

All we know about the early Greek ships comes from literature and sculpture; and it is clear that the ships were developed from Phoenician designs. However, all attempts to interpret the terms bireme, trireme, and quinquereme have been unsuccessful. If we assume that they mean so many rowers to an oar, then the end man is so far from where the oar pivots that he has to move an impossible distance. If we assume them to mean so many banks of oars, then the oars of the top row are impossibly long. The only solution is to find a Greek wreck, but so far we have not been lucky enough to make such a discovery.

Neither have we found any Carthaginian ships, but they must have been very similar to the Phoenician. Roman ships, presumably copied from all the types available, were carvel-built, had many closely spaced ribs, and the planks were fixed with wooden pins or copper nails.

Although carbon-14 dating would seem to be the most obvious

Part of a frieze showing Roman ships nearing a lighthouse. Carved about A.D. 200, it came from Ostia, the port for Rome.

method of fixing the age of the ancient wrecks we find, it has its drawbacks. The wood of any wreck is bound to be impregnated with modern marine organisms which throw the count off. The only reliable method is analyzing the wreck's cargo. But the underwater archaeologist is interested in the cargo for purposes other than dating alone. It is a primary-source sample of objects which were all in use at the same time, and from the items making up the cargo we can deduce the ports of call on the voyage, and therefore the nature of the trade between these points.

Early mariners of the Mediterranean nearly always hugged the coast and limited their voyages to the summer season, unless famine or outbursts of piracy forced them to set out during the winter. For purposes of navigation, a rugged coast with easily identifiable landmarks was preferable to a flat one with no points of reference. For this reason many of the conspicuous headlands and islands of the Mediterranean are mentioned in the *Odyssey*.

Such was the fear of the low Egyptian coast line that all ships on an east-west route across the Mediterranean sailed north of Cyprus into the lee of the Taurus Mountains, past Side, Phaselis, Myra, and Patara to the southern side of Rhodes. From here they continued on to Crete, north past Cythera, Zacynthos, and Corcyra, across the Strait of Otranto to Hydruntum, along the coast of Magna Graecia to Sicily, then by Pantelleria to Utica and Carthage, and finally along the coast of North Africa to the Pillars of Hercules. It was possible to cross the Isthmus of Corinth overland by roller tramway, but the tolls were so heavy that most cargo ships sailed round the dangerous shores of the Peloponnesus.

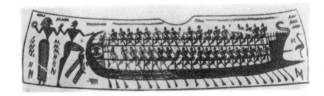

This Theban vase of the eighth century B.C. shows a steersman about to board a Greek ship fitted with two banks of oars.

All along the busy routes the sailors were never out of sight of one mountain peak or another. Dotted around the Mediterranean are hundreds of minute islands and volcanic mountains which bridge the gaps between the major land masses, and these were indispensable guides to the early navigators. A perfect example is Pantelleria, a volcanic cone between Africa and Sicily, rising more than 2500 feet high. Although the island was completely barren it was an important link in the Phoenician trade system. With this brief background about the key civilizations of the classical world, and something about their ships and methods of navigation, let us now turn to the underwater archaeologist and his methods of "digging" under the sea.

Archaeologists at Work

A diver brings a first-century B.C. Greek amphora to the surface near the island of Corfu. It was found at a depth of 130 feet.

By far the greatest amount of work in underwater archaeology has been done in the Mediterranean, and for obvious reasons. Although the Mediterranean may not be the only cradle of civilization, it was certainly the cradle of maritime trade and communications, so it is natural that we turn to this region in our quest for knowledge of ancient coastal cities and forgotten wrecks.

Even though the Egyptians were the first to sail the high seas, they were surpassed in skill and daring by the Minoans and Phoenicians. Consequently the greatest concentration of early shipping was on the east-west route along the south coast of Turkey, to this day one of the most treacherous coasts in the world. This explains the predominance of ancient wrecks in the eastern Mediterranean.

The large number of sunken cities around the Mediterranean is easy to explain if we examine the region geographically. The Mediterranean is almost surrounded by mountains of the Alpine system – which includes the Atlas, Pyrenees, Alps, Carpathians, Caucasus, Himalayas, and the island chains of the East Indies. This chain of mountains is fairly recent, geologically speaking, having been uplifted in the Tertiary period. Throughout recorded history the earth has been, and still is, adjusting itself to the residual stresses of this upheaval; consequently there are continual earthquakes, tremors, faults, and volcanic outbreaks over the whole area. Apart from its southeast corner, the entire Mediterranean coast is bordered by mountains of this system, and so the coastal cities of the ancient civilizations were peculiarly liable to devastation and subsidence.

While past geological conditions made the Mediterranean the natural graveyard of many maritime remains, present conditions are ideal for the recovery of these relics. The water is warm and clear, the weather is good, and many countries in the region encourage the exploration of ancient sites.

Because underwater sites are nearly always related to the local archaeology and history of the land area near which they are found, the only men who can assess the site accurately must be expert in the area's local archaeology. For this reason, no professional archaeologist – who specializes in a limited geographical area and a certain period – will take an interest in the subject of underwater archaeology as a whole. In a few places, however, there are senior archaeologists who do take an interest in the underwater work in their area, such as Professor Fernand Benoît, in the south of France, and Professor Nino Lamboglia, in northern Italy. But because it takes many years to become an established archaeologist, most men who have achieved this eminence have neither the time, nor the athletic ability required to become divers as well. As a result, all the diving has to be done by amateur archaeologists, or by people who are not archaeologists at all. It is remarkable and regrettable that so few young archaeologists today are learning to dive.

When searching for an unknown archaeological site – either a wreck or a submerged city – it is a waste of time, money, and trained men to survey at random many miles of coast in the hopes of stumbling onto something. Like a newspaper reporter in search of a story, an underwater archaeologist needs a "tip." He may find his tips deliberately by combing the files of libraries and museums, or he may find one accidentally by talking to a local fisherman. Let us see how this works, first with sunken wrecks, then with lost coastal cities.

The inevitable penalty of navigating close to a precipitous, rocky shore was the risk of being wrecked, not only because of the inherent danger of unseen rocks, but because the winds near the promontories were often violent and unpredictable. Cape Malea had a particularly bad reputation from this point of view, and was used as an excuse by the Corcyrans when they arrived late to help the Athenians at the battle of Salamis. Thus in antiquity the head-lands achieved dual significance for sailors: friend and guide from afar, but deceiver and wrecker from close to. To ensure that a headland would serve as friend and guide, temples were built on cliff edges, even in the remotest spots. Today the bleached columns of Sunion towering above the dark sea is a sight to make even the most hardened globe-trotter pause in genuine wonder.

The greatest danger to classical mariners were submerged rocks rising from the sea floor to within only a few feet of the surface. Called a *sec* by the French, and a *secca* by the Italians, these rocks are fatally common off all the steep coasts of the Mediterranean. Often they are not marked on charts – which does not matter much since large ships rarely go near the shore nowadays – but they can be seen from the air or from a hilltop and they can be found with an echo sounder. *Secs* serve as a valuable tip to a diver, for if he searches around these submerged pinnacles on a known trade route, he has a very good chance of finding not one, but several wrecks. This was the method Gianni Roghi used at Spargi, and which will be discussed in detail later.

Local fishermen and sponge divers often can be helpful to a diver investigating a small area in detail. Peter Throckmorton, mentioned later, achieved almost incredible results while he was working from a sponge boat off the coast of Turkey. Sometimes the local authorities offer rewards to fishermen who bring in antiquities. But this can be expensive, especially if the antiques happen to be Roman anchors, since the reward must exceed the current price of lead. And a man discovering a complete cargo is tempted to deliver it to the local authorities piece by piece without revealing the site, in order to obtain a steady income and to avoid the risk of a small down payment for the whole cargo. This results in the systematic destruction of the arrangement of the objects *in situ*, which is often the primary value of such finds.

Fishermen are not the only guilty ones. Tourists with their own diving equipment sometimes pillage a site for what amounts to an archaeological cheap thrill. This was the fate of the wrecked cargo of Roman amphorae at Anthéor, which is now no more than a smashed heap of fragments. It is all but impossible to protect wrecks from looting. Nothing short of an armed police launch with day and night guards permanently over the site would keep the vandals at bay. In spite of the laws against stealing antiquities, divers continue to work at night by torchlight, and fishermen continue to drag their anchors over wrecks in hopes of catching one amphora, but smashing hundreds in the process.

Finding a submerged city requires search techniques quite different from those used in searching for wrecks. The diver-archae-ologist must refer to ancient geographers and historians, such as Strabo, Herodotus, and Thucydides, and the itineraries of Antoni-nus and Peutinger. He also should consult the many excellent classical atlases and the Admiralty charts which show coastal ruins.

The remains of a temple at Lindos, Rhodes, dedicated to Athena. Lighthouses of the ancient world, many such temples were built on the cliff edges of dangerous promontories to warn and guide mariners from afar.

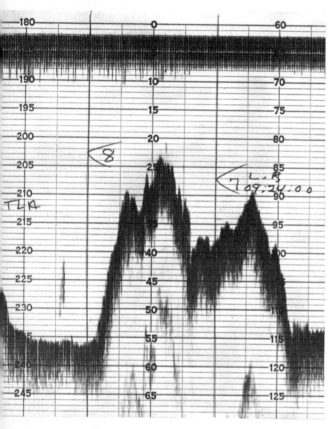

Secs, *pinnacles of rock rising to within a few feet of the sea surface, sent many ships of classical times to the bottom. These rock formations serve as valuable guides to divers searching for old wrecks. The one shown here was traced by an echo sounder.*

The real problem is not that of finding a classical harbor town, but of establishing its relation to the present coast.

This can sometimes be settled quite simply by finding a person who has been swimming in the area with a mask and fins, as I was lucky enough to do at Apollonia. Normally the most reliable course is to refer to the archaeological journals that contain details of past work on a particular site. It is ridiculous to expect to discover a lost city without a clue. What is more usually the case is that a classical port in some remote place was recognized by a traveler in the eighteenth century, noted by a chart surveyor in the nineteenth century, and studied by archaeologists in the twentieth century.

Once a suitable site has been chosen and the precise nature of the "digging" problem worked out, the next step is to obtain permission to work there – both political and archaeological. The type of site to be explored in part determines the work methods and equipment. The basic gear – mask, fins, and snorkel – enables a diver to work easily in shallow water. With this simple equipment he can survey a complex structure in ten feet of water, and dive down to a hundred feet for a short time, but such dives are not recommended for beginners.

If the water is deep, or if it is shallow but dirty, a diver must be able to stay submerged for long periods, and must therefore have an air supply. If he intends to stay down for long, he will also need to wear a suit for warmth; even in the Mediterranean the water is always cold below a hundred feet.

Not counting the use of pure oxygen, there are three common ways of feeding air to a diver. The oldest is the "standard" system which provides a diver with a loose, watertight suit connected to a heavy brass helmet, and heavy lead boots. The air supply is fed continuously through a pipe from the surface, at a pressure only slightly above ambient water pressure. Air floods the suit and helmet, the surplus bubbling out through a valve. This system enables a diver to stay down for very long periods, it keeps him warm and comfortable, and provides telephone communication with the surface. The enormous disadvantage is that the diver is cumbersome and slow-moving, and a boat at least twenty-five feet long is needed to house the air compressor, diving attendants, and spare gear that is usually needed.

The aqualung, perfected by Jacques-Yves Cousteau and Emile Gagnan, is the exact opposite of standard gear. In this system the diver swims with fins, carrying on his back a tank of air compressed to 120 atmospheres, and the duration of his dive depends on the capacity of the tank. The diver is fed air only when he breathes in, and it reaches him at the ambient water pressure. The advantages of this equipment are its lightness, mobility, and versatility, both underwater and at the surface. And diving attendants are not essential. The disadvantages are the limited time it permits a diver to stay down, lack of communication with the surface, and during deep dives the divers must wear protective clothing for warmth. Aqualungs have been used for most of the archaeological work done since 1945.

The new "surface-demand" system combines advantages of both standard and free-diving systems. The air is fed to the diver from a tank or compressor at the surface, and he breathes through a demand valve attached to his back by a simple harness. The connecting hose is extremely light and flexible, never carrying a pressure of more than ten atmospheres. In case the hose should be cut, or the surface supply should fail, the diver carries a small high-pressure cylinder which gives him several minutes of air, depending on his depth. As with the aqualung, the diver must wear a suit for warmth, and he may wear either fins or boots, according to the nature of his work.

Two devices scarcely off the secret list promise important breakthroughs for submarine archaeology. One is Cousteau's plunging saucer, a disk-shaped, miniature, two-man submarine propelled by water jets and fitted with outside mechanical arms. Almost more remarkable is the self-contained breathing apparatus designed by the Swiss, Hannes Keller. With it he has dived to 720 feet, and it has been tested in a tank to a depth of 820 feet. This is an enormous achievement when we consider that the normal, absolute limit for safe diving with regular air is 300 feet. Below this depth both oxygen and nitrogen become poisonous. In 1956, however, a British team made a series of dives off Norway culminating in George Wookey's world-record dive of 600 feet. But Wookey used an advanced form of standard gear and was supplied with an oxygen-helium mixture in which the proportion of oxygen was much less than in natural air, so that it was not toxic. The total time for the dive was more than twelve hours. In contrast, one of Keller's dives to 510 feet took only 58 minutes!

Salvaging a wreck or surveying a city usually means removing tons of mud or sand from around the hull, or from the buried street. To do this work the archaeologist depends on two bulky but standard pieces of equipment called the "air-lift" and the "tunneling-lance." The air-lift consists of a large, flexible pipe through the bottom end of which a supply of air is blown. As it rises up the pipe, the air expands and draws a mass of water (and mud or sand) with it, acting like a huge vacuum cleaner. The tunneling-lance is nothing more than a glorified fireman's hose that produces a continuous jet of water strong enough to loosen packed mud, sand, or shingle, which is then carried away by the suction of the air-lift.

For the most part, a diver's life underwater consists of long hours of drudgery, sweat, and routine. But nearly every diver thrills to the exhilarating sensation of being alone in the silence of deep water, and seeing for the first time an object made by a man many thousands of years before. Divers who work together usually develop a sixth sense for understanding each others' signs and grunts underwater. If they do not, they are not good divers. Communication with the surface party is a different matter. If a telephone system is not available then the diver cannot dictate his notes; he must record them himself. His plastic board, on which he must record all survey measurements, is as indispensable as his knife, underwater watch, depth gauge, and compass.

If the site is small, such as a wreck and its cargo, then the best surveying approach is to lay a grid of plastic tapes over the wreck, as was done by Richard Garnett at Chios, and by Gianni Roghi at Spargi. It was Roghi who made the first real attempt to plot the arrangement of a cargo in three dimensions.

The archaeologist who surveys a larger area, such as a city, must use more complex techniques. Usually he begins by orientat-

The aqualung, a free-diving system perfected by Cousteau and Gagnan, is here demonstrated by a diver (Sandri Khan) at a depth of a hundred feet.

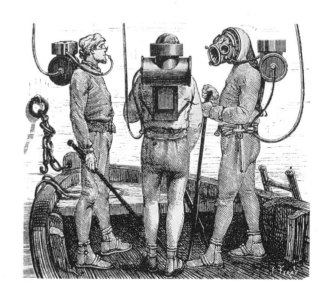

This late nineteenth-century engraving shows an early version of diving equipment. As with present day "standard" gear, air was fed to the diver from a boat at the surface.

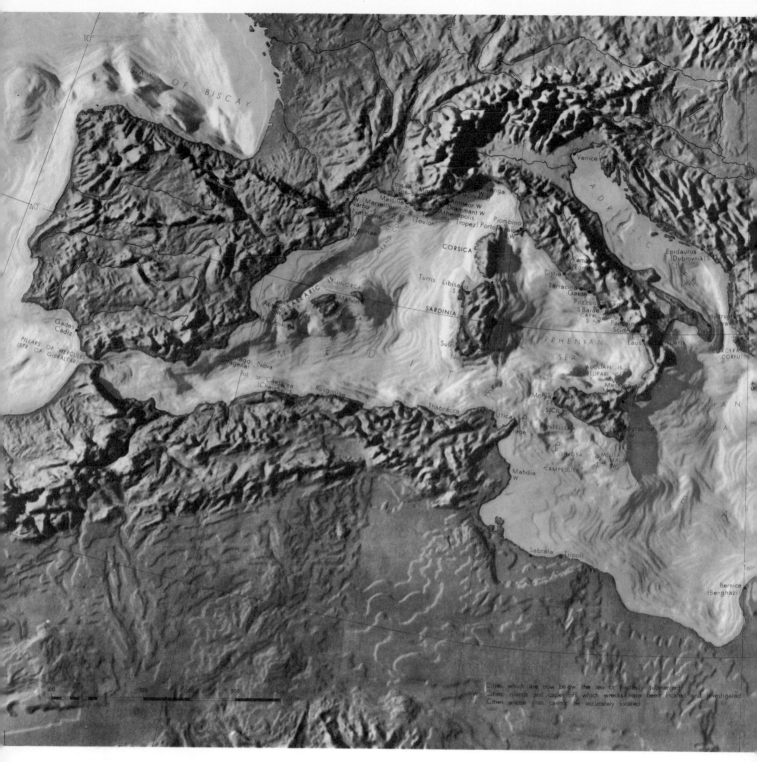

Map labels (as visible on the map):

BAY OF BISCAY
10°
40°
10°
Venice
A D R I A T I C
Epidaurus
(Dubrovnik) S
Genoa
Fossae Marianae
Massilia
W (Marseille)
Narbonne
Narbo
Antheor W
Drammant W
Athenopolis
Theopolis
St Tropez Porto
W (Toulon)
Piombino
Portoferraio
W
Rama
Rome
Ostia
GRAND CON
CORSICA
Turris Libisalis
S
Tarracina
Gaeta
Pozzuoli
S Baiae
S Salerno
Paestum
Scidri
Hydruntum
Otranto
MINORCA
San
Antonio BALEARIC IS
Mahon
IVICA
Emporiae
W
SARDINIA
Gades
Cadiz
PILLARS OF HERCULES
(STR OF GIBRALTAR)
M E D I T E
Carthago Nova
Carthagena
Iol or Caesarea
(Cherchel)
Rusgoniae
Sulci
Nora
TYRRHENIAN
SEA
Laus
Sybaris
CORFU
AEOLIAN IS
(LIPARI IS)
Messina
Motya
S
SICILY
Thabracca
Utica
Carthage
PANTELLERIA
Syracuse
W
Mahdia
W
LINOSA
LAMPEDUSA
MELITA
MALTA
Sabrata
Tripoli
Bernice
(Benghazi)
Tolr

Legend (bottom right):
Cities which are now below the sea or partially submerged
W Cities, islands and capes off which wrecks have been located and investigated
Cities whose sites cannot be accurately located

Scale:
100   0   100   200   300   400

This map of the Mediterranean shows most of the sites of the submerged cities and ancient wrecks mentioned in this chapter. Sunken cities for which there is evidence, but which have not yet been explored, are also plotted.

ing the survey in relation to the coast, and a base line must be set up on land. From this line key points such as rocks, islands, and important buildings are fixed by theodolite, or alidade and plane table. Submerged buildings can be marked with buoys, and these, too, are fixed from the shore. For more detailed work divers can then operate with plastic tapes and rules to measure city block dimensions, wall thicknesses, street widths, and so on, which reveal the detailed plan of the submerged city.

Aerial and underwater photographs both are a great help where the water is clear enough. While aerial photographs reveal the general plan of a submerged city, underwater photographs provide the diver with a permanent record of what he has found, and

Three divers of Jules Verne's imagination, equipped with self-contained breathing apparatus and rifles, explore the sea floor near the fictitious island of Crespo.

exactly where he found it in relation to other objects. But with the limited field of view of a camera, even with a wide-angle lens, accentuated by the refractive index of water, it is always difficult to photograph buildings in a way that does not make them look like heaps of rocks. A cargo of amphorae presents no special problem to the photographer; he can always hover above it and photograph it in plan. Buildings, however, are usually at a depth of twenty feet or less, so it is impossible to get high enough above them to take good plan view pictures. With this background of the underwater archaeologist's equipment and working methods, let us now turn to some of the submerged cities and lost wrecks that have been discovered.

Cities under the Sea

Changes in sea and land levels have altered the coast line of Amalfi, south of the Bay of Naples, many times. In the early Middle Ages part of the town built on the coast sank into the sea. Around the fifteenth century the land began to rise, but since that time it has started to sink again.

To judge from the earliest reports of Aristotle and Pausanias, the destruction of Helike aroused widespread interest, and people came from many miles away to see the city beneath the waves. Spyridon Marinatos, a Greek archaeologist, has carried out the most recent study of the area, but he has failed to locate any of the mud-covered ruins. Apart from Helike, some of the most interesting ruins of sunken cities, which can be seen by any archaeologically-minded tourist, are along the shores of Italy.

In the first half of the nineteenth century Guiseppe de Fazio, an engineer, studied the remains of several Roman ports in the Bay of Naples. Working with sponge divers who knew the area well, he found the submerged remnants of quays, breakwaters, and bollards at Misenum and Pozzuoli. Recognizing them for what they were, he realized that there must have been a drastic change in sea level after Roman times. Since de Fazio's day many of the coastal towns of Italy have grown so extensively that the ancient ports which he described have been destroyed by modern construction, and the water is sometimes so polluted that free-diving work in it is impossible.

Between 1901 and 1903 the Bay of Naples was again surveyed for ruins, this time by Robert Theodore Günther, an Oxford don. (Günther explains that he was able to carry out this work because of the inordinate length of vacations at Oxford.) The fishermen in the Bay of Naples, in the habit of raking for shellfish in the cracks and hollows of the submerged buildings, were a great help to Günther. By much wading and using a glass-bottomed bucket to observe the floor of the Bay, he mapped the ruins for many miles along the shore.

Stretching from Naples to the weird rock that guards the headland of the Scoglio di Virgilio, just to the west of Posilipo, today there is a cliff that forms a series of little headlands and bays, each backed by a beach. But the coast did not look like this to the Romans. The sea then was sixteen feet lower, and at the foot of the cliffs ran a great highway, bordered by luxurious villas. The quarries from which the Romans obtained stone for these buildings are now partly submerged caves which thunder and roar as the storm waves crash into their dark mouths.

The buildings of southern Posilipo were in three principal regions, which Günther called Gaiola, Marechiano, and Roseberry. The islands of Gaiola were joined by an arch of rock as late as the beginning of the nineteenth century, but it then collapsed and blocked the passage beneath. In Roman days these islands formed a promontory jutting a quarter of a mile beyond the present shore. Around a small hill on the promontory stood splendid villas, colonnaded temples, and little pavilions by the sea — like those painted on many of the walls in Pompeii. In the lee of the promontory was a row of massive concrete piers rising brown out of the blue water — the breakwater of the harbor — and on the heights above were the theater and the temples.

Seaward of the islands today there are concrete foundations in an area that would have been underwater even in the Roman period. These were once summer villas or pavilions built right in the sea and supported by raised foundations, as seen in the pictures from Herculaneum. Surrounded with covered galleries and ornamented with statues, at Gaiola they were so close to the water, and

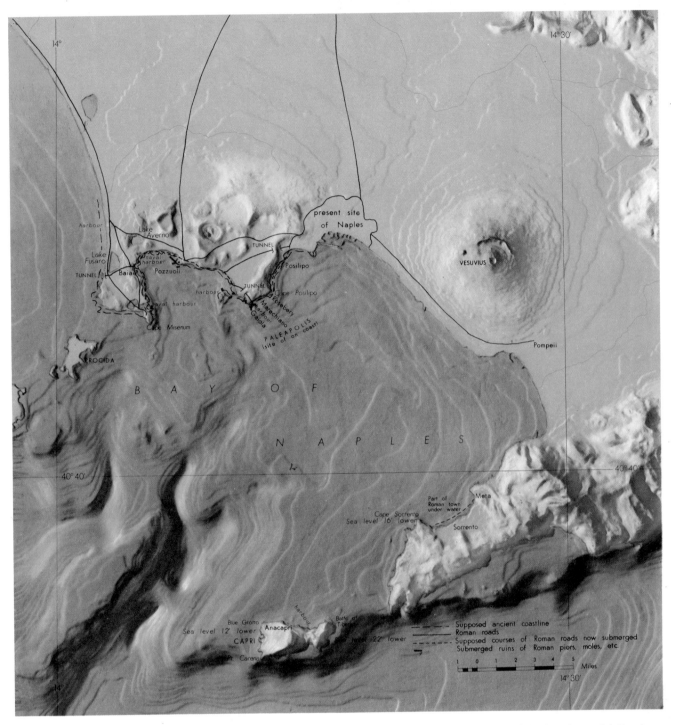

Labels on map:
14°
14°30'
present site of Naples
VESUVIUS
harbour
Lake Averno
Lake Fusaro
naval harbour
TUNNEL
Baiae
Pozzuoli
TUNNEL
Posilipo
Cape Posilipo
harbour
TUNNEL
Rotobery
Marechiano
harbour
Gaiola
Cape Misenum
naval harbour
PALEAPOLIS
(site of on coast)
PROCIDA
Pompeii
B A Y   O F
40° 40'
40° 40'
N A P L E S
Part of Roman town under water
Meta
Cape Sorrento
Sea level 16' lower
Sorrento
Blue Grotto
Sea level 12' lower
Anacapri
CAPRI
Pt. Carena
harbour
Baths of Tiberius
level 22' lower
Supposed ancient coastline
Roman roads
Supposed courses of Roman roads now submerged
Submerged ruins of Roman piers, moles, etc.
1 0 1 2 3 4 5 Miles
14°30'
14°

Map of the Bay of Naples shows details of the work carried out by R. T. Günther when he examined changes in sea level that have taken place since Roman times.

in such an exposed position, that a protective wall had to be built fifty yards seaward of the villas to check the onslaught of storms. Of the rich men who had these houses made for their pleasure, Horace had this to say:

"You on the verge of death contract for blocks of marble to be hewn, and unmindful of the grave, are rearing mansions and are all eagerness to thrust back the shores of the sea that roars against Baiae; for not enough does the bound of the land enrich you."

On the east side of the Gaiola promontory is a row of submerged structures which the fishermen have always regarded with mixed feelings. In calm weather they are a rich hunting ground, but in a storm they are a menace to small boats. These obstacles rise from twenty-five or thirty feet of water to within a few feet of the surface and are regularly spaced. Close investigation has shown that they are made of concrete; they are, in fact, the piers of a Roman harbor

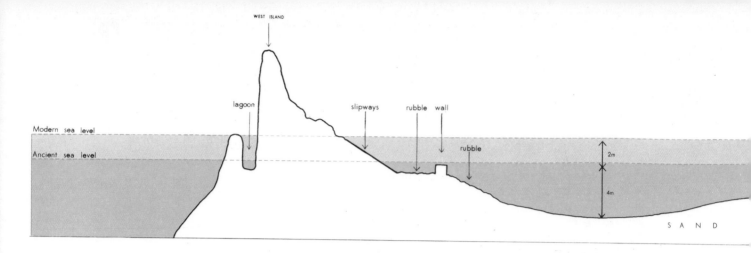

WEST ISLAND

lagoon   slipways   rubble   wall

Modern sea level

Ancient sea level

rubble

2m

4m

S A N D

wall of the type known as *opus pilarum*. The tops of the piers might have been joined by arches to form a *progressus*, as shown in the fresco from Gragnano. Günther considers that the Roman buildings at Gaiola, and the harbor at Posilipo, were built on the site of the earlier Greek colony of Parthenope, or Palaeopolis, which is otherwise not located.

The most perfectly preserved house in Posilipo is that called La Casa degli Spiriti, but because of its remote location and the "white-robed ghost" which haunts it, it is rarely visited. The lower two floors are Roman and are still partly covered with the original plaster, but the third floor is a later addition. Since the ground floor is now eight feet below water, it is amazing that the building should have survived so long. The restoration of the third story was carried out probably to make the place into a tavern, which could be reached only by boat. In the easternmost room there is a line of erosion on the plaster sixteen feet above the present level of the sea, which shows that since Roman times the sea level has been higher than it is now.

East of La Casa degli Spiriti is the ancient and silted harbor of Marechiano, today outlined by submerged, continuous walls. With a present entrance thirty-eight yards wide and twenty-six feet deep, the harbor contains the ruins of a villa which is supposed to have belonged to Vedius Pollio – a friend of Augustus – who was in the habit of throwing disobedient slaves into tanks full of moray eels. Incidentally, the association of the villa at Gaiola with the name of Virgil is almost certainly inaccurate. "Virgil had a villa here" seems to have been as popular a saying in Italy as "Queen Elizabeth slept here" is in England, or "George Washington slept here," in the United States.

At the extreme east of the Posilipo area is the Roseberry region, near Capo Posilipo. Here, outside a breakwater built by convict labor to protect the villa of the Bourbon Prince Luigi, is a large area of submarine ruins. But only one concrete block, the Pietra Salata – eleven yards long and two yards wide – breaks the surface of the sea. The block is part of a huge wall, reinforced with massive bastions, that encloses a rectangular area within which are three large rock-and-concrete foundations. Judging by their size and complexity, these must have been villas of the type found at Gaiola, but on an even grander scale.

At Pozzuoli, four miles west of Posilipo, is the most well-known Roman breakwater, commonly called the Bridge of Caligula. This imposing structure once consisted of fifteen tall piers of concrete joined by arches. Each pier was fifty-two feet square and rose from

The temple at Pozzuoli built in the third century A.D. By the fifteenth century the columns were totally submerged. Since then the sea level has changed and the columns have emerged. Today, at low tide, most of the temple floor is visible.

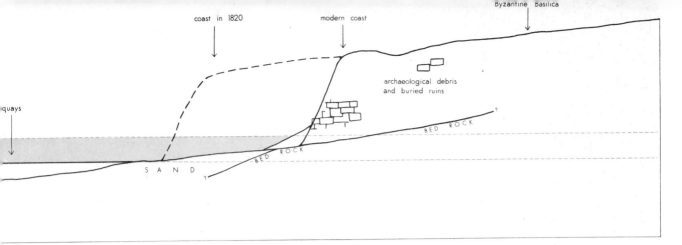

coast in 1820   modern coast   Byzantine Basilica

archaeological debris
and buried ruins

BED ROCK

quays

BED ROCK

SAND

forty-nine feet of water to sixteen feet above the surface. De Fazio dived around these piers and found stone mooring rings six feet below the surface, proving a subsidence of at least ten feet. The outermost pier has marine borings in it to a height of twelve feet above the present water level, showing that the land has been lower in the past. Unfortunately the Roman breakwater has been used as the base for a modern sea wall; the result is that little of it is now to be seen.

Continuing west, we come to the submerged ruins of Baiae, a Roman pleasure resort of infamous luxury, and finally to Misenum, the great Roman naval port. The harbor of Misenum was protected by a double row of piers erected by the engineers of Agrippa in twenty-five feet of water. They were arranged in such a way that waves passing between the piers of the first row broke against those of the second, but this ingenuity was not enough to prevent the port from silting up. The tops of the piers are now hidden nearly six feet below the surface of the water; even so, the indefatigable de Fazio found a mooring ring on one of them, again indicating subsidence of more than ten feet.

Günther continued his survey all round the Sorrentine peninsula and Capri. Everywhere the erosion line on rocks and buildings, together with the positions of the buildings themselves, told the same story. The shore line, when the Romans used the great coast road, was about sixteen feet lower than it is today. By the twelfth century the land had fallen some thirty to sixteen feet below the present level, and it remained that low for at least three hundred years. But by the sixteenth century it had risen almost to its present level. On Capri itself, clues provided by the numerous grottos, the Roman harbor at Annacapri, and the partly submerged Baths of Tiberius, indicate that the island has pivoted: it has been uplifted by about twenty-two feet in the east, but by only twelve feet or so in the west.

The roof of the famous Blue Grotto is about twenty feet above sea level today, and the walls have erosion marks sixteen feet up from the floor. This is the twelfth-century land-level mark. At the back of the grotto is a flight of Roman steps which are supposed to continue twenty feet down into the water, showing that the Roman land level was twenty feet higher than at present. At the Roman level is a great opening in the rock wall, but the opening is now completely submerged. Even so, sunlight is filtered through by the clear water so that it rises blue into the cave, as if from the depths of the ocean itself. You can enter the Blue Grotto through a second, although minute, opening half above the present water

This section through the harbor at Apollonia shows the rise in sea level since Roman times and the retreat of the coast line over the past 150 years. Positions of some of the more important parts of the ancient harbor, excavated by the author, are also shown.

The famous Blue Grotto on Capri contains clues to the remarkable cycle of subsidence and uplift that has occurred around the Bay of Naples. When the Romans of the first century B.C. used the cave, its floor was at least twenty feet higher than it is today. The mysterious blue light that fills the cave is thought to come through the submerged Roman entrance.

level, but it can be penetrated only by very small boats, and the mysterious blue light of the cave is best seen when this entrance is closed. The Blue Grotto contains within it all the clues to the remarkable cycle of subsidence and uplift which has apparently occurred all around the Bay of Naples. How far this cycle can be traced to the north and to the south of Naples has yet to be determined by someone.

Philippe Diolé, the learned French journalist, was only too well aware that it was useless to attempt anything in underwater archaeology without adequate finance and modern machinery. His book, *4000 Years Under the Sea*, is the most thorough survey of the topic to date, and in it he shows how rare it is to have interested archaeologists, adequate finance, suitable equipment, trained divers, and enough time, all focused on the same site. While this may sound simple to achieve, it seldom happens in practice.

Diolé is such an individualist that, rather than dive with a team, however reliable, he prefers to work alone to savor in oceanic solitude the presence of the past. His most important work has been on the ports of Saint Tropez, Marseilles, Fos-sur-Mer, and Cherchel.

At Saint Tropez (ancient Athenopolis) there is an ancient stonemason's yard about 650 feet from the shore and in a depth of about twenty feet of water. What caused this change of level and when it occurred are unknown. In September 1950 the Club Alpin Sous-

Marin began to dive on a cargo of marble blocks just outside Saint-Tropez harbor. The blocks were lying in less than twenty feet of water, and when they were photographed and measured they turned out to be nine large pieces of column and one architrave. The weight of the architrave was calculated at thirty-eight metric tons, and the weight of the total cargo at about 250 tons. When the crust of these large blocks was scraped away, the stone proved to be white Carrara marble.

By chance, a large floating crane was at Saint-Tropez to do some work for the navy, and the Club Alpin Sous-Marin was lucky enough to be given use of it. Under the direction of Professor Benoît and Henri Broussard, and with the help of a professional helmet diver, half of the blocks were brought up. By January 1952 all but one had been raised, and they stood forlornly on a jetty, draped with tattered weed and surrounded by rusty cables and scrap. Professor Benoît has suggested that these columns were being carried by freighter from Italy to Narbonne, where the temple was rebuilt during the reign of Antoninus. The temple had been destroyed by fire in A.D. 149 and a rich shipowner and merchant, Fadius Musa, offered to rebuild it at his own expense. The trademark of the Fadii has been found in Ostia and many places in Gaul; it would have been simple for a man of such wealth and business connections to carry marble over the Mediterranean from Carrara in his own ships.

Along the coast at Marseilles, during excavation to clear war damage near the Vieux Port, workmen uncovered stakes of unseasoned pine and holm oak. These balks of timber proved to be part of the Greek harbor of Massilia, of about the sixth century B.C. Nearby, at the water's edge, an Ionic capital was found in a confusion of rubble and masonry. Since this is the only piece of Greek architecture ever found in Gaul, it has become an extremely important archaeological document.

Still farther west, on the Rhône delta, is Fos-sur-Mer, a favorite summer beach for tourists from Marseilles. Here, by the cove of Saint-Gervais, lie columns and cut blocks in only fifteen feet of water. In spite of the thick mud and weed one of the columns was raised, complete with an impost to support an arch or the lintel of a door. Dr. Beaucaire started diving at Fos-sur-Mer with voluntary assistants in 1948. During four years' work they removed layer after layer of sand, clay, and sticky mud deposited over the centuries by the Rhône, until at last they reached the foundations of old Roman villas. This is a perfect example of how conscientious work can produce results on a difficult site.

Before we leave the Mediterranean to examine a notorious sunken city of the New World, we should mention a few cities that are truly lost. In the eighth and seventh centuries B.C. the Greeks expanded with enormous energy, colonizing the whole of southern Italy, and other places as well. Of the fabulous and prosperous cities of Magna Graecia – such as Paestum and Tarentum, which are well known today – some are lost without trace. Of all the cities of Magna Graecia, Sybaris was the most luxurious and the most renowned, yet its site is unknown as are those of its colonies Scidrus and Laus.

The fantastic wealth of Sybaris came from two principal sources – its rich, "virtuous" soil, and land routes for trade across the toe

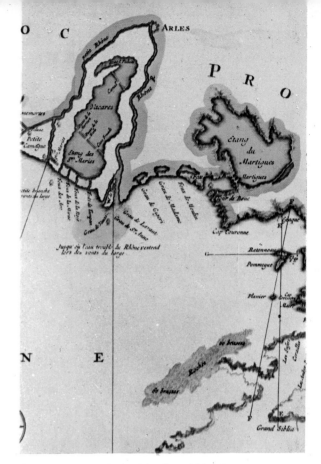

This map drawn in 1725 by Count Marsigli shows the position of Fos-sur-Mer (Fox) and its relation to the Rhône. It was at Fos-sur-Mer that Beaucaire discovered the foundations of old Roman villas buried in mud deposits brought down by the Rhône.

A head of Aphrodite, Greek goddess of love and beauty, found at Fos-sur-Mer. Carved in ivory, it is of Hellenic design and dates from about the first century B.C.

145

These coins recovered from sunken cities of Magna Graecia show a variety of sea motifs: crab, from Motya; octopus, from Syracuse; scallop from Oxentum; and the dolphin from Tarentum.

of Italy to Scidrus and Laus. This saved a long sea journey and enabled ships to avoid the dangerous Strait of Messana. The overland route probably took about two days. Recently the Italians have excavated in the area of Laus and have discovered enough to show that they are on the right trail, but the site of Scidrus, like that of Sybaris, is completely lost.

Sybaris was founded about 720 B.C. and was razed to the ground in 510 B.C., after about two hundred glorious years. The city was destroyed by the citizens of the neighboring colony of Croton, which was famous for its athletes. The account of Phylarchus states that the Sybarites murdered thirty ambassadors from Croton and threw their bodies over the city wall to be eaten by beasts. Although the Sybarites put three hundred thousand men into ensuing battle against the Crotoniates, this was not enough. Led by Milo, the greatest athlete of the ancient world, the Croton forces crushed their enemy. To quote Strabo: "Because of their luxuriousness and their insolence all their high fortune was wrested from them by the Crotoniates in seventy days." All stragglers were killed, and the waters of the river Crathis were diverted to flow over the site of the ruined city.

So far we have spoken only of lost cities of the Mediterranean. In 1959, Edwin Link, the American of Link aviation trainer fame, extended the scope of underwater archaeology by his work at Port Royal, in Jamaica. Two-thirds of this town was destroyed by an earthquake that struck at about 11:40 A.M. on June 7, 1692. Here is an eye witness account of the event, which compares nicely with the Greek geographer Pausanias' vivid description of the destruction of Helike.

"The earth heaved and swelled like the rolling billows, and in many places the earth cracked, open'd, and shut with a motion quick and fast . . . in some of these people were swallowed up, in others they were caught by the middle and pressed to death. The whole was attended with the noise of falling mountains at a distance, while the sky was turned dull and reddish like an glowing oven."

Port Royal was reputed to be the wickedest town in the world. It was Henry Morgan's base for operations against the Spaniards and was the headquarters of pirates and buccaneers. They spent their ill-gotten wealth recklessly on the usual pleasures of sailors, and the town was well equipped to provide them. As the merchants prospered by selling and trading, the town expanded dangerously to the very edges of the sand spit on which it was built, but apparently no thought was given to the stupidity of building four-story houses on sand and shingle.

On the fatal June day the whole waterfront was precipitated into the sea in a few minutes, and, as crevasses opened to swallow buildings and people, a vast wave roared in from the sea. Warehouses and docks were smashed, and ships were battered to splinters. The frigate *Swan* was carried high over the roof tops. Two thousand people were killed.

In the 270 years since the earthquake, sand has deposited and enlarged the spit, and the ruins of the town lie deep in mud. To cope with this difficult situation, Link had a special diving and salvage ship built, called the *Sea Diver*. The water was so dirty that aerial photography was hopeless, so a great search was made for reliable old charts to give the divers some idea of the town plan

The *Sea Diver*, *the research ship owned and used by Edwin Link when he uncovered the remains of Port Royal, Jamaica.*

before they started work. Eventually the best map was found in London, in the British Museum. The first stage of the work on the site was an echo sounder survey by Captain P.V.H. Weems, who worked from the launch *Reef Diver*. When he located Fort James and Fort Carlisle, at either end of the town, it was then possible to calculate the positions of other buildings.

Link next fixed the *Sea Diver* by four anchors above the point where he thought the king's warehouse should have been and lashed a steel pontoon barge alongside. In the barge was a ten-inch diameter air-lift to pump mud to the surface. The position was worked for several days with the assistance of six U.S. Navy divers, but only mud and gravel, broken bits of modern bottles, and china came gushing out of the air-lift. Even when the *Sea Diver* was moved to another position, Port Royal remained obstinately concealed beneath its cloak of mud.

At last, by the east wall of Fort James, the past was forced to reveal its secrets. Wine bottles, clay pipes, bones, bits of coal, and broken dishes came pouring to the surface in a steady stream. The best finds, however, were those which the divers rescued from the air-lift at the bottom. Among these were onion-shaped rum bottles

Sir Henry Morgan.

The brass watch which, when X-rayed, showed the time of the Port Royal earthquake.

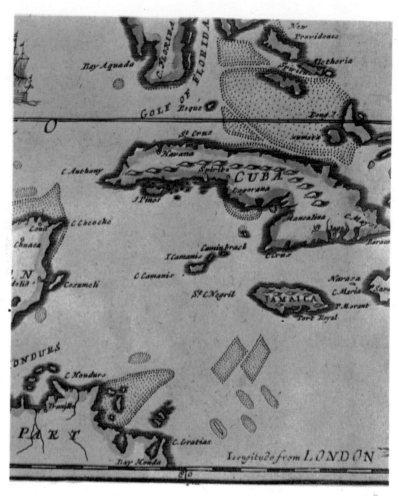

which were made of greenish-black glass, and one ladle made of brass.

Working forty feet down in the inky blackness of the mud stirred up by the air-lift, the divers soon began to uncover the brick walls of the old town. They had to work entirely by feel, and the risk of the collapse of the walls was added to the usual dangers of diving in tropical waters. Only in the early morning, before the work day had started, was it possible to see through the water, which became cloudier as the day wore on.

Among the finds were many cooking pots, one of which still contained several bones left from a stew. The divers also found charred bricks, and an iron grill, which must have been part of a cooking range for a large kitchen. This kitchen possibly supplied the fort or, alternatively, a house marked on the chart as belonging to a Mr. Littleton, who may have been a tavern-keeper. During a systematic survey of the entire site, divers found in Fort James several cannon balls, including two joined with an iron bar so that they would smash through the rigging of a ship. On the site of Freeman's House they found an onion bottle with the cork still in place and secured by twisted wire. Some of the rum was extracted with a hypodermic syringe, but on sampling it Ed Link proclaimed that 1692 must have been a bad year.

The number of bottles dredged up seems to indicate that the inhabitants of Port Royal had been conscientious drinkers at all

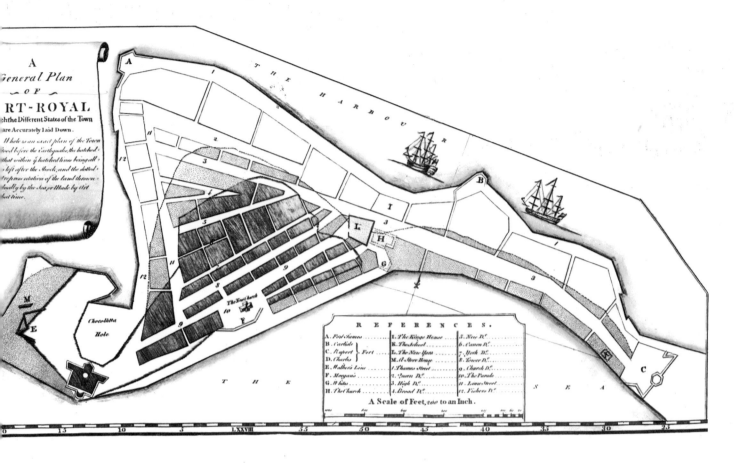

times. As the air-lift sucked its way down, it exposed first Coke and beer bottles, then nineteenth-century bottles of many shapes, then eighteenth-century hand-blown rum bottles, and finally, among the shattered brick walls, the onion-shaped rum bottles which were contemporary with the earthquake.

All of the ferrous objects were heavily encrusted with coral, and in most instances the metal beneath had corroded away. An iron beam balance was found, as well as a swivel gun of the type made in Spain during the fifteenth century. What this gun was doing in Port Royal is still a mystery.

The most bizarre find of all was made by Al Barnesky, one of the navy divers. It was a brass watch, complete except for the glass and hands. When the calcareous growth covering the face was X-rayed to reveal the original position of the hands, it was found that the watch had stopped at seventeen minutes to twelve, the time of the earthquake. The name of the maker, Paul Blondel, was inscribed inside, and researchers at the Science Museum in London later confirmed that the watch had been made in Amsterdam about 1686.

All of the findings at Port Royal have yet to be analyzed in detail. The excavation has shown that an awkward and unpromising site can be worked successfully, provided that a wide range of resources of science, modern engineering and salvage techniques are all used to maximum advantage.

At the left is a map of the West Indies drawn in 1685 by Anthony Williams. It shows Jamaica (center) with the town Port Royal. The plan (above) shows Port Royal after the earthquake of 1692, the dark areas indicating the streets and docks that still remained above water after the earthquake. The dotted line shows the area that had risen above sea level by 1749.

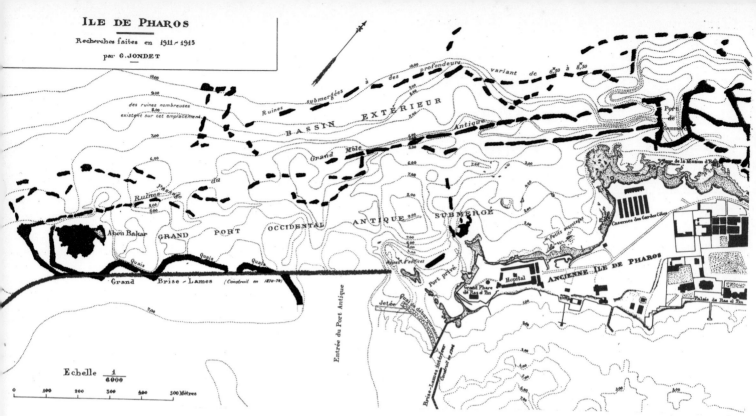

Echelle $\frac{1}{6000}$

0   100   200   300   400   500 Mètres

Lost Harbors

*Jondet's chart drawn in 1911 details the
submerged breakwaters and moles (in blue) of
the Minoan port of A-ur near Alexandria,
shown here in a painting of 1472. The
ancient port dwarfed many modern ones.*

The oldest known artificial harbor in the world was near the present site of Alexandria, at A-ur, on the Canopic branch of the Nile, and it was here that the voyages of Seneferu came to an end about 3000 B.C. By 2000 B.C. the site of A-ur was lost and the Great Harbor of Pharos was built nearby; it was on a colossal scale which dwarfs many of our ports today. Its layout and the skillful use of the configuration of the sea bed might have been the work of a modern harbor engineer. Possibly this work of genius was built by the Minoans who were the dominant sea power at the time; even so, it could not have been built without the co-operation of the reigning Pharaoh, possibly Sensuret.

When M. Gaston Jondet investigated the submerged ruins of the Great Harbor of Pharos between 1910 and 1915, he found that it had been formed by joining the island of Pharos to the rock of Abu Bakar with a series of breakwaters, thus enclosing two basins with a total area of more than three hundred acres. The most amazing parts of this system were the two parallel breakwaters, the outer one of which faced the open sea, and the inner one separating the basins. The breakwaters were each 8500 feet long, 200 feet wide, 30 feet high, and were situated 650 feet apart. Each one was faced with a wall 40 feet thick, and the space between the walls was filled with large blocks.

The upper surface of both breakwaters had a slight camber, and was made of flagstones often fifteen to twenty feet across, some of which were arranged in a typically Minoan pattern. No cement or mortar was used anywhere in the harbor; the large blocks, quarried at Mex, were packed in with sand and small stones. There is no need here to go into the details of the wharfs and quays which surrounded this magnificent port, but one cannot help agreeing with M. Jondet when he said that "it was the work of a realistic genius."

All attempts to find records of the construction of the Port of Pharos have failed. By the time Alexander reached it, it had already disappeared beneath the waves. Having just destroyed Tyre, he

This engraving of the old wall of the Port of Tyre (view toward the mainland) shows that part of the wall was visible as late as 1836. Alexander's causeway, which he built to capture the port, is now covered by sand.

was determined to build a port which would outshine its glory, but the site he chose, just to the east of Pharos, was not so good as that of the original harbor. Not only were the reefs dangerous, which led to the construction of the famous lighthouse by Ptolemy, but the surrounding sea there was fairly shallow and it tended to fill with sand.

From 1931 to 1934 Père Antoine Poidebard worked on the great Phoenician port of Tyre and greatly improved on the methods of Günther and Jondet. For one thing he used aerial photography to get a general outline of the submerged site; then he surveyed it in detail by using helmet divers and by taking many underwater photographs.

Herodotus dates the foundation of Tyre at 2750 B.C., but this is probably incorrect. At any rate, the fame of the city was widespread by 1400 B.C., and by 900 B.C. its sailors had passed Gibraltar and received their baptism of the Atlantic. It was probably at this time that the northern, or Sidonian, harbor was built. Hiram, who was king of Tyre from 970 to 936 B.C., was a friend and ally of Solomon, and it was during his reign that engineers from Tyre built the temple at Jerusalem. When Hiram came to the throne, Tyre was separated into three islands by arms of the sea. He filled these channels and by so doing greatly increased the strategic strength of the city. Along the south side of the reclaimed land he built the Egyptian harbor, which was protected from the action of the sea by a mole 2500 feet long.

As late as 332 B.C., Alexander regarded Tyre as the key to the East. He cunningly captured it by building a colossal causeway to the island. Over the years following his destruction of the city, sand began accumulating along both sides of the causeway, with the result that land was built up and the site is no longer an island.

During his survey of Tyre, Poidebard relied on local divers who knew the bottom very well, and who could guide him to points of interest. But he found that the helmet divers were so clumsy that men with no equipment at all had to swim down to help, and to point things out. These men could dive down fifty feet and work there with enormous strength for periods of more than one and a half minutes. Considering that prodigious work was accomplished in this way by Poidebard, it is probable that the Phoenicians themselves used divers of similar ability to position the foundations of the harbor walls. If so, it would be interesting to know if the Phoenician divers ever used an artificial air supply.

A group of photographs taken with a camera made at the naval base at Beirut showed Poidebard that the moles had foundations of carefully laid blocks, the upper parts faced with stone and filled in with concrete. Some of the blocks were keyed together with dowels of iron and packed with lead. The south part of the mole was twenty-six feet wide, and the west part, where it was exposed to the full force of the open sea, was thirty-three feet wide. The Quai de la Source was once a massive concrete wharf which divided the east basin in two, the easternmost part used as a shipbuilding and repair yard.

North and south of the island of Tyre there stretched extensive reefs and ridges of rock running parallel to the shore. These certainly helped to protect the approaches to the harbors, but the ingenious Phoenicians improved on nature by building vast walls along the reef tops. These breakwaters were a hundred feet wide,

Little more than fragments of masonry remain to mark the once proud harbors of the classical world. This photograph shows what were possibly foundation stones of the rectangular shore frontage of part of the harbor at Carthage, founded about 814 B.C. and destroyed by the Romans in 146 B.C.

several thousand feet long, and contained some blocks weighing fifteen tons. Traces of these rugged walls were still visible as late as the nineteenth century.

North of Tyre is the small island of Arvad, a very early Phoenician colony whose engineers demonstrated to perfection their ingenuity in coping with the sea. This island, where there was no soil, no fresh water, and which was swept by storm waves, was made to support human life. The engineers excavated lagoons to act as wave traps on the seaward side of the island, and built apartment houses many stories high. They even found a spring of fresh water beneath the sea, not far from the island, and placed a lead hemisphere over it. With a pipe led from the hemisphere to a boat equipped with a storage tank.

The early Phoenician and Carthaginian military harbors of North Africa are of an interesting type called a cothon. These primitive artificial basins were cut entirely out of the land so that the port was snug within the city walls. Motya, on the west coast of Sicily, and Utica, near Carthage, were both founded about 900 B.C., and were on islands. The cothon at Utica was cut into the island and measured 338 feet by 108 feet; that at Motya was 167 feet by 121 feet.

Before the foundation of Carthage the island site of Utica had already become too small and the city was expanding onto the mainland. Here engineers built a greatly improved cothon, 781 feet by 607 feet, with rounded corners, a heavily fortified palace on an island in the middle, and a strong breakwater to protect the seaward side. The breakwater was ingeniously built with rows of holes leading to a central channel or tunnel which ran within the masonry along the entire length of the breakwater. This elaborate system was most likely devised to reduce the shock of breaking waves. The moles at Thapsus and Hadrumetum are of the same design.

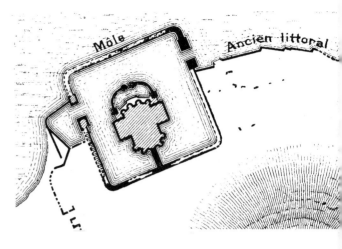

The "cothon," or military fortress of a harbor, was an artificial basin cut into the land. The plan of the one shown here is for Utica, founded about 1000 B.C.

As early as the ninth century B.C. men were using artificial breathing apparatus for underwater work. This relief shows Assyrian divers with air tanks of inflated animal skins.

Apollonia, the port for the once-proud city of Cyrene, is today half submerged. Eroded marble columns embedded in sand mark its remains on land. Under Roman domination in 96 B.C., Apollonia was one of the chief export centers of the North African coast.

In 1958 and 1959 the present writer led expeditions to the sunken Greek city of Apollonia on the Cyrenaican coast of Libya. The expeditions were financed and supported by the Royal Geographical Society, the British School at Athens, the British Academy, and the Faculty of Archaeology at Cambridge. The divers were all members of the Cambridge University Underwater Exploration Group.

Herodotus gives two versions of the foundation of a Greek colony in Libya – one the Therean story, the other the Cyrenaican. According to the Cyrenaican version, Battus, the son of one of the chief citizens of Thera, founded the city of Cyrene in the mountains (in 631 B.C.), and on the coast nearby he founded the port of Apollonia. In 525 B.C. Cyrene came under Persian domination; Alexandrian in 331 B.C.; and Roman in 96 B.C. The main exports of the area were chariots and sylphium, a drug used by the priestesses of the oracles. Under Roman rule Cyrene became fabulously rich by exporting enormous quantities of grain from the port of Apollonia to Ostia, the port of Rome.

Today Cyrene has only a single street, shaded by whispering eucalyptus trees and twisting between the low, white Arab shops. All round the village lie magnificent ruins of the old temples, market places, baths, and theaters. Beyond these are the scattered remains of the suburbs of the once-great city, now half-buried in sand and overgrown with thorns.

At Apollonia itself there is a little fishing village to the west of the ancient city, and some of the poorer members of the community today live in the dark tombs and fallen ruins. Now more than half of the city is beneath water. In rough weather the waves plunge and boil over the outermost walls, thunder across the ruined harbor

This Greek plate (in Attic style) shows
Arcesilaus, King of Cyrene, supervising
the weighing of ballast. Apollonia was
Cyrene's chief port and grew fabulously
rich on her exports to Rome.

— faltering and tumbling over the submerged buildings — and
finally collapse, roaring on the sandy beach.

Our first task when we arrived in August 1958 was to get a
rough idea of the extent of the underwater site. At the west end of
the city we found that the great fortified gate tower was being
undermined by the sea, and half of it had already collapsed. Swimmers with masks, fins, and snorkels dived into the water by the
tower, taking plastic drawing boards and pencils with them. From
the submerged foundations of the seaward part of the tower the
western city wall stretched out beneath the waves toward the reef.
Halfway along the wall was a square fort, and from this many more
walls ran eastward into the bewildering maze of the city itself.

While the swimmers were making their sketches, another group
worked on land setting up the base line, which extended 2953 feet
from the west gate to the theater. During all of our work on land

we were watched attentively by a circle of Arab children who were always willing to help and carry things for us, or to sell Roman coins for cigarettes.

We soon became acquainted with a team of Arab divers who were spending the season at Apollonia. They lived on the jetty beneath a canvas shelter supported by oil drums. For furniture they had cushions to sit on and a radio, and would have been very happy had it not been for the bends. The wrecked ammunition ship which they were cutting up for scrap lay in eighty feet of water, and they were in the habit of working in standard gear for eleven hours at this depth, then surfacing without stops. As a result, one man lay in agony on a heap of rugs while his companions comforted him by singing and waiting for him to get better before they continued their work. We tried to explain that the pains would not occur if they dived for a shorter time and stopped on the way up. They would hear none of it.

"It is the will of Allah," said the afflicted one. "All divers die young. My father died at twenty-seven. I will soon be dead. It is the will of Allah."

After plotting the main points of the city, we measured the buildings in detail. At the northwest of the site was a cluster of rocks which just broke the surface and which we called the Grotto Reef. This was a natural outcrop which had been carved artificially in such a way that its sides were straight and vertical. Through the rock was a submerged tunnel sixty feet long, four feet wide, and six feet from floor to ceiling. In one place where the roof had collapsed the sunlight filtered through the watery darkness and glowed greenly against the ancient walls. At the northern boundary of the city were two islands, and outside each was a lagoon sheltered from the sea by a barrier of rock. Cut artificially, the lagoons most likely served as wave traps, like the lagoons at Arvad. On the inside of the west island were ten Greek slipways, each 23 feet wide, 92 feet long, and sloping at four degrees. Greek warships were kept on land except when they were needed in combat; even the merchant vessels were taken out of water for the winter.

On the other side of the harbor was a group of solid parallel structures, probably quays. By burrowing in the sand between them we found several complete pots, jars, and small dishes that must have fallen overboard while the ships were being loaded. Scattered over the whole site were thousands of broken amphorae. East of the quays was a square block building keyed together with hollow lead dowels which probably were packed in cold rather than melted in – a technique exactly parallel to that found at Tyre by Poidebard.

The central wall of the harbor stretched northward toward the west island and ended as a massive block fortress which guarded the harbor entrance. On the opposite side of the channel was a similar fort. Our 1958 work led us to the conclusion that there had been a fortified harbor between the mainland and the west island, and that it had been protected by a sea wall running between the island and the Grotto Reef. It also seemed that the harbor entrance had been between the west and east islands.

In 1959 when we returned to Apollonia we searched in the deep water to the east of the site and found scattered rubble and blocks of marble stretching northward from the foot of the acropolis and

terminating in a group of massive stones, each twelve feet by four feet by four feet. These were the remains of the east breakwater that had originally enclosed a second harbor basin. On the east island, across a narrow gap of water from the end of the east breakwater, we discovered the foundations of a huge circular tower that probably served as a beacon to guide ships from afar.

Apollonia was a perfect two-harbor city with an inner fortified port separated from the outer commercial port by a narrow channel and a broad quay which could be defended. The connecting channel was flanked by long walls so that any ship attempting to get into the military port had to run the gauntlet between the massed ranks of the defenders, and at the end of the channel a spiked boom or chains would be hung between the towers.

It is important here to point out the similarity of the general design of Apollonia to the Phoenician plan, not the Greek. The Greeks were used to a highly indented coast line, where natural harbors needed few improvements, so their methods of construction were not as sophisticated as those of the Phoenicians. Instead

Built on a Phoenician plan, the Greek port of Apollonia was a two-harbor city. The outer harbor received ships of commerce, while the inner harbor was fortified to protect the city from attack. An enemy ship attempting to enter the inner harbor would have to pass through the connecting channel, which could be defended by soldiers standing on the walls.

The author, N. C. Flemming, is caught by a second camera as he takes motion pictures during the 1958–59 Apollonia expedition.

Richard Everington, one of the Cambridge divers at Apollonia, examines grain silos cut out of rock in classical times.

of laying carefully cut blocks below the water level, the Greeks dumped in rubble until the mound broke the surface, then they built a wall along it. As at Tyre, Apollonia has one harbor inside the city fortifications, the other outside. It was general practice for the Greeks to build two interconnected harbors, but they usually had separate entrances so that a ship could enter port in any wind. It is difficult to see how there could have been a separate entrance to the inner harbor at Apollonia, and so the plan becomes more like the cothon and commercial port system of the Phoenicians in North Africa.

Just inside the east breakwater we found a large submerged *piscina*, or fish tank, divided into many compartments and connected to the open sea by narrow channels. The Romans cultivated fish in such tanks, regulating the small tide of the Mediterranean with stone or bronze sluice gates. It was the *piscina* that gave us our most important clue to the city's subsidence of six and a half feet, since it was built more than 2500 years ago. Unplanned finds such as the *piscina* can be rewarding.

Another find was made by Hugh Edwards. One day while Natalka Czartoryska and I were filming the tunnel in the Grotto Reef, Hugh was measuring a small building near the Roman quays when suddenly he saw the corner of a block of stone sticking out of the white sand, and in it was a hole about three inches across. He swam down to it, scoured away the sand, and found himself looking at a prize – a wedge-shaped Greek anchor. He pried it out of the mud, clutched it, then struggled toward the surface. But it was too heavy, and since he was without an aqualung he had to drop the anchor and race to the surface for a breath. But Hugh is not a man to be defeated by a small engineering problem. Taking a deep lungful of air he dived down again, clasped the precious stone to his chest and began to walk slowly along the bottom toward the shore. After a minute or so he had to drop anchor and surface again, then dive once more. It took a quarter of an hour to reach the beach, where he sat down exhausted but happy.

This kind of anchor is one of the earliest types known. From the *Odyssey* we know that the Mycenaeans used heavy stones to anchor their ships, and the first development was a stone with a hole in it for a rope. At Syracuse, in 1959, divers found several oddly-shaped stones that might have been primitive anchors, but their use is not yet certain. The hole in our Apollonia anchor probably took a long crossbeam to control the position of the anchor when it struck bottom. At the opposite end were two holes perpendicular to the first one. They probably took short stakes that dug into the sea bed. The rope would have been attached to the longer beam on either side of the stone. Anchors found on the earlier Roman wrecks were made of wood and lead. One diver discovered many lead anchor stocks from Syracuse harbor during 1955 and 1956. The largest one weighed 702 pounds, the smallest about ten pounds. It is not clear when the first iron anchors were introduced, although some of the very primitive types found in Sicily may be late Roman or early Arabic.

The prosperity of Cyrenaica in Roman times was such that the coastal settlements were very close together. We visited three of these known minor harbors, and discovered a fourth. Naustathmos and Erithrium had very little to show for themselves; but at

Phycus, Natalka Czartoryska and I found an extraordinary complex of channels, tunnels, passages, caves, and tanks, most of them designed presumably for the storage of goods for export and ships' provisions. From the relation of these structures to the water, it was clear that there had been a subsidence of the land of between three and six feet.

We searched the island chain west of Apollonia for any signs of ancient ruins, but it was only after we had been given a clue by an Arab friend that we found some about three miles away. On a tiny island was a maze of tanks and storage bins which we had been expecting to find. The items stored in these bins would have corresponded to what was carried in amphorae – including grain, oil, wine, fresh water, fish, and shellfish. It is easy to imagine a few ships lying in the shelter of the island while their crews transferred the local produce into amphorae and then loaded them into the cargo holds.

The incredible engineering genius of the Romans brought about a revolution in harbor construction. By the third century B.C. they were using arches, hydraulic cement, and watertight cofferdams. Vitruvius, an engineer of the first century B.C., gave a detailed description of the methods of construction of breakwaters. The most advanced system then was one devised for coping with a soft sea bed. When Claudius was building the new harbor at Ostia in A.D. 43, he formed one section of the breakwater by filling a huge barge with concrete and sinking the barge in position.

Günther has revealed the details of the elaborate Roman ports in the Bay of Naples, and Diolé visited many of them in North Africa. The one he studied most thoroughly was Cherchel, in Algeria. This is a very old port, probably in use even before the Phoenicians arrived, calling it Iol. The Romans called it Caesarea, and it was their most important naval harbor between Carthage and Gibraltar. But there is one problem: although Caesarea was such an important military base, there is no evidence on the surface of any harbor, except a small one created by the shelter of the island of Joinville. René Cagnat, an authority on the Roman colonies in North Africa, could not see how the harbor could have held more than thirteen ships, a number totally inadequate to cope with the pirates and political problems of the time.

Diolé, after braving the town sewers of Caesarea and struggling with rusty cables and tangled wreckage, learned the truth about the Roman port. He found vast areas of submerged masonry and concrete, columns, and a section of a huge arch. From these he concluded that the remains of a mole at the east of the city, first reported in 1932, really did exist. After many long days of swimming and searching, he decided that originally there must have been four basins to the Roman harbor, and that there had been a complex system of moles and breakwaters to protect them. If this is the case, then the old harbor would have been large enough to rank as a major Roman naval base.

In summary, the sequence of development of harbors runs from the Minoan-Egyptian port of Pharos, to the Phoenician port of Tyre, the Carthaginian ports of North Africa, and culminates with the advanced Roman constructions. The Greeks, because their coasts offered so many natural harbors, did not develop such ingenious ports as the other powers of the ancient world.

Hugh Edwards, an Australian diver who worked with Flemming at Apollonia, displays his Greek stone anchor. Pieces of spiked wood, fitted through the holes, dug into the bottom and prevented the anchor from slipping.

Forgotten Wrecks

In 1832 a Piombino fisherman brought this bronze statue of Apollo up in his nets. It is dated about 460 B.C. and is now on display in the Louvre, Paris.

The sea is so vast, and men must move so hesitantly within it that a widespread, systematic search for lost wrecks would take hundreds of years. Besides, a lost wreck of the past is concealed like a timid fish whose coloring is so perfect that it has only to lie still and the hunters will pass by, unseeing. Luck is the leading lady in this drama. Divers may search for a wreck for days or weeks and give up in despair before seeing encrusted pottery protruding from the mud and weed at a particular angle, or the linear pattern which means the work of man.

Fishermen who drag their living from the sea sometimes bring up in their nets carved stones which are of no apparent value to them. Most submarine archaeological discoveries have been made this way. A novel variation of this theme was provided recently when a classical wreck was revealed accidentally by television during the search for the Comet aircraft that crashed off Elba in 1954. The chance finds that have been made over the last 150 years fascinate archaeologists and divers alike, particularly if it is possible to place the wreck, or a fragment of its cargo, in the proper historical context.

When the Romans ransacked the temples of Greece, many of their ships, loaded to the gunwales with sculptures, columns, and furniture, were wrecked by storms. In 1832 a fisherman at Piombino hauled up in his net a statue of Apollo dating from the fifth century B.C. It can now be seen in the Louvre. A beautiful bronze of a boy was found at Eleusis in 1829, and nearby at Livadhostro, a bronze of Poseidon. But it is more likely that both of these statues fell into the sea during the looting of temples, and are not part of the cargoes of wrecks.

A team of sponge fishers were working off Anticythera near Cape Malea in 1900 when they noticed a coagulated black mass twenty-five yards from shore and 180 feet deep in the crystal-clear water. It turned out to be a corroded heap of marble and bronze statues in and around a wreck 150 feet long. The Greek government sponsored the salvage, and divers, who could work only five minutes at a time at that depth, raised statues, utensils, tiles, and amphorae. Most of the marbles were so corroded that they were unrecognizable, but one statue of Aphrodite was intact, as was a gigantic marble Heracles. A perfect bronze of Perseus was also discovered, plus broken limbs of dancers, athletes, boxers, and the head of a philosopher. When they were examined, many of the statues were found to be copies of famous works made for export. On one of the objects, a metal dial of a curious astronomical instrument, appeared the name of a month which was not introduced until 30 B.C., and since there were some early types of pottery among the wreckage, the date of the voyage is thought to be Augustan. The ship was probably sailing from Athens to Rome.

In 1925 a boat fishing off the sandy shore near Marathon brought up a perfect bronze statue of a boy, four feet, three inches high, in the style of Praxiteles. In the same nets was a bronze base of a candelabrum and some planks. Since there are no temples or shrines in the vicinity, there is almost certainly a wreck here, but no search has been made for it.

The fishermen who found the bronze arm of a statue at Artemison, in 1920, brought it secretly to Athens and tried to sell an option on the rest of the statue to a variety of local dealers. The

This bronze head of Poseidon, part of a
statue six feet, ten inches high, was found
in a wreck off Cape Artemison, Greece. The
Greeks honored Poseidon as a "savior," and
regarded him as god of the sea.

A grotesque in bronze from the Mahdia wreck.

This marble head of Aphrodite, eroded by sea water, was found in the wreck off Mahdia, Tunisia. The wreck may be the remains of one of the ships that took part in the capture of Athens by Sulla in 86 B.C.

government heard of the scheme and forced the men to reveal the site. The wreck was seven hundred yards from shore in 144 feet of water and contained a magnificent fifth-century Zeus, a statue of a small boy, and the forepart of a galloping horse. Pottery from this wreck dates it from about the first century B.C., and the ship seems to have been another Roman loot ship.

Random finds aside – and they could continue for many more pages – wrecks with their cargoes clustered in place are to the archaeologist-diver a much more rewarding find, and there have been several of these.

The wreck of Mahdia, off Tunisia, was discovered by Greek sponge divers in 1907, and from then until 1913 a series of expeditions to explore the wreck were organized by Alfred Merlin, Director of Tunisian Antiquities. The wreck was three miles from the shore in 130 feet of water. Lying on the bottom were sixty slime-covered columns, each twelve feet long and twenty-five inches in diameter; and scattered around were overgrown masses of broken amphorae and statues. Beneath the columns the divers found a layer of rotting timbers eight inches thick, which they believed to be the deck. When they cut their way through they found a cargo of artistic masterpieces to which no description can do justice. This amazing hoard, perilously lifted from its envelope of mud, now fills six rooms in the Bardo Museum in Tunis. The main items included a bronze Eros fifty inches high; a herma of Dionysus, by Boethus of Chalcedon; two large cornices; eight statuettes, of which three are grotesques; and many decorative motifs, fragments of furniture, and candelabra. The marbles include a bust of Aphrodite, a Pan, a Niobe, two Niobids, and two satyrs. A lamp of characteristic design puts the date of the wreck in the early first century B.C., and the presence of so many Athenian sculptures suggests that this was loot from the capture of Athens by Sulla in 86 B.C.

In 1948 a team of nine free-divers, under the leadership of Cousteau and Philippe Taillez, revisited the wreck of Mahdia on board the sloop *Elie Monnier*. They had great difficulty finding it because the original fixes had been so vague. As a result, they had so little time left for work that they managed to bring up only four of the columns and two anchors. However, this operation did prove that there was still a lot more to be found on the site.

In 1954 the search was taken up again, this time by members of the Club d'Etudes Sous Marines de Tunisie, who found the wreck after only two and a half days' search. They drew a plan of her and, by using two air-lifts, cleared most of the mud, then moved the remaining columns clear of the ship. The following year they discovered the keel, which was $19\frac{1}{2}$ inches wide and 85 feet long, and estimated the original cargo at 200 to 250 tons.

On August 8, 1948, Henri Broussard discovered a large heap of amphorae off Anthéor Point. At first there was no suspicion of a wreck, just rows of amphorae. The following year Taillez worked the site from the *Elie Monnier*, but it was so overgrown that work was difficult and slow; nevertheless they did bring up several amphorae in good condition. In August 1950, Capitaine de Fregate Rossignol returned with the *Elie Monnier* and succeeded, with an air-lift, in exposing the ribs of the wreck. He found that the copper nails from this ship had almost exactly the same composition as

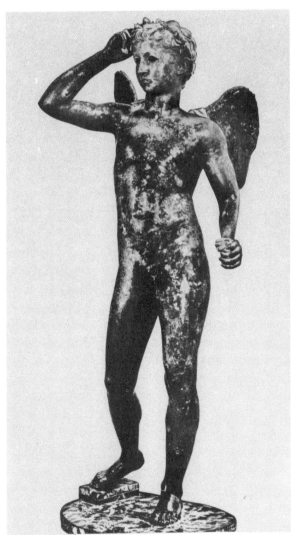

This marble head of Pan was also found in the wreck off Mahdia. Like the head of Aphrodite, it has been eroded by water.

Another prize from the wreck of Mahdia is this statue of Eros, Greek god of love. His hand is extended, probably to hold a lyre.

those from the wreck of Mahdia. The amphorae, which numbered about two thousand, probably date from the first century B.C. Regrettably, there is nothing left to be seen at Anthéor today, save the broken and scattered debris left by hundreds of diving tourists searching for souvenirs.

One of the most exciting wrecks found to date is the thousand-ton Roman freighter salvaged by Cousteau at Grand Congloué, a tiny limestone islet near Marseilles. It was discovered by standard divers working on a new sewer for Marseilles, and Cousteau began excavating it in August 1952. In about 140 feet of water, the wreck appeared to be a weed-covered grave from which the necks of amphorae and assorted pottery projected. The mound was 120 feet long and 12 feet wide.

Cousteau managed to recruit a volunteer salvage team and a large air-lift was installed in the *Calypso*. But the wreck was so close to the cliff wall that after several setbacks from rough seas they decided to suspend the air-lift from a boom on shore. This problem solved, they immediately met another. When they had cleared away the mud they found that several huge chunks of the cliff had fallen onto the wreck, some of them weighing more than seven tons. After several attempts to split the boulders with small charges of plastic explosive failed, they resorted to large charges tamped into drilled holes. The results were just what they had hoped for, leaving the wreck exposed and undamaged. Next began the work of examining the cargo. More than a thousand amphorae were raised during several thousand dives, together with hundreds of pots, thousands of pieces of black dinnerware, and many objects of lead. The date for this wreck seems to be about 250 B.C., and its significance is that it is one of the oldest seagoing ships yet discovered.

Another wreck of interest, because of the salvage technique used, is off Spargi. The archipelago of Magdalena, between Corsica and Sardinia, is on the ancient route from Etruria and Campania to the colonies on Sardinia, and possibly to the old ports of Massilia and Narbo. The navigation here is tricky and dangerous; treacherous rocks cause many wrecks even today. Just south of the Isola di Spargi lies a *secca*, and on the west of the *secca* is a pinnacle of rock rising from a depth of sixty feet to within nine feet of the surface. About three hundred feet from the danger point is the last resting place of the wreck of Spargi.

The cargo consisted of a batch of amphorae thirty-three feet by twenty-four feet, all aligned in the same direction and stacked in layers. The first layer contained 120 amphorae, and in a sandy area nearby were scattered black varnished ceramics and many plates and cups. In 1957, Gianni Roghi began to work the wreck with a team of seven divers. His method was to lay a yellow plastic tape grid with two-meter squares. Each square was marked by black letters written on a white plate, and if an amphora was removed a tag was tied to the grid to mark the exact position. The wreck has been dated at about 120 to 100 B.C. Although the excavation was still in progress when this was written, Roghi's work on it is perhaps the most thorough and accurate survey of any wreck to date.

These four wrecks – at Mahdia, Anthéor, Grand Congloué, and Spargi—all appear to be of about the same period. And they are all Roman cargo wrecks. It may seem odd, but not one warship of the

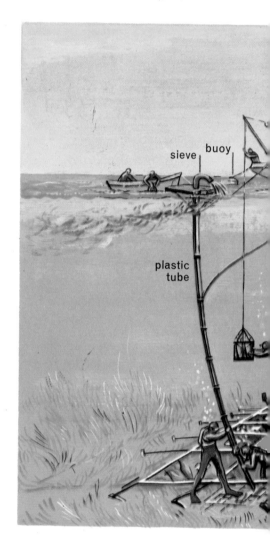

Between 120 and 100 B.C. a Roman cargo ship struck a rock and sank off the coast of Spargi between Corsica and Sardinia. When he began salvaging the wreck in 1957, Gianni Roghi laid down a grid of plastic tapes so that he could mark the position of each amphora in the cargo. This diagram shows a variety of activities carried out during the salvage operation.

sieve   buoy

plastic
tube

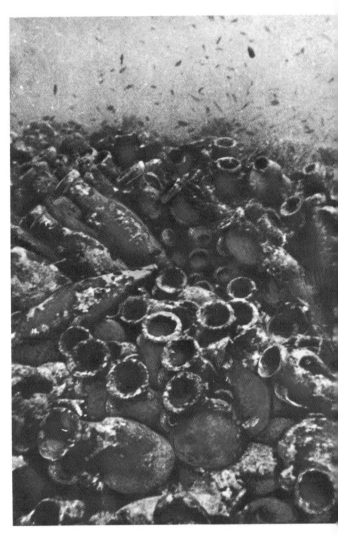

Remains of a cargo of about 700 amphorae (first century B.C.) found off Toulon near the island of Levant in 1948. These amphorae were stacked on the sea floor in much the same way as the amphorae found in the wreck of Spargi (left).

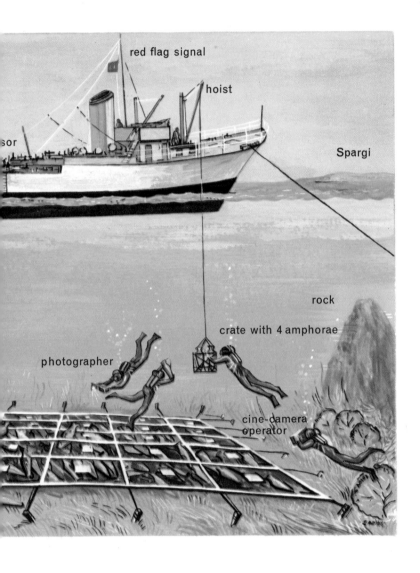

red flag signal

hoist

sor

Spargi

rock

crate with 4 amphorae

photographer

cine-camera operator

classical world has been found since our search for wrecks began.

Cargo ships of the classical world usually carried large sails, heavy cargoes, and possibly had a special fitting of lead on the hull to make the ship stable in heavy seas. If such a ship capsized during a storm it would sink rapidly, and at least part of the hull would be protected from corrosion by the cargo. In contrast, military vessels carried more rowers, lighter sails, less lead, and very little cargo. If one of these ships capsized it might not sink at all, and would be broken up by the waves or dashed to pieces against the shore. If it did sink, there would be no cargo to protect the hull, and all the planking would rot. This may explain why no classical warships remain to be found.

The most spectacular and successful salvage of an old wreck

Site of the Roman wreck salvaged by Cousteau at Grand Congloué in 1952. The wreck was dated at about 250 B.C.

ever carried out is that of the *Vasa*. In 1956 Anders Franzen located the wreck of this seventeenth-century warship in Stockholm Fiord, beneath 110 feet of dark, ice-cold water. The *Vasa* was constructed by order of King Gustav Adolf II in January 1625, and on Sunday afternoon, August 10, 1628, she was towed downstream against a light breeze to start her maiden voyage. After passing close to the rocks of Södermalm, with her mizzen, topsails, and foresail set, a sudden squall struck the ship and she heeled violently to port. With all flags flying she went down only a hundred yards from shore. It was a national disaster.

Three years later, Ian Bulmer, engineer to the King of England, tried to raise the wreck. Although he managed only to put the vessel on an even keel, this helped engineers who made subsequent attempts. In 1629 the Royal Swedish Navy began to work on the wreck, and from then until 1663 many Swedish and foreign experts tried to salvage it. On April 1, 1664, under the supervision of Andreas Peckel, the first cannon broke the surface after thirty-six years of submersion. By the time most of the guns from the upper deck had been recovered, Peckel had worked out a way of extracting the lower deck cannon through the gun ports, but how he achieved this fantastic operation is a mystery. During 1664 and the following year fifty-three of the sixty-four cannon were recovered. Considering the conditions in which the men worked – the blackness of the water, no artificial light, and the cold – this was a stupendous feat of endurance and skill.

Soon after Franzen had rediscovered the *Vasa*, a committee was formed with Commodore Edward Classon as chairman, and in February 1958 the committee produced a report recommending complete salvage of the wreck. The plan was to move the ship into shallow water where she could be more carefully investigated; meanwhile preparations could be made for raising her, if this seemed

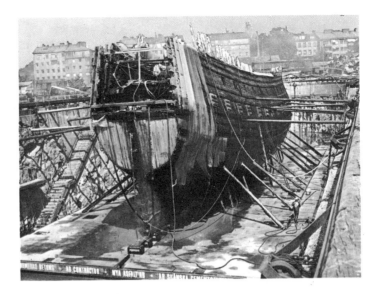

In 1628 the Swedish warship Vasa set sail on her maiden voyage, but a squall hit her and she sank just a hundred yards from shore in Stockholm Harbor (engraving shows Stockholm at the time the Vasa was built). After several attempts she was finally raised (see diagram below). When eventually she is restored, complete with wooden carvings (far left), she will be the oldest fully documented ship in the world. The photograph above shows the Vasa in dry dock after she was raised.

possible. With the help of King Gustav Adolf VI, the divers of the Royal Swedish Navy, and the resources of the Neptune Salvage Company, the project seemed assured of success.

The first stage was to blast six tunnels beneath the hull so that lifting cables could be passed under the ship. This task alone required more than a thousand diving hours and had to be carried out in total darkness. Add to this the divers' unpleasant knowledge that they were working under several hundred tons of stone ballast, and the risk of the collapse of the mud walls of the tunnel itself. While the tunnels were being scooped out and the wreck was being cleared for the lifting operation, the divers found thousands of objects that had fallen off the ship — among them superficial decorations of carved wood in the baroque style. Items recovered during the salvage work include a skull, a boot, rigging blocks, plates and tankards, coins and jugs, and even a keg of butter. The wooden sculptures, a few of which still have part of their gilt finish, required immediate treatment to prevent them from disintegrating after they were removed from their three hundred-year bath in salt water.

After the tunnels were completed, forty-five hundred feet of six-inch steel wires were looped under the hull and fastened to two lifting pontoons. As water was slowly pumped out of the pontoons, the *Vasa* rose a few feet from her grave. In eighteen laborious stages of lifting, the pontoons were towed 500 yards to a point near Kastellholmen in fifty feet of water. This operation was completed in September 1959.

At this writing the *Vasa* can be seen in full view, propped upright by braces and bathed constantly to prevent her drying out too rapidly. When she is finally installed in a special museum, with all her decorations replaced and her wood preserved, the *Vasa* will be the oldest fully documented ship in the world.

In the spring of 1959 I heard a rumor which I just could not believe. The story was that a wreck had been found by an American on the Turkish coast, and it was dated about 1500 B.C. Certainly, a wreck might have been found — but not so early. To everyone's surprise, it was true. This incredible discovery has pushed the time barrier back more than a thousand years past the date of the oldest wrecks mentioned so far.

In 1958, Peter Throckmorton and Mustafa Kapkin boarded a sponge boat belonging to Kamal Aras to begin their search for ancient wrecks. After two hours' sail from Bodrum they came to the island of Yassi in the Chuka channel, and around the reef that rises near the island they found no less than sixteen classical wrecks before the season ended! Each ship had the same story to tell: each had been split open by the rocks and lay buried beneath its encrusted cargo. At the end of the season another diver told them of a cargo of bronze. The more he talked, the more keenly Throckmorton and Kapkin listened. From the diver's detailed description they began to realize the possible age of the wreck and immediately drew up plans to return and examine the site the following year.

In 1959 they set sail with John Codran in the *Little Vigilant*, a seventy-foot steel ketch, to search for the wreck off Cape Gelidonya. The search dragged on day after day under a merciless sun and their seemingly endless work brought on a state of general depression. Just after deciding to give up the next day, they found the wreck by accident. It lay shimmering below them in ninety feet of water on the side of a ridge that joined two islands. On either side the ridge sloped sharply to the bottom to a depth of 150 feet.

On reaching the cargo they found that it consisted mainly of copper ingots in the shape of oxhides. There were also bronze axes, picks, spear points, and some crude pottery. The ingots were similar to those shown in Egyptian paintings of about 1500 B.C. Copper was exported from Cyprus in this form, samples having been found in Mycenae and Sardinia on sites dating between 1600 B.C. and 1200 B.C.

The following year another team returned to the site, this time under the auspices of the University of Pennsylvania, and set up a camp near Cape Gelidonya. Their finds included more ingots, ivory scarabs, haematite weights, delicate knife blades, plowshares, and ax heads. As the work went on, bits of wood and shreds of rope began to turn up among the ingots. In early August they lifted away a huge mass of concreted copper, and there below were dark timbers of the ancient ship. It was a piece of the hull about a yard square, complete with dowels and fragments of broken ribs.

The precious lump of soggy wood, encrusted with shattered splinters, folded bits of metal, and other debris, was prized from the bedrock after three weeks of chiseling. The wreck has been dated at about 1300 B.C., presumably on the basis of the cargo, and this puts it in the period of Mycenaean or early Phoenician navigation. Here, at last, is tangible proof that the ships of the great seagoing nations were built with ribs, while the ships of Egypt were still fragile and frameless.

Even in such a young country as Australia divers have successfully found part of their history beneath the sea. Hugh Edwards has described a series of expeditions sponsored by Australian newspapers to investigate wrecks around Rottnest Island, near Perth,

Ingots like the one shown here, about three feet long and in the shape of an ox hide, were used by eastern Mediterranean peoples during the Bronze Age. Many were found in the wreck at Bodrum.

and near the Murchison River, four hundred miles farther north.

The oldest and most interesting find was the wreck of the *Zuytdorp*, which belonged to the Dutch East India Company. The first suspicion of a wreck was reported by a bushman, Tom Pepper. He found broken glass, scraps of copper, and silver coins dated 1670, 1690, and 1711 on a part of the coast where few white men had been before.

The *Zuytdorp* left Wielingen on August 1, 1711, bound for Batavia. After eight hellish months she arrived off the Cape of Good Hope with 174 men left alive of her original crew of 286. On March 27, 1712, she set sail from Table Bay and was never seen again. It was an ill-fated voyage, even by the standards of the eighteenth century. Sometime in 1712 she must have been thrown up against the towering red cliffs of Australia, where a few survivors struggled ashore onto the barren rocks.

In 1958 an expedition – the second, in fact – was organized, but again the lethal pounding of the surf made diving impossible. However, they found the camp of the survivors on the cliff top, and scattered around it were many coins, keys, the bases of square glass bottles, and a twenty-five-foot length of a broken mast. The fact that no cooking pots, knives, or muskets were found leads Edwards to suppose that the Dutchmen had eventually succeeded in building themselves a boat and had sailed away to their death, taking all their utensils with them.

The *Zuytdorp* is supposed to have been carrying a treasure of one hundred thousand guilders, but the wreck itself has yet to be found. Although the local people swear that the sea is sometimes calm for days at a time, this seems to be so rare that the *Zuytdorp's* treasure will probably remain safe from divers forever. For the most part, wrecks found in the New World are of less historical interest than those found in the Mediterranean, simply because the ships that went to the bottom around the Americas and Australia are well documented and their cargoes can tell us little that we do not already know.

Dutch painting (top) shows sailors of the same period as the wreck of the Zuytdorp. The ship went down off the west coast of Australia, forty miles south of Shark Bay (above). A coin (top right) found on the coast is dated 1711, about a year before the wreck.

New Frontiers

Around the shores of the Mediterranean there are about forty submerged cities that have yet to be excavated. This task can be carried out only by archaeologists who have also been trained as divers. To date there are few such scholars, but the aqualung and underwater camera are gradually becoming standard archaeological equipment in some universities.

From 3000 B.C. to the fall of the Roman Empire more than three hundred major ports and coastal cities were constructed in the Mediterranean. Between these cities were thousands of fishing villages, minor trading ports, and seaside villas. Since their construction there has not been a large eustatic change in sea level, but there have been many localized earth movements and many great estuaries have been silted up. As a result, about half of the original cities are now below sea level, together with their associated minor ports and villas. Of these 150 submerged cities, half again are obscured by modern buildings or have been completely destroyed, so that there are probably seventy-five submerged or partially submerged sites to be explored. During the last hundred years nearly forty of these have been studied, so that there are only about thirty-five to forty left.

As the number of large and obvious targets dwindles, divers are paying more and more attention to the minor sites, and searching farther afield for more obscure and exotic ones. An example of this trend is shown by Count Gargallo, an enthusiastic underwater archaeologist from Sicily, who set out in 1960 to find the lost island of Chryse, which is mentioned in the *Odyssey* as being on the route to Troy. It was here that the Greek archer Philoctetes was fatally bitten by a viper after refusing the advances of a local nymph.

Chryse was known to be near the island of Lemnos. After studying the naval charts Gargallo selected the Kharos bank as the most likely site. The bank is nine miles east of Lemnos, ten square miles in area, and only about forty feet deep. Here he found heaps of rectangular white stone blocks, which are thought to be the remains of the temple of Apollo, but the site will require further investigation before this can be confirmed.

Today there are many small groups of divers scattered around the Mediterranean working the remains of the submerged villages and villas that can be found on every coast. In the next few years the emphasis will probably be on the development of a detailed over-all picture of these coastal settlements and their relations to one another.

Of the large sites still to be tackled it is doubtful that any of those involving the removal of thousands of tons of mud and silt will be excavated in the near future, if ever. Unless there is a very strong reason to believe that finds of extreme artistic, architectural, or historical importance can be made, it would not be worth spending the enormous amount of money that would be needed to uncover a city or port that might turn out to be little more than a duplicate of one we already know about. Thus Helike and Epidaurus will probably lie forever beneath the mud. So far as cities are concerned, the great pioneering days seem to be over.

With ships the situation is different. Although Egyptian and Roman trading vessels have been studied in some detail, we still know practically nothing about ships of the Minoan, Mycenaean, and Phoenician civilizations, nor of the warships of any period. We have already seen that it is not worth excavating every wreck that is found, but there are still so many gaps in the story of classical shipping that some dramatic excavations may be undertaken in the next few years. If a Greek warship were found in the mud of Syracuse harbor, or a Minoan trading vessel in four hundred feet of water off the coast of Crete or Turkey, then the enormous expense of excavation would be justified. With the new techniques of deep diving which are now under development – Cousteau's plunging saucer, and Keller's new gas mixtures and decompression tables – it is becoming possible to investigate a wreck below three hundred feet. But if, as is quite likely, these new methods are taken over by the military authorities and classified as secret, it will be many years before civilian diving reaps any benefit from them.

There is yet another branch of submarine archaeology that we have not mentioned at all – the study of caves. Although little has yet been done in this line, my own hope is to find signs of human occupation in caves down to depths of 150 feet or more. A cave at a depth of a hundred feet below present sea level would have been high and dry from 70,000 B.C. to 18,000 B.C. and could easily have been inhabited during that period. The prospect of excavating submerged cave dwellings, and thereby linking the archaeological periods of the stone ages with the eustatic changes of sea level, is one of the most exciting possibilities of the near future.

After talking about submerged cities of the past, it is difficult to resist the temptation of making prophecies about our present coastal cities, such as London and New York. London has, in fact, been subsiding gently since Roman times. However, while it is impossible to say whether the next big eustatic change will be up or down, we have no reason to believe that the sea should remain at its present level indefinitely, and changes of a hundred feet up or down would be equally awkward. In any case, a change of this order would take three thousand or so years, so that we can comfort ourselves that it will not occur in our lifetime.

This bronze head of a wild boar decorated the prow of a Greek ship 2000 years ago. Before its discovery the only evidence of the shape of Greek warship prows was to be found on vase paintings, like the one above.

New Attack on the Sea

Modern technological devices, coupled with a theoretical study of the sea, are bringing oceanographers closer to a real understanding of the inner workings of the oceans. Leonardo da Vinci, whose wave drawing appears above, was one of the first to make a study of the dynamics of water. Today scientists are aided by devices such as the wave-recording buoy, here being lowered over the side of Britain's Discovery II. *This instrument helps to show how the wind affects the shape of waves.*

The Endless Search
G. E. R. Deacon

The scientific exploration of the oceans, even more than the record of geographical exploration, is a history of personal achievements. It is a record of men wanting to find things out for themselves rather than of any widespread public demand for knowledge. The seas are still not as accessible to science as we would like, partly because ships are very expensive to run, and largely because mariners and other professional men of the sea are not sufficiently convinced of the need to know more about the sea's' forces and motions, in which they are hourly concerned.

We have never had to wait very long for some enthusiast to give the work a new turn or thrust, but we are still only on the threshold of a real understanding of the inner workings of the ocean. As President Kennedy of the United States said in March 1961, "knowledge of the oceans is no longer a matter of curiosity, our very survival may hinge upon it." It is difficult to urge the need for a new and more intensive approach without risk of minimizing the value of what generations of careful seamen and quite a number of enthusiastic scientists have done, but what is now required is the determined application of theoretical and practical techniques as advanced as those of any other branch of science, and technical exploitation of the ocean on as large a scale as the major operations in the Antarctic and our rush into space.

An international maritime congress led by the American naval officer Matthew F. Maury in the mid-1800s resulted in systematic collection of information on winds and currents all over the world, and it was the start of our meteorological offices. The wind and current maps resulting from these observations shortened the ocean passages of sailing ships by as much as one third, and also made them safer. Even though the need to find the quickest and safest routes for ships to follow was widely acknowledged, some mariners were reluctant to help collect data. One of the earliest meteorological registers received in 1855 says: "remarks not so full or complete as I would have wished" . . . "most of my officers being members of what is called the old school cannot or will not see the utility of bothering themselves (as they term it) with these new affairs."

Oceanographers today, if they are lucky, have their own research ships in which they can stay and work in the same bit of ocean for weeks on end if the work requires it, but often they find it difficult to persuade the sailors that they ought not to be "going somewhere." We are now attacking problems more complex than those of a century ago, such as predicting day-to-day changes in wave conditions and currents. Although the practical rewards are neither so obvious or immediate – nor at first sight so spectacular as they were in the days of sailing ships – the results we are obtaining are accurate and reliable enough to be immediately useful to the community.

The research ship *Atlantis*, belonging to the Woods Hole Oceanographic Institution in Massachusetts, has sailed more than one and a quarter million miles (equal to fifty times around the world) since she was launched in 1931. Built of steel, she is 142 feet overall with a beam of 29 feet, and she is rigged as a ketch with a mainmast of 112 feet. Powered by a 400 horsepower Diesel engine, she can carry her complement of nineteen officers and men at a speed of nine knots. The *Atlantis* has been used extensively for studying

Matthew Fontaine Maury.

the Gulf Stream and the western half of the North Atlantic, the Caribbean Sea and the Gulf of Mexico, the Mediterranean Sea and the waters of the coasts of Africa and South America, and the Peru Current. She is now getting old and is to be replaced by a new and larger steam-turbine vessel incorporating the tradition, experience, and advances of the past thirty years.

The British Royal Research Ship *Discovery II*, formerly operated by the Discovery Investigations, and now by the National Institute of Oceanography, was launched in 1929. She has made six voyages

to the Antarctic, going to the ice-edge in winter and summer and sometimes through heavy ice in the Ross, Weddell, and Bellingshausen seas. She is 234 feet overall with a beam of 36 feet and is powered by a 1250 horsepower, triple-expansion steam engine. Her cruising range could be about 10,000 miles, but it is generally much less because of the time she spends hove-to for the scientific work. During the past ten years she has been working mainly in the North Atlantic on all aspects of oceanography in collaboration with scientists from other countries. Like the *Atlantis*, she is getting old and is being replaced by a larger ship.

Discovery II, *here seen leaving Woods Hole, Massachusetts, belongs to Britain's National Institute of Oceanography. She is 234 feet overall and has a cruising range of about 10,000 miles. Like the* Atlantis, *of Woods Hole, she is being replaced by a new ship.*

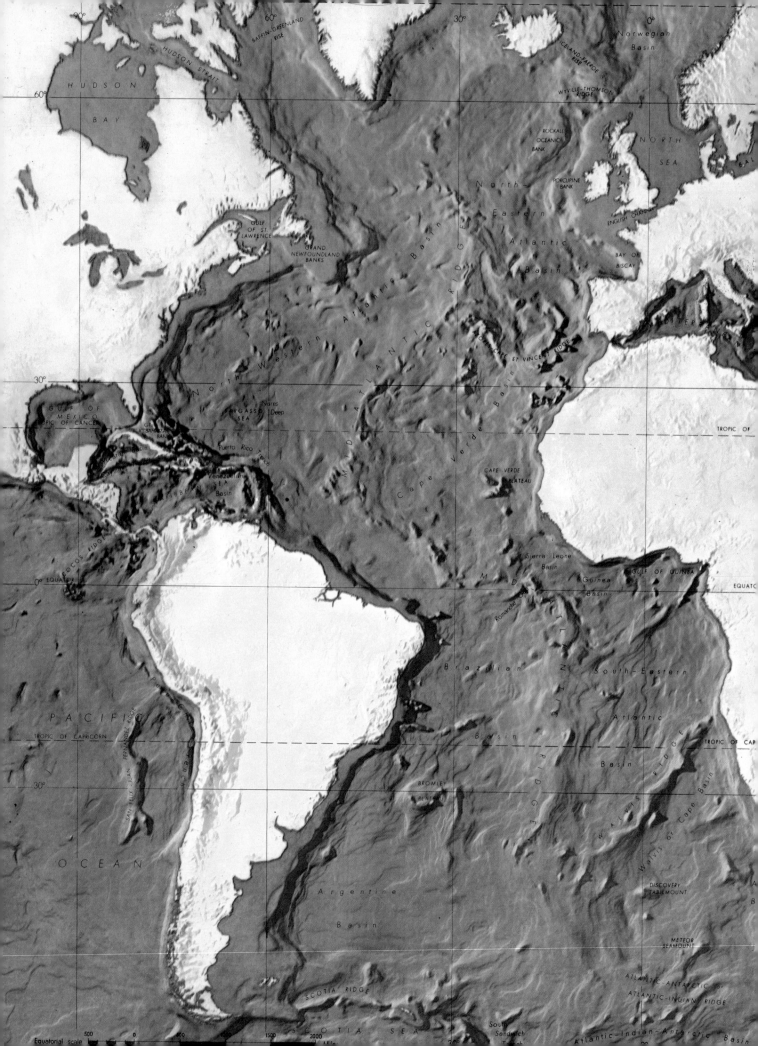

90°　　　　　60°　　BAFFIN-GREENLAND RISE　　30°　　　　　0°

Norwegian
Basin

HUDSON STRAIT

ICELAND-FAEROE RISE

60°

HUDSON
BAY

WYVILLE-THOMSON RIDGE

NORTH SEA

ROCKALL OCEANIC BANK

North-
Eastern

PORCUPINE BANK

BAL

GULF OF ST. LAWRENCE

Atlantic

North Western Atlantic Basin

Basin

ENGLISH CHANNEL

BAY OF BISCAY

GRAND NEWFOUNDLAND BANKS

M
I
D
-
A
T
L
A
N
T
I
C
　
R
I
D
G
E

CAPE ST VINCENT RIDGE

30°

30°

GULF OF MEXICO

SARGASSO SEA

Nares Deep

TROPIC OF CANCER

Cape Verde Basin

TROPIC OF

GT BAHAMA BANK

Puerto Rico Trench

CAPE VERDE PLATEAU

Venezuelan SEA Basin

CARIBBEAN

Sierra Leone Basin

Guinea Basin

GULF OF GUINEA

COCOS RIDGE

0° EQUATOR

Romanche

EQUATO

M
I
D
-
A
T
L
A
N
T
I
C

Brazilian

South-Eastern

PACIFIC

JUAN FERNANDEZ RIDGE

Basin

Atlantic

BROMLEY PLATEAU

Basin

Basin

TROPIC OF CAPRICORN

R
I
D
G
E

TROPIC OF CAP

SAN FELIX - JUAN

30°

W
A
L
V
I
S
　
R
I
D
G
E

Walvis or Cape Basin

30°

DISCOVERY TABLEMOUNT

A

OCEAN

Argentine

Basin

METEOR SEAMOUNT

ATLANTIC-ANTARCTIC

SCOTIA RIDGE

ATLANTIC-INDIAN RIDGE

SCOTIA SEA

South Sandwich Trench

ATLANTIC-INDIAN-ANTARCTIC Basin

Equatorial scale　500　0　500　1000　1500　2000　Miles

Both ships have extensive laboratory space, winches for lowering instruments on wires and electric cables, for mid-water trawling, bottom dredging, sediment coring, and other heavy tasks which are described later in this chapter. Because the scientific teams usually change from cruise to cruise, much special apparatus has to be installed and removed at the beginning and end of each voyage. When the ship reaches a "station," a variety of work begins, the scientists usually standing watches like the seamen. One task may be to take samples of the water at different depths. To do this, a series of water-sampling devices (with thermometers) are attached to one of the wires and lowered until the bottom one is near the sea bed. They are all tripped and closed by small "messenger" weights that slide down the wire, each sampler releasing a similar weight to operate the one below, so that they all close one after another. Fine silk nets may be hauled vertically and towed horizontally and obliquely to sample the plankton. Deep-sea cameras may be lowered to the bottom, and different kinds of dredges used to sample the bottom-living fauna, or to collect rock samples. Many other observations are made as the ship steams along – temperature recordings, echo-sounding profiles, wave records, records of total magnetic and gravimetric field, and meteorological observations. There is not much rest for anyone until the ship returns home. Even then, each scientist usually spends many weeks or months analyzing his findings.

For centuries the depths of the oceans have puzzled men. Later in this chapter Dr. Laughton tells of early speculations about the ocean depths and shows that new moves to gather factual information started in the eighteenth century. Count Luigi Marsigli, the Italian soldier and scientist who published a *Histoire Physique de la Mer* in 1725 wrote: "The fishermen working on that slope where they are in the habit of finding coral at 150 and 200 fathoms, and their lines not allowing soundings in greater depths, imagine that the bottom cannot be found, and call it in their exaggerated jargon a bottomless abyss, impossible to be sounded. This idea entertained by people of experience in marine matters, as well as by the simple fishers, appears to be absurd, and founded merely on the fact that nobody has yet cared to undertake the trouble and expense required for such soundings, which according to all appearances will never be made unless some Prince orders for that purpose special vessels with suitable instruments."

It was indeed from a King's ship, H.M.S. *Racehorse*, that the first deep sounding was made, and in two young Queen's ships H.M.S. *Erebus* and *Terror*, that Sir James Clark Ross, as we saw in an earlier chapter, made deep soundings all around the world. The next step was made by Midshipman Brooke on the other side of the Atlantic Ocean. One of Lieutenant Maury's assistants, he used a hollow tube, a forerunner of modern core samplers, running through the middle of the sounding weight (actually a cannon ball). There were catches to release the ball as soon as it touched bottom. This made recovery of the sounding line much easier and allowed the use of thinner lines. Soon after this, cable ships began to sound out routes for submarine cables, and they used a wire sounding machine developed by Lord Kelvin. In spite of these advances and increased interest, the total number of deep-ocean soundings recorded by 1914 was only about 6000.

A water color by John Clevely shows H.M.S. Racehorse in pack ice during her 1773 voyage toward the North Pole. Commanded by C.J. Phipps, she made the first deep-sea sounding between Iceland and Norway.

This relief map of the Atlantic Ocean shows the most prominent features of the sea floor. The mid-Atlantic Ridge runs almost parallel to the coast of America on one side, and to the coasts of Europe and Africa on the other. There are side ridges which divide the east and west basins, one of the sharpest being the Walvis Ridge. The Scotia arc which joins South America to Graham Land is a prominent feature in the south, and there is a deep trench east of the South Sandwich Islands. The greatest depth is 30,246 feet off Puerto Rico.

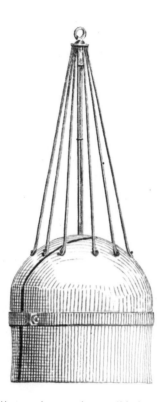

To get the most accurate possible temperature reading of deep water, De Saussure coated a thermometer bulb with wax, then placed the device in a wooden box to prevent too much movement of water. He then left the device in deep water for twelve hours.

The development of underwater acoustic methods during the First World War stimulated new interest and advances, and it was not long before we had echo sounders able to record a continuous profile of the deep ocean floor as the ship crossed the ocean above it. Some of the older scientists were not very enthusiastic about this new method, because at first it tended to cut off the supply of samples of bottom sediments produced by the wire soundings, but the interest and progress awakened by the new profiles soon brought more extensive and specially planned sampling and coring programs. We now know quite a lot about a few small areas of the sea floor, but there are many large areas about which we know little or nothing.

The more inquisitive of later sea explorers began to take an interest in the temperature of the deep sea almost as soon as reliable thermometers were invented. The first record of any measurements at great depths is that of Captain Henry Ellis' observations in 1749 at depths of 650 and 891 fathoms, north of the Cape Verde Islands. He used a stout wooden barrel, about the size of an ordinary pail, with top and bottom valves which stayed open while the sampler was being lowered but which closed while it was being brought up. It was hauled up as fast as possible so that the temperature of the water inside would not have much time to change.

George Forster made three such series of deep measurements during Captain Cook's circumnavigation. One of them made in Antarctic waters southeast of Cape Town is remarkable because it showed a warm undercurrent moving south and replacing the outward spread of cold water at the surface. The fact that Forster made only three sets of observations in three years suggests a lack of opportunity. Captain Cook, like most practical seamen, may not have had much time for what might have seemed to him rather pointless enquiries. He did not try to sound the oceans, only the approaches to the land. William Scoresby, the whaling explorer and scientist, also used wooden samplers, but he found that they did not stand up for very long to the soaking up of water at high pressures, so he made metal containers coated with insulating material.

Not all the temperature measurements depended on attempts to haul insulated water samples to the surface. H. B. de Saussure, the great Swiss mountain climber, used an alcohol thermometer with its bulb insulated with a three-inch mixture of wax, resin, and oil to measure the temperature at a depth of 320 fathoms off Nice. He left it down for twelve hours, pulled it up as fast as possible, and estimated that his reading was correct to within a fraction of a degree.

Maximum and minimum thermometers promised to make the task of measuring deep temperatures much easier, but at first the effect of pressure on the thermometer bulb was overlooked. The thermometers used by Sir James Clark Ross read about 1°C. too high for every 500 fathoms because the mercury was squeezed this much up the stem by the pressure on the bulb. At about 50° S. latitude in the Antarctic Ocean, where the temperature at the surface is about 4°C., and at the bottom in 2000 fathoms 0°C., Ross found 4°C. all the way down. He accepted the idea previously put forward by the French Admiral Dumont d'Urville that the deep ocean basins, like the bottom of deep, fresh-water lakes, were filled with water at 4°C. They both should have known that sea water does not have a point of maximum density at 4°C. like fresh water, and that earlier explorers using the older method of hauling up water in an insulated vessel had found bottom water with temperatures below the freezing point of fresh water.

It took a long time to get all the thermometers properly protected, and then the method was changed again. For the past sixty years we have been using protected thermometers that turn upside down when a catch on the water sampler is released by the 'messenger' weight. This reversal separates a column of mercury proportional to the temperature of the water and provides a temperature reading accurate to a hundredth of a degree.

Unhappily, we have too few observations to tell us whether the oceans as a whole are now getting warmer or colder. However, we know a good deal about the seasonal changes, and in one or two areas, such as the approaches to the Arctic, we have evidence that the sea has become warmer in the past few decades. It is quite remarkable how much we know about the large-scale features of temperature distribution in the depths of the ocean as well as at the surface, but we know much less about the fine structure and the day-to-day changes. The interchange of heat and water vapor between the atmosphere and ocean, together with the part played by ocean currents in determining where most heat is going to be fed into the atmosphere, is being studied in the new attack on the sea. The surface temperature of the oceans increases from freezing point in high latitudes to nearly 30°C. a little north of the Equator, but the isotherms (lines of equal temperature) are not always parallel to the lines of latitude. They are often bent toward the poles by warm currents moving into higher latitudes, and toward the Equator by cold currents moving away from the polar regions. Because the temperature of the sea generally decreases with depth, welling up from below tends to lower the surface temperature.

Temperatures of the oceans generally decrease with depth because the lower layers are filled with water from higher latitudes. A sea like the Mediterranean, on the other hand, largely shut off from the ocean outside, is covered with a sun-warmed layer some thirty to forty fathoms deep in summer. Only in such deep basins shut off from the open ocean does the bottom temperature rise above 2.5°C. Over most of the world ocean the bottom temperature is lower – only about 1°C. or less.

If the oceans were evaporated and all the salt spread evenly over the earth, there would be a salt layer about two hundred feet thick. We do not know just how and when the ocean acquired it all – how much was formed at the same time as the oceans themselves, and how it has been leached out of the land. Perhaps the salts accumulated at a great rate to begin with, or perhaps as a gradual process. The minerals brought down by the rivers today look rather like the less soluble residues. The total annual addition of salt to the ocean is now less than a ten millionth of what is already there.

Robert Boyle was the first to make a detailed study of the salt content of the oceans. In 1673, when he published his *Observations and Experiments about the Saltness of the Sea*, he realized that many observations would have to be made in all parts of the world before anyone could generalize about the amount of salt in the ocean. He

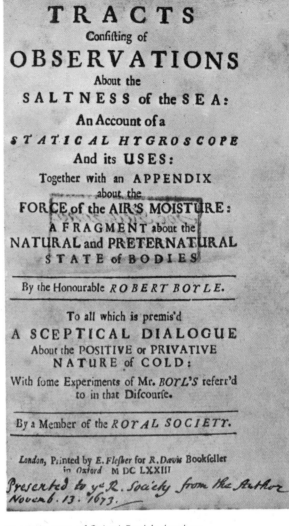

The title page of Robert Boyle's tract on "saltness of the sea." In 1673 Boyle knew that the amount of concentration of salt in any region of the sea depended on the balance between rainfall and evaporation.

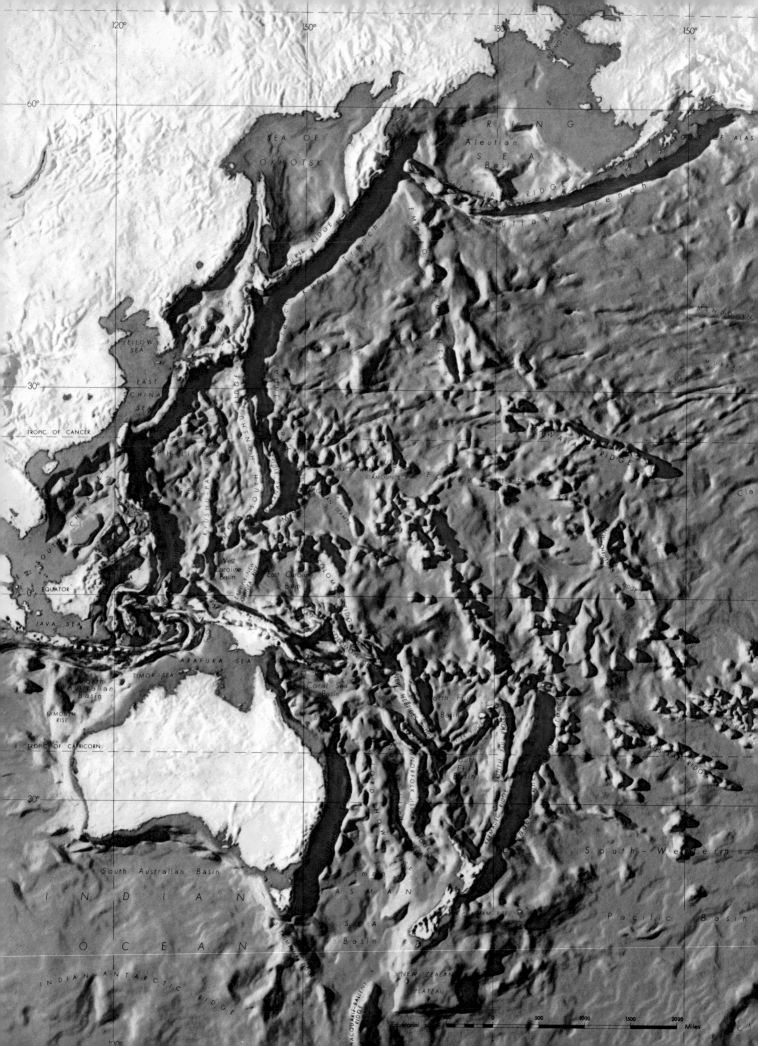

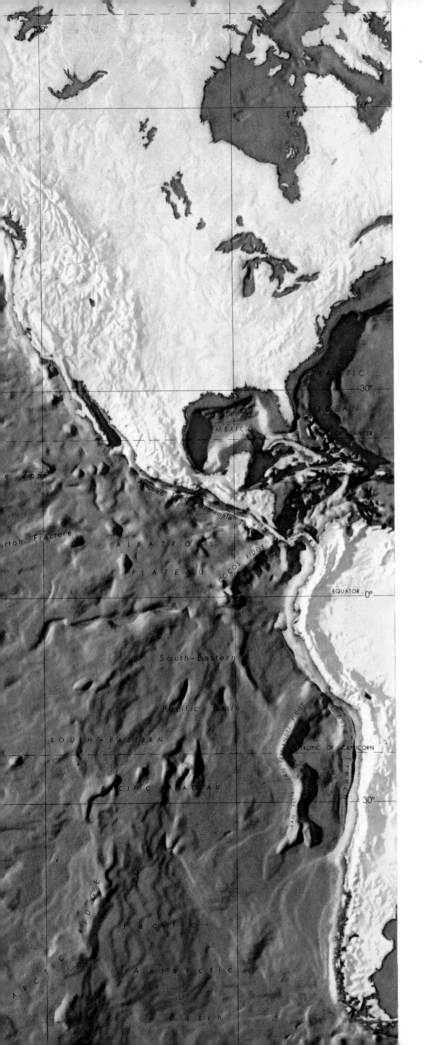

The Scripps Institute of Oceanography was established at the end of the last century by Dr. William E. Ritter in San Pedro, California. In 1905 it was moved to La Jolla where it was made part of the University of California.

The western (especially the northwestern) Pacific Ocean contains the most extensive continuous area of sea floor deeper than 16,400 feet, and wide areas of a depth greater than 19,700 feet. Deep-sea trenches are a feature of the western marginal region, and the greatest depth in the ocean, 35,800 feet, is in the Marianas Trench.

also realized that the concentration of salt in a particular region depends on the balance between evaporation and rainfall. In one of his experiments he showed that the specific gravity of salt water gave a more accurate measure of the salt content than he could obtain by evaporating sea water to dryness because the final weight of the remaining salt depends on the degree of heat applied during evaporation.

In 1819 Alexander Marcet, a retired London doctor, made a remarkable discovery about the constancy of composition of sea salt. He knew that samples would differ in the proportion of salt to water, but said "all the specimens of sea water which I have examined, however different their strength, contain the same ingredients all over the world, these bearing the same proportions to each other, so that they differ only as to the total amount of their saline contents." It was almost a guess because he had only fourteen samples, but his findings were later confirmed by Professor G. Forchammer, who published the results of 150 analyses, and by Professor William Dittmar, who analyzed 77 samples brought home by H.M.S. *Challenger*. Today we have more accurate means of determining the chemical and physical properties of sea salts, and we know that there are small but significant differences.

The highest salinity in the oceans is found in the Red Sea (37 to 41 parts per thousand) and the Persian Gulf (35 to 40 parts per thousand); the lowest in the Baltic Sea (2 to 7 parts per thousand), the Black Sea (18 parts per thousand), and in fjords and estuaries.

This 1894 map of the Skagerrak shows relatively low salt content compared with that of the Atlantic. High rate of evaporation in the subtropical Atlantic accounts for high salinity. Low evaporation rate in the Baltic, and the many rivers carrying melted snow into the sea, account for lower salinity.

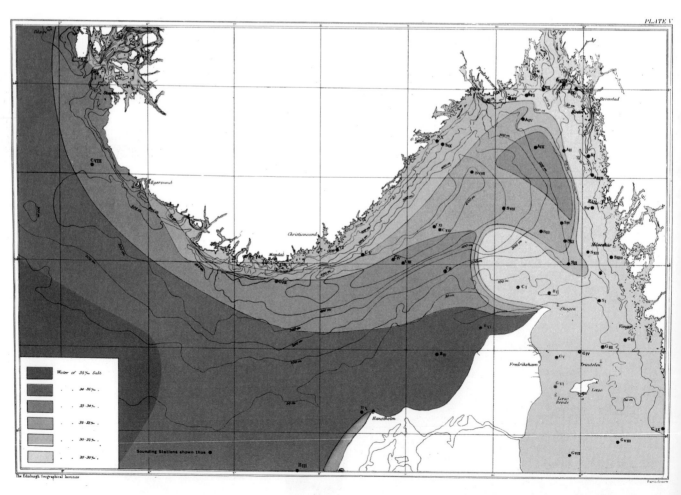

In the Atlantic Ocean it rises to 37.5 parts per thousand in the northern subtropical region, where descending dry air leads to high evaporation, and is lowest in the subpolar regions where the rainfall is heavy, and in the doldrums where there is also a lot of rain. The Atlantic Ocean has higher salinities than the Pacific Ocean, probably because it has greater evaporation, and possibly because it is more influenced by dry winds off the land, but the deep-water circulation may also play a significant part. As we will see in Dr. Swallow's section on currents, salinity as well as temperature determines the layering of ocean water. The warm subsurface water found on Cook's voyage is now known to be more saline than the colder water above it. Nansen found cold, relatively fresh water above warmer, more saline water in the Arctic. Salinity differences between one part of the ocean and another contribute to the density differences which affect the circulation of the water.

Ocean currents have always been of interest to seamen. The effect of the wind on the water, always the most striking thing about the sea to sailors, has been generally held responsible for currents. But this has not prevented other explanations — such as the early misconception that the westward flow of water in the equatorial region is caused by a tendency for the water to be left behind as the Earth rotates eastward underneath it. Objects at the Earth's surface feel the effect of the Earth's rotation, but not in such a simple way. Except right on the Equator, every bit of the Earth's surface has some horizontal rotation around, say, a post standing vertically on it.

We can perform an experiment to demonstrate this. If a pendulum bob is suspended on a very long cord and set in motion, it will continue to swing in the same direction; but if the direction is marked on the ground every hour or so, the mark will be seen to swing slowly around, because the Earth's surface is going around the opposite way underneath. At the North Pole the line would perform a complete counterclockwise rotation in twenty-four hours. But at the Equator the line would not rotate. At intermediate latitudes the time of rotation varies between twenty-four hours at the poles to infinity at the Equator.

So every part of the Earth's surface has a different sort of rotation. This means that water moving from one place to another — whether horizontally or vertically — is affected by this *geostrophic* effect, or Coriolis effect as it is sometimes called. Although this effect is well known, it requires someone with a good knowledge of fluid mechanics to judge exactly how the motion of the ocean water is affected. The application of this specialized knowledge is the mainspring of the new attack on all studies of ocean circulation.

Major James Rennell, surveyor for the East India Company, was an outstanding pioneer in the study of ocean currents. His first chart and *Remarks on the Agulhas or South African Current* appeared in 1778, and his most comprehensive work, *Currents of the Atlantic Ocean*, was published by his daughter in 1832 after his death. Another pioneer in charting currents was Benjamin Franklin, who published a chart of the Gulf Stream in 1770; and twelve years later Sir Charles Blagden published a useful account of the same current. Described as the creator of statistical studies of ocean currents, Rennell was followed by Heinrich Berghaus and Matthew Maury. In 1835 Maury persuaded the United States government

Major James Rennell.

This section of Rennell's chart of the North Atlantic clearly shows the trend of the Gulf Stream. Heavy arrows show estimated mean current flow. Thin arrows: current observations. Thin dotted arrows: wind observations. Heavy figures: sea temperature. Italics figures: sea soundings.

to invite Belgium, Denmark, France, Great Britain, Holland, Norway, Portugal, Russia, and Sweden to send representatives to a meeting in Brussels to discuss a universal system of observations at sea. It was the first international meteorological conference ever to be held.

Two years later Britain's Board of Trade started a meteorological department under Admiral Fitzroy, and by 1857 about two hundred merchant ships had been fitted out with instruments. Among the inducements offered to shipowners was a promise of free copies of all charts and books resulting from the work. They were to contain information about wind, ocean currents, and the surest and quickest sea routes.

Today's charts compiled in Britain, Germany, Holland, Japan, the United States, and U.S.S.R. are about as good as charts showing average conditions can be. They divide the ocean into small squares, and then all the information available for each square over the past

Average current conditions are shown on "current roses." The ocean is divided into squares and then all the information available for each square over past years is sorted into months and averaged over each square for each month. In some squares a single direction is predominant, suggesting a prevailing current, but in others there are two or more favored directions, suggesting a variable current. This chart is for the North Pacific and clearly shows the eastward-flowing Kuro Shio Current. (Compare with the currents chart on pages 204–05.)

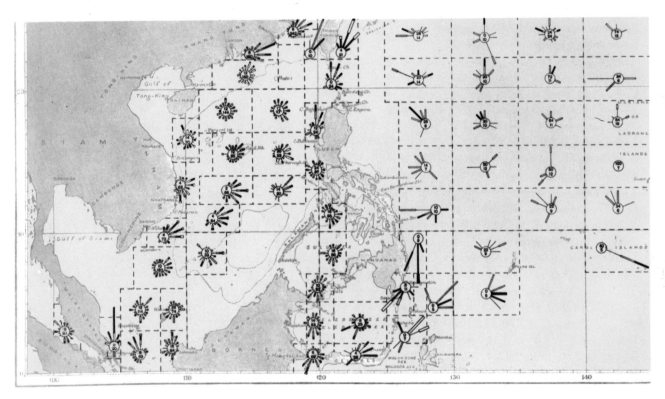

150 years is sorted into months and averaged over each square for each month. The resulting summaries are generally shown as "current roses," compasslike diagrams showing what percentage of all the measurements fall in each direction. In some squares a single direction is predominant, suggesting a prevailing current; in others two or more favored directions show a moderate range of variability. But in others there is so much variation that the current cannot be said to favor any particular direction. Even strongly prevailing currents can vary a good deal from day to day. In addition, there are many regions of variable current where the navigator would like to know how his ship is likely to be influenced by local and general meteorological conditions prevailing at the time. Here is another of the many ways in which oceanographers can help merchant shipping.

The whole problem of currents is too complex to be solved

The Arctic Ocean is divided into two basins, each about 13,000 feet deep, by a region of more complicated topography that incorporates the Lomonosov Ridge. It is surrounded by the large, shallow shelf-seas north of Europe, Asia, and America.

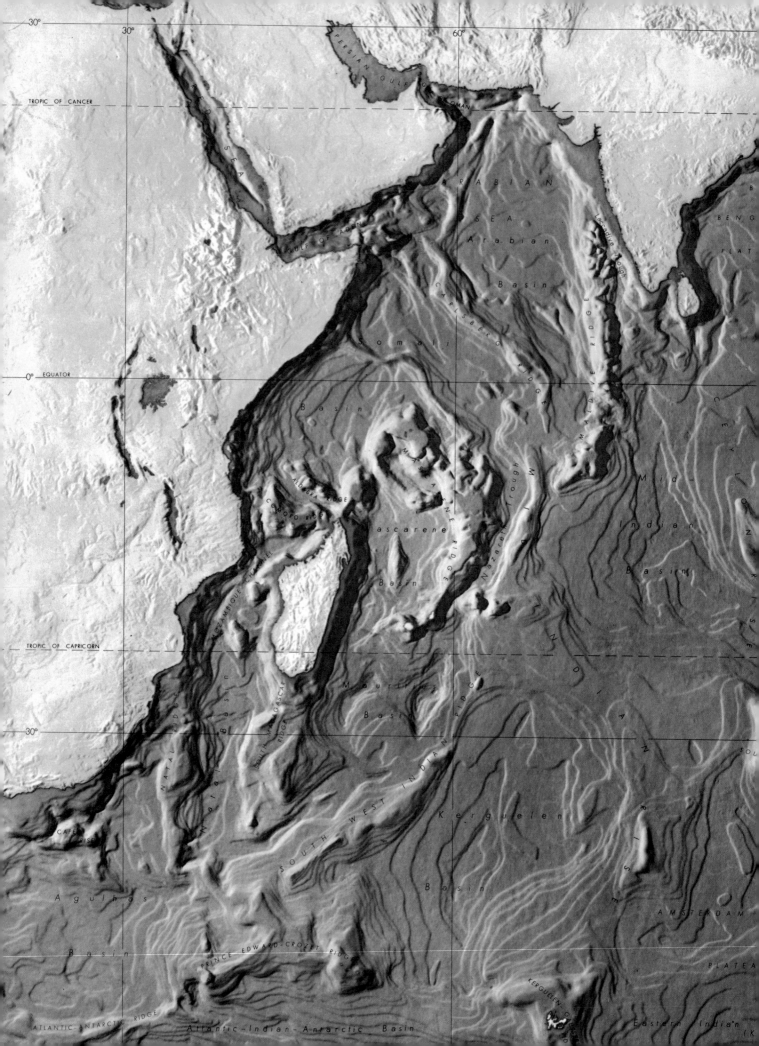

30°   30°   60°

TROPIC OF CANCER

PERSIAN GULF OMAN

ARABIAN
SEA
Arabian
Basin

BENG
PLAT

GULF OF ADEN

Laccadive Trough

Somali

CARLSBERG RIDGE

MALDIVE RIDGE

0°   EQUATOR

Basin

Mid-

MASCARENE

Indian

ALDABRA RIDGE

Nazareth Trough

Basin

COMORO RIDGE

ascarene

Ridge

Basin

MOZAMBIQUE CHANNEL

INDIAN

TROPIC OF CAPRICORN

Mauritius

Basin

NATAL RIDGE

SOUTH MADAGASCAR RIDGE

RIDGE

30°   30°   SOU

SOUTH WEST INDIAN

Kerguelen

CAPE RISE

Basin

Agulhas

AMSTERDAM

Basin

KERGUELEN

PRINCE EDWARD-CROZET RIDGE

PLATEA

ATLANTIC-ANTARCTIC RIDGE

Atlantic-Indian-Antarctic Basin

Eastern Indian

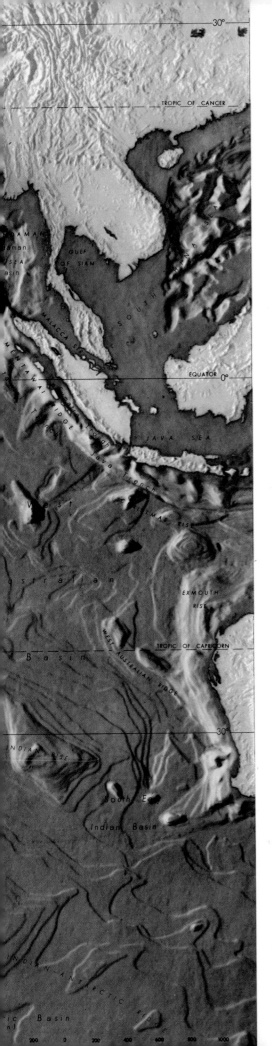

When the Challenger stopped at St. Paul's Rocks to make astronomical and magnetic observations, her small boats found it almost impossible to land because of the strong currents surging among the channels.

The topography of the Indian Ocean floor is not so well known as that of the other oceans, but there is evidence of a mid-ocean ridge running northward as far as Kerguelen through New Amsterdam to the Seychelles and Chagos islands. The Maldive Ridge is a remarkably sharp feature. The greatest depths are in troughs near the Sunda Strait, 24,459 feet deep; and near the Andaman islands, 17,247 feet.

187

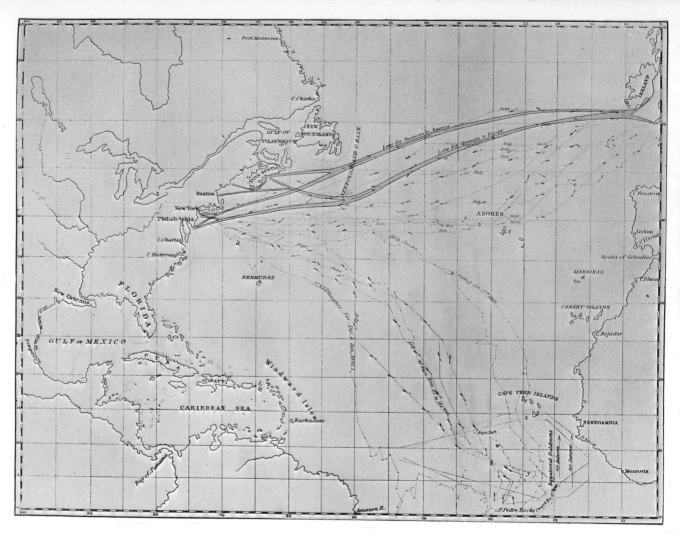

By studying a great number of current and weather observations made by merchant ships, Matthew Maury was able to work out the most favorable routes for commercial ships to follow during their crossing of the Atlantic. This chart prepared by Maury shows the quickest routes to and from Europe.

simply by plotting careful observations. We have to find *how* the currents are generated. For the past 150 years the main question — still not completely answered — has been: How do the winds and differences of water density between one part of the ocean and another conspire to cause surface and deep-water movements and exchanges between them? Franklin and Rennell were convinced that the winds were the main cause of the surface currents. Rennell, however, knew that when water is piled up against a coast by the wind, there might be a "stream current" away from the area of accumulation — not necessarily in the direction of the wind.

Temperature measurements soon showed that there was very cold water at the bottom of the tropical oceans. As early as 1812 Alexander von Humboldt maintained that this was evidence of bottom currents flowing from the polar regions toward the Equator. Jean Arago, the French physicist, said that the inability of the polar bottom currents to get into the Mediterranean Sea would explain why the temperature at the bottom of the Mediterranean was higher than at the same level outside. (He knew about the relatively warm undercurrent flowing out through the Strait of Gibraltar.) Humboldt made a clear distinction between the general circulation of the water in the ocean and the rapid surface currents that had most bearing on navigation.

Emil von Lenz, the German physicist who reviewed all the evidence available up to 1845, said that a flow of warmer water from the Equator to the poles must take place at the surface. Further, this surface flow must be constantly supplied at the Equator

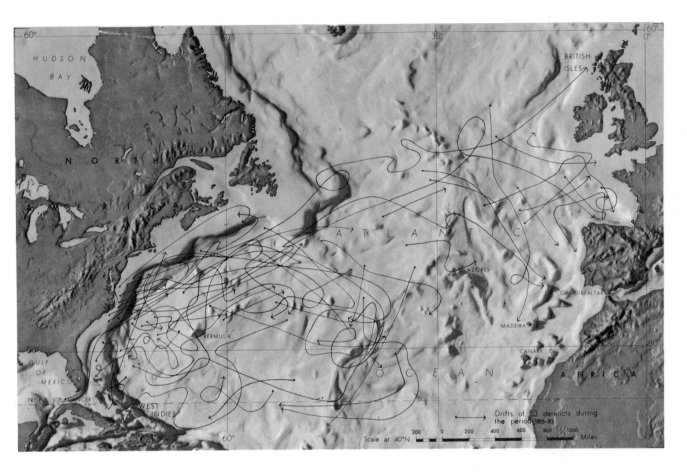

Labels on map: HUDSON BAY, NORTH AMERICA, GULF OF MEXICO, TROPIC OF CANCER, WEST INDIES, BERMUDA, ATLANTIC OCEAN, AZORES, MADEIRA, CANARY IS, OF GIBRALTAR, AFRICA, BRITISH ISLES

Drifts of 53 derelicts during the period 1886-93

Scale at 40°N 200 0 200 400 600 800 1000 Miles

by an undercurrent flowing down from high latitudes. Throughout most of its journey the undercurrent would flow in an almost horizontal direction, but under the Equator it must well up to the surface. He was aware that the actual directions of such movements might be greatly influenced by the action of the Earth's rotation and by the winds.

New information about the temperature and salt content of the deep layers led Professor William Carpenter, one of the leading biologists of the 1870s, to say that the ocean circulation was due mainly to heat, cold, and evaporation. He could not see how the wind could cause a deep current. The uncompromising nature of this man brought him into collision with James Croll, an eminent physical geographer who tried to show him that forces due to small differences in density between the polar and equatorial regions could not produce currents as fast as those that were known at the surface. Both men, as it turned out, raised important issues, but neither knew enough about fluid mechanics to get a complete enough grasp of the subject to convince the other. Only today are we beginning to get somewhere with these complex questions. Although there is still plenty of room to argue about the relative importance of wind and density differences, we are beginning to put forward fairly realistic theories that take account of both.

With this brief historical summary, which shows our constant indebtedness to the earlier scientists and seamen, let us now look in more detail at some of the work being done today and what new information it is revealing about the oceans.

Between 1889 and 1893, Captain A. Hautreaux plotted the courses of tree trunks and masses of driftwood as they were carried by currents across the Atlantic. The map on this page shows the drift courses of fifty-three objects (compare with map on page 204).

The Floor of the Sea
A. S. Laughton

A sailor takes soundings from an Egyptian boat journeying up the Nile in about 1422 B.C. The painting was found in the tomb of Menna, a "field scribe," who made the voyage up the Nile with his wife.

Throughout the long history of travel over the sea, has there been a sailor who has not wondered what marvels and mysteries lie hidden by the dark and restless water beneath his ship? For thousands of years speculations about the unknown depths grew almost entirely out of fantasy, often based on fear of imagined monsters lurking below. Without a background of facts it was impossible for early sea explorers to picture what the bottom of the ocean is really like.

Yet, as today, there have always been places where the sea floor rises closer into view, and it is in these shallow regions around the coasts that sailors of old had to plumb the depth of the bottom to avoid running their ships onto sandbanks, jagged rocks, and reefs. So it is not surprising that the earliest records of soundings appeared almost as soon as the first pictorial records of ships themselves. In Egyptian wall paintings we see sailors lowering a weighted line over the side and calling out the depth at the moment the weight touched bottom. This simple method of sounding has survived over the centuries and is still used today.

But what of those parts of the ocean far from land where the depth of the water is no longer a navigational hazard? How deep are these? The Greek philosophers, more interested in logic than in facts gained by experiment, argued on purely logical grounds that the depths of the oceans must be about the same as the heights of the mountains on land, and it turns out that they were just about right. Many explorers in the seventeenth and eighteenth centuries attempted to find the depth of the bottom in the open ocean but failed because their sounding lines were not long enough. Captain Constantine John Phipps, later Lord Mulgrave, in command of H.M.S. *Racehorse* on a voyage towards the North Pole, in 1773 succeeded in making the first sounding beyond the edge of the continental shelf in a basin between Iceland and Norway. Following is a description of the method he used:

"September the fourth, at two in the afternoon, we sounded with all the lines, above eight hundred fathoms. Some time before the last line was out, we perceived a slack, and that it did not run off near so quick as before. When we got the lines in again, the first roll came in very easily and twenty fathoms of the next, after which it took a great strain to move the lead; a mark was put on at the place where the weight was perceived and the line measured, by which the depth was found to be six hundred and eighty-three fathoms. The lead weighed above one hundred and fifty pounds, and had sunk, as appeared by the line, near ten feet into the ground, which was a very fine blue soft clay."

Not only did Captain Phipps get a depth measurement, but he also got a sample of the bottom, and with thermometers attached to the line he was able to take a temperature measurement of the deep water. His sounding of 683 fathoms is still on Admiralty charts today. But a half century or more passed before oceanographers found the bottom far out in the oceans. In some attempts they paid out as much as six thousand fathoms of line before they reached bottom, but they soon discovered that currents and surface winds, by carrying the ship far off to the side, were giving them an exaggerated reading.

Sir James Clark Ross, who voyaged to the Antarctic in 1840, solved this problem by sounding from an open boat that was held in position against wind and surface current by a second rowing boat. He had a sounding line four miles long wound on a large drum that allowed a weight to pull the line off freely. By carefully timing each successive one hundred fathoms of paid-out line, he was able to mark the change of speed when the weight hit the bottom. His sounding, made in the South Atlantic (lat. 27° 26′ S., long. 17° 29′ W.) established an accurate depth of 2425 fathoms. The whole operation, including recovery of the weight, took about four hours.

Around this time talk of laying a trans-Atlantic submarine telegraph cable stimulated a great wave of effort to find out about the depths of the ocean. As a result, sounding techniques were streamlined: detachable weights rather than fixed ones eased recovery of the line; wire lines replaced rope lines; and a steam-powered winch was used for reeling in. The expedition of H.M.S. *Challenger* around the world, between 1872 and 1876, returned with an impressive collection of deep-sea soundings. With this new data cartographers finally were able to draw charts showing several main features, such as basins and mountain ranges of the ocean bottom. The expedition also brought back new information about the sediments that range over the sea floor. Since the three-year *Challenger* voyage, which laid the foundation of modern oceanography, many other expeditions have studied particular problems and particular areas; but when we consider the giant size of the oceans and the many difficulties of peering and probing into them, all the work that we have done to date seems a mere skeleton which has yet to be clothed in flesh.

The submarine geologist now has an impressive battery of new instruments and techniques for exploring the deep-ocean floor and

Ross took soundings from an open boat held in position against wind and surface currents by a second boat. His sounding line, which was paid out and recovered by a rotating drum, was four miles long.

An engraving of the Great Eastern *battling a heavy sea as she lays the first transatlantic cable, June 30, 1866.*

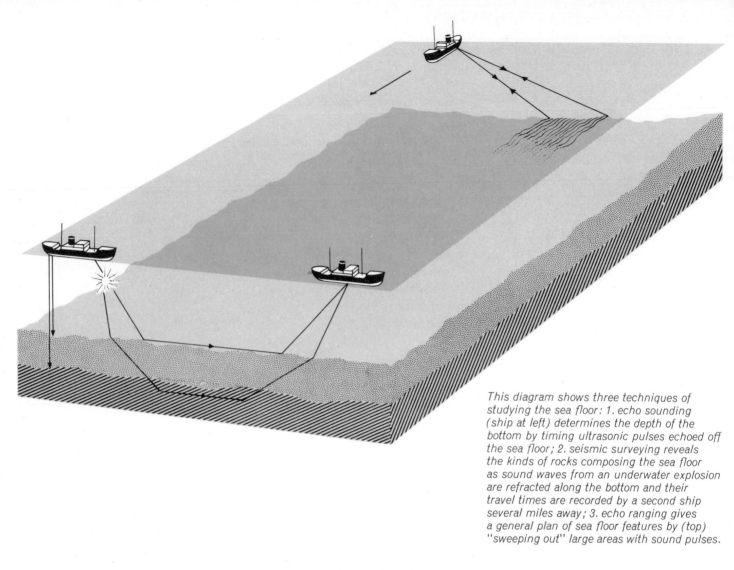

This diagram shows three techniques of studying the sea floor: 1. echo sounding (ship at left) determines the depth of the bottom by timing ultrasonic pulses echoed off the sea floor; 2. seismic surveying reveals the kinds of rocks composing the sea floor as sound waves from an underwater explosion are refracted along the bottom and their travel times are recorded by a second ship several miles away; 3. echo ranging gives a general plan of sea floor features by (top) "sweeping out" large areas with sound pulses.

its geological structures. For the purpose of charting the ocean depths, sounding with lead and line has given way to precision echo sounding, which traces on a moving sheet of paper a continuous profile of the sea floor as the ship moves above it. An echo sounder performs its task by sending to the sea bottom a succession of ultrasonic signals, or "pings," which bounce off the sea floor and return to the ship as an echo. The time interval between transmitting each ping and receiving its echo gives a measure of the depth, since the velocity of sound in sea water is known. Modern echo sounders can make a record of the depth once every second and to an accuracy of one fathom in three thousand.

In recent years we have found another use for sound echoes. It is called echo ranging. Instead of directing a series of pings straight down to the ocean floor, we direct them nearly horizontally in a narrow beam so they strike the sea bed obliquely. Echoes from rock outcrops and even shipwrecks are recorded and form a picture similar to that obtained by radar on the surface. With echo ranging we can sweep out large areas of the sea floor and quickly obtain a general plan of its features.

To get a close look at the features of the bottom we have to abandon sound echoes and turn to bathyscaphes, undersea photography, or television. So far, it is from underwater photography that we have learned the most.

To collect samples of the rocks and sediments covering the sea

The existence of currents on the deep sea floor is confirmed by underwater photographs. This one shows ripple marks, ten inches between crests, in sand on a seamount at a depth of 1700 fathoms.

floor, we use the age-old technique of dredging and the modern technique of coring. To dredge for loose rocks and boulders we simply tow a large steel-framed wire-mesh bag on the end of several miles of cable. The great difficulty lies in trying to find out whether the dredge is dragging along the bottom or skimming just above it; frequently we come up with only an empty bag. However, some very successful hauls have been made from depths of nearly three thousand fathoms and have given the geologists good specimens to examine.

We get samples of the soft sediments by driving a long, hollow tube into the bottom. When the tube, called a corer, is brought up, the soft core of sediments — sometimes up to a hundred feet long — gives us a geological and biological record ranging over the past few million years, when the sediments were being laid down.

The sediments tell only part of the story of the sea floor. To

Left: Fifty pounds of TNT are exploded in the Arctic ice. Seismic surveying of this kind reveals not only the thickness of the ice and the depth of the sea floor, but also the nature of rocks making up the sea bed (see diagram on opposite page). Right: A piston coring tube is prepared for its journey to the sea floor where it will cut its way into the sediment layers and withdraw a sample of ocean bottom deposits, some of which were laid down millions of years ago.

understand how the rock floor of the sea was formed when our planet was young, we must penetrate the full thickness of sediments, some two thousand feet, and find out about the solid rocks beneath. Buried rock masses often have physical properties different, if only in a small way, from surrounding masses of rock. If the density of the buried rock is greater than the density of surrounding rock, then this difference results in minute but detectable variations in gravity around the rock – the greater the density, the stronger the pull of gravity. Magnetic properties of one rock mass also may differ from those of a nearby mass, and this leads to local distortions in the Earth's magnetic field. And so it is possible to locate and identify the character of these buried rocks by making gravity and magnetic field surveys.

A more powerful tool for identifying the deep-lying rocks is that of seismic surveying. The submarine geologist can detonate an underwater explosive and so generate a series of sound waves that fan out to the ocean bottom and to the rocks underlying the sediments. The echoes that come back to the ship, or move horizontally through a layer of rock to a distant listening point, vary as the rocks refracting them vary. Quite simply, we know that sound waves travel faster through some rocks than through others. So by comparing the acoustic properties of known rocks with those of the sea bottom, geologists can try to identify the rocks making up the sea floor.

The ocean floor itself presents a landscape of canyons, valleys, trenches, abyssal plains, and mountains. Most of the bottom lies either at an average depth of about a hundred fathoms or else at an average depth of between twenty-five hundred and three thousand fathoms. In other words, there are two important levels – one associated with the edge of the continents, the other with the ocean basins. This is not to say that greater depths do not exist; they do, but they are comparatively rare.

If we could walk out from the coast of any typical continent, say the west coast of Portugal, and stroll toward the center of the ocean, we would find that as soon as we were clear of the immediate shore line and its eroded cliffs we would be standing on a plateau

Many continental slopes are incised with steep-walled canyons that are scoured out by turbidity currents which carry sediments out into the ocean basins. Shown here is a detailed map of a typical canyon, the Black Mud Canyon on the continental slope southwest of Brittany, France. The map is based on soundings made by Britain's National Institute of Oceanography.

that extends seaward for some fifty miles. This plateau, known as the continental shelf, slopes gently downward away from the coast, and on the whole it is remarkably flat at depths between fifty fathoms and a hundred fathoms. As far as we can tell, its rocks and sediments are similar to those on the continents. We find areas sometimes of sand and mud, sometimes of coarse gravel and shells, and occasional mounds indicating that solid rock must be sticking up through the sediment. We are not sure whether the flatness of the continental shelves is the work of currents and waves cutting into the edge of the continents and leveling it out, or whether the shelves are great dumping grounds where the eroded products of the land are accumulating, as they do in a delta at a river mouth.

As we reach the outer edge of the shelf, quite suddenly we find the ocean depth increasing and we descend the continental slope. The slope continues for forty or fifty miles, plunging down to the deep-sea floor. Some of the slopes drop at a rate of one in twenty, others at a rate of one in four, comparable with the sides of the mountain peaks on the land. It is the continental slope, not the coast line, that marks the true boundary of each continent. It is here that the thickness of the Earth's crust – that thin shell of hard rocks lying above the world-encircling mantle – changes abruptly from a thickness of about thirty miles under the continent to about five miles under the ocean. The continents, then, appear as great "rafts" of lighter rock floating in the heavier mantle rock, whereas the oceanic crust is a mere layer of scum.

Each continental slope is under constant attack from erosive and other destructive forces in the sea. Many slopes are incised with steep-walled canyons that serve as passageways through which the continental sediments flow out into the ocean basins. For many years we thought that these canyons were cut by ancient rivers that flowed at a time when the sea level was much lower and the edges of the shelves were exposed to the air. But it does not now seem likely that the sea level could ever have dropped as much as six hundred feet below its present level; furthermore, we still have to explain how those parts of the canyons that lie thousands of fathoms below the surface could have been cut.

Most submarine geologists today think that these giant canyons – however they were formed originally – are kept scoured out by currents of sediment-laden water hurtling at great speeds down the continental slopes. These turbidity currents, as they are called, may be set in motion when an earthquake or some other violent disturbance creates sliding and slumping in the sediments heaped on the edges of the continental shelves. When this happens, some of the sediments are stirred up into the water and create a local body of water that is denser than the surrounding water. The denser, sediment-laden water begins to flow down the slope, picking up more sediment along the way. As it becomes still denser it travels faster, and by the time it reaches the base of the slope it may be moving at enormous speeds – up to fifty or sixty miles an hour. Such a turbidity current south of Newfoundland was touched off by an earthquake in 1929 and broke several submarine telegraph cables along its path. The exact time when each cable was broken could be worked out accurately from the interruption of services, and so it was possible to measure the speed of the current as it passed.

A turbidity current begins to deposit part of its sediment load as

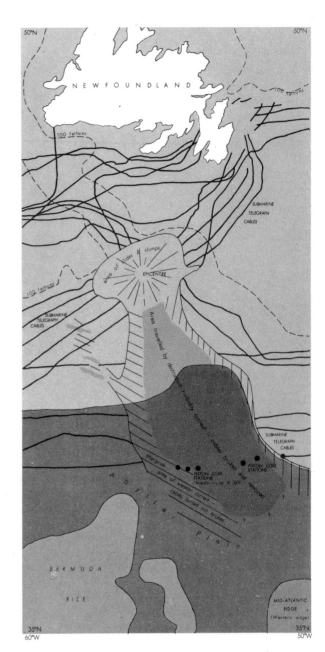

The destructive force of a turbidity current can be enormous. In 1929 an earthquake started a turbidity current south of Newfoundland. As the mud-laden water rushed down the slope it broke several telegraph cables along its path, as shown in this chart. Core samples taken near the lower end of the turbidity current revealed graded layers of silt (laid down by the current) in the upper part of the core, and clays of the abyssal plain in the bottom part of the core.

soon as the slope begins to level off, and so the speed of the current decreases. At the bottom of the continental slope the current adds the remains of its deposit to those of earlier currents; so we find deep-sea deltas in the shape of shallow, conical fans leading up to the bottom of the canyons. Often these fans are crossed with small channels, rather like river beds, that have been formed by smaller turbidity currents.

A turbidity current has a remarkable capacity for retaining its identity and flowing hundreds of miles over very gently sloping bottoms. It will not completely die until it has reached the greatest depths of the basin that confines it, and here finally with nowhere to go it comes to rest and the remaining sediments settle out. It is by this means that the bottoms of basins adjoining the continent have become filled with sand and silt from the land and that the amazingly flat floors of the vast abyssal plains have been formed. We can travel for hundreds of miles over the abyssal plains and find slopes no greater than one in several thousand.

Turbidity currents are not alone responsible for the sediments covering the deep-ocean floor. These currents flow only along the paths of greatest depth, and then only spasmodically. A constant rain of sediments showers down from the great water canopy high above the floor of the sea. In many areas this rain comes primarily from the minute shells of plankton that live and die in the sunlit waters near the surface. Century after century the shells drift down over all parts of the ocean floor and lodge in the cracks and crevices of the bottom. Because these shells are sometimes pure calcium carbonate, sometimes pure silica, the sediments may be the white chalky oozes we find in temperate regions, or the siliceous oozes of colder waters.

Along with these organic remains there are very fine clay particles that rain down on the sea floor. They are washed into the sea by erosion of the coasts and by the thousands of rivers that terminate in the sea. These minute particles sink so slowly that they may travel hundreds of miles before finally settling to the bottom. There are other contributors to the deep-ocean sediments: wind-blown sands and dust from the deserts, volcanic ash thrown high into the atmosphere, and minute particles known as cosmic spherules that come from the melting of meteorites as they enter the atmosphere from outer space.

We might expect the sediments covering the abyssal floor to be perfectly smooth, like a field of new-fallen snow. Undersea photography shows that the surface of the deep-ocean sediments is far from being smooth. It is disturbed by animals that live in the inky darkness of the bottom – sea cucumbers, sea urchins, starfish, and worms, all of which produce an array of mounds and burrows, tracks and subsurface galleries that churn up the top few inches.

We believe from seismic measurements that the sediment carpet of the sea floor is nearly half a mile thick, the result of millions of years of slow accumulation, an inch or so every three thousand years. But even this slow rate, assuming that it remained constant throughout the history of the Earth, would produce much more sediment than we have found; so we have to ask: What has happened to the older sediments? Have they been transformed into the solid rocks that lie farther down in the crust? What, in fact, are the deeper rocks? The only satisfactory way to answer these questions

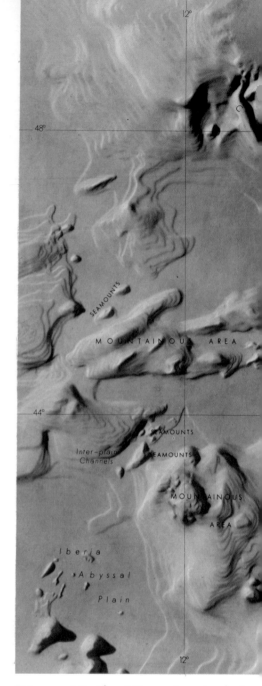

This map of the Bay of Biscay shows in relief coloring typical features found on the sea floor – abyssal plains, seamounts, valleys, and continental slopes. All of the features shown here are based on the most recent detailed soundings made by Britain's National Institute of Oceanography.

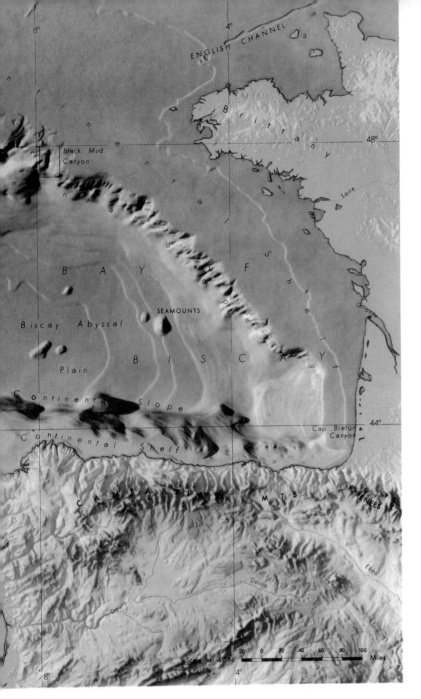

The first stage in an attempt to drill a hole through the Earth's crust down to the mantle was carried out in March 1961. The drilling apparatus of the ship shown here penetrated two miles of water, 500 feet of sediments, and 50 feet of rock. The ship was held in position above the drill by signals transmitted by electronic marker buoys.

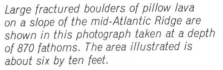

Large fractured boulders of pillow lava on a slope of the mid-Atlantic Ridge are shown in this photograph taken at a depth of 870 fathoms. The area illustrated is about six by ten feet.

would be to drill a hole right through the bed of the ocean and find out. Not only would we learn about the rock floor beneath the carpet of sediments, but we could complete our geological calendar of the sediments themselves, whereas now we have sampled only the top few feet. As this book is being written, engineers are attempting to drill such a hole off the west coast of Mexico (p. 14).

As we continue our journey along the ocean floor and move toward the center of the Atlantic by crossing fields of sediments undulated by deeply-buried basement rocks, we find that the depth gradually decreases, the bottom becomes rougher, and there are more and more volcanic peaks sticking up through the sediments. Eventually we find ourselves facing an enormous mountain range rising ten thousand feet from the ocean floor, and in places breaking the surface of the water. Such mountain peaks are the Azores in the North Atlantic and the St. Paul's Rocks, Ascension Island, and Tristan da Cunha in the South Atlantic.

Known in the Atlantic as the mid-Atlantic Ridge, this vast

From time to time submerged volcanic peaks erupt and become new islands. This photograph shows the 1946 eruption of Myojin, part of the 1500-mile-long chain of islands extending from Japan to Guam.

mountain range extends about a thousand miles across its base and stretches down the middle of the Atlantic for more than ten thousand miles. Recent surveys suggest that similar ridges in other oceans link with the mid-Atlantic Ridge and form a chain of world-encircling mountains some forty thousand miles in total length. A feature on such a vast scale must be explained along with the formation of the oceans and continents themselves.

We know very little about the composition of the mid-Atlantic Ridge. Photographs and dredge hauls show that the peaks are submarine volcanoes that have erupted many times over the years, spilling their lava flows out over the surrounding sea bed. Under the influence of the cold water, the flows have cooled rapidly and have subsequently been broken up by internal stresses. We know from a study of the distribution of earthquakes over the world that one belt of shallow earthquakes runs right down the ridge itself and that it is a region of quite intense crustal movement today. Deep seismic refraction work has shown that under the ridge the oceanic crust has been thickened, possibly by low density material rising up out of the mantle, giving "roots" to the range.

In the center of the ridge in many places is a deep valley running along its length. In the North Atlantic we have followed this valley for about a hundred and fifty miles, and noticed in some places that it has been blocked by volcanic outpourings from neighboring volcanoes. Studies of other mid-ocean ridges reveal similar median valleys, and it now appears that such a valley is common to all ridges. How do we explain such a feature? By comparing the mid-Atlantic Ridge valley with the African Rift valley and the trench in the Red Sea, some geophysicists conclude that these are tears in the Earth's crust — weak seams that are gradually widening as our planet slowly expands.

One problem of the ocean floor that has puzzled geophysicists for many years is the pattern of features associated with island arcs. Island arcs are found in the West Indies and in the Scotian arc southeast of South America, but mostly on the western and northern sides of the Pacific Ocean. The pattern consists of a curving arc of islands about a thousand miles long enclosing an inland sea, usually rather shallower than the typical ocean. Outside any typical island arc, and running parallel to it, is a deep trench where the greatest ocean depths are found. It was in the Marianas Trench in the western Pacific that man eventually conquered the greatest known depths. In 1960, Jacques Piccard, son of Professor Auguste Piccard, and Lieutenant Don Walsh of the U.S. Navy descended to a depth of 35,800 feet in the bathyscaphe *Trieste*, a vessel designed by Professor Piccard and his son. During a twenty-minute stay on the bottom they confirmed by direct observation what dredge hauls and photographs had shown us — that there is life even at these enormous depths, where the pressure of the water is more than seven tons per square inch.

These deep-sea trenches, where the sea depth is almost double the average, are rare gashes in the oceanic crust. We believe that they may be regions which, when filled with sediments, are for some reason subsequently thrust up as new mountain ranges. The full story of the sea floor's trenches has yet to be told.

In nearly all the oceans we find underwater mountains of one kind or another. Some are called "seamounts," and may be mere isolated bumps on the bottom, or they may reach up to the surface. These are submarine volcanoes that form wherever the floor of the ocean is weak enough to allow the molten magma to burst through. Seamounts are found singly, in groups, or in long lines associated with fracture zones. Underwater photographs reveal them in splendid variety, often showing vertical cliffs of exposed rocks with corals, crinoids, gorgonians, and many other beautiful deep-sea animals attached. At the base of these cliffs are scattered boulders and piles of rocks or pebbles, and trapped in valleys and on ledges are accumulations of sediment.

Often the fine particles of sediment have been winnowed away by the currents, and only sand composed of calcareous shells is left. This material is ideal for currents to work and shape as sand ripples, and many seamounts at a variety of depths have ripple markings. Until quite recently geologists believed that ripple marks found in sedimentary rocks indicated that the rocks were formed in shallow water, since the currents of the deep ocean were thought to be too mild to form them. However, underwater photography has shown us that ripple marks are common in depths down to at least sixteen hundred fathoms.

Among the most unusual shapes of seamounts are those found in the North Pacific. Dotting the sea floor are hundreds of flat-topped structures called "guyots," rather like truncated cones, the tops of which are submerged to a depth of several hundred feet and capped with limestone. For a long time it was hard to see how the guyots' tops could have been flattened, since they are far too deep to be worn smooth by wave action. The history of the guyots, as we now understand them, is very interesting. In the first stage, a volcano erupts through the ocean floor and builds a cone reaching far above sea level. Gradually, at the water line the guyot is eaten

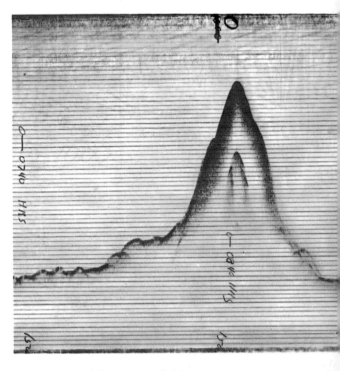

This echogram of a seamount rising 900 fathoms from the floor of the Caribbean was made by an echo sounder. Seamounts may be mere bumps on the ocean floor or they may reach up to the surface. The top of this seamount is 300 fathoms below the surface, here represented by the top edge of the illustration.

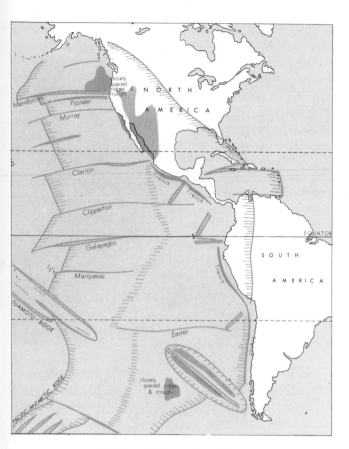

Faulting in the eastern Pacific is shown by this diagram. Turquoise lines mark the major fracture zones; dark shading shows areas of ridges and troughs; heavy turquoise lines indicate trenches.

away by waves and the top is eventually cut off. During this time corals grow over the truncated part. Meanwhile, the great mass of the entire cone presses into the oceanic crust, gradually the crust yields, and the cone begins to sink. Provided the guyot is sinking slowly, the coral reefs can grow upward fast enough to remain near the surface, and so great thicknesses of coral limestone can be built up. But if the guyot sinks too rapidly, or if the coral becomes less active, then the whole column sinks below the surface until it finds its equilibrium level, floating, as it were, in the mantle rock far below.

Most of the seamounts cause some degree of local variation in the intensity of the Earth's magnetic field. This happens because the magnetic property of the volcanic rock forming them is different from that of the sediments the seamounts displace. But there are some seamounts near the continental slopes without magnetic anomalies and without the exposed lava flows that are found on the magnetic seamounts. These have certain properties rather similar to continental rocks, so it may be that they are pieces of continent that have broken off and separated from the shelf edge.

In recent years American scientists have uncovered a striking pattern of features in the Pacific Ocean. Extending westward for thousands of miles from the edge of the continent are four or more enormous fracture zones – represented as escarpments and chains of submarine volcanoes. Now if the two sides of a fracture had moved only up and down, we would expect to find the pattern of magnetic anomalies across the fracture to be more or less continuous. But detailed magnetic surveys have shown that the pattern on one side of the fracture has been shifted horizontally relative to the other side. The first fracture studied in this way showed that a shift of eighty miles had occurred across the fault line; but the most recent work on the Mendocino Escarpment shows that the northern side has shifted 750 miles to the west, relative to the southern side.

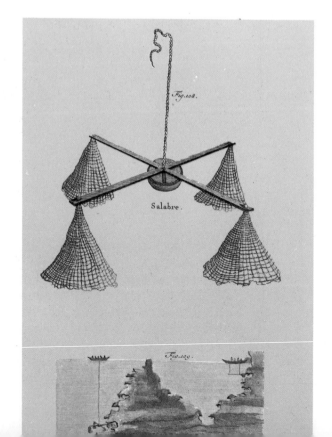

Here is irrefutable evidence of what geologists call a transcurrent fault, with a displacement an appreciable fraction of the size of the oceans themselves! What are the giant forces capable of bringing about such large-scale movement in the crust underlying the sea floor? And what happens to the displacement if it bites into a continental margin? Quite simply, we do not know; there is no evidence of faulting on such a grand scale along the American coast itself.

If we have faith in our data, and in our present interpretation of them, we must admit the possibility that enormous blocks of the Earth's crust *can* be moved around on a scale envisioned by those who favor the theories of continental drift. Further evidence – the ancient positions of the Earth's magnetic poles, deduced from the fossil magnetic properties of rocks – also leads us to believe that the continents themselves have been able to float about in the mantle rock. And we must include the mid-Atlantic Ridge in any discussions of continental drift, as well as many of the smaller features, such as the median valley on the ridge and the non-magnetic seamounts off the continental margins.

The deep-sea floor is still defying our attemps to pry out its secrets. Only slowly and with painstaking care can we fit together the thousands of pieces of the jigsaw puzzle and see the whole picture. In time, deep-diving submarines and bathyscaphes will permit us to wander about at will through the ocean depths and peer through the foggy gloom; deep holes through the oceanic crust will test our conclusions about the deep structure. We will be able to fill in the details, now unknown, and delve further into the problems of the sea floor. Inevitably, the more we find out, the more questions and puzzles will arise. Yet in this field we are on the brink of discoveries and explorations quite as exciting and just as rewarding as man's first steps into space.

The illustrations along the bottom of these pages show techniques, past and present, to gain information about the sea floor: a dredging device used by Count Luigi Marsigli, who maintained that the deep ocean was not a "bottomless abyss"; William Beebe's bathysphere which is lowered from a ship and takes its occupant to the ocean bottom; A. S. Laughton's automatic camera which takes pnotographs of the sea bed; and Auguste Piccard's bathyscaphe, capable of taking men to the deepest regions of the oceans. Its occupants ride in the small sphere attached to the gasoline-filled float. Because gasoline is lighter than water, the bathyscaphe rises to the surface when ballast is dropped.

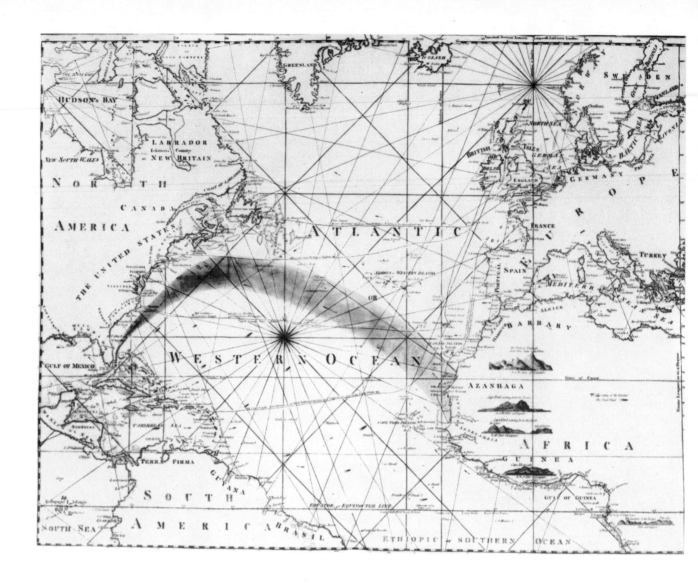

The Currents
J. C. Swallow

The most impressive of the world's currents is the Gulf Stream, shown above on a chart prepared by Governor Pownall in 1787. Its volume transport is more than a thousand times that of the Mississippi River.

There are about three hundred million cubic miles of water in the oceans, and all of it is moving about. The water is moving in many different ways; in shallow water the waves move back and forth every few seconds, and the tidal streams ebb and flow twice a day. Currents, which are set up by the drag of the local wind on the sea, vary with the changes in the wind itself. Besides these fluctuating movements there is, almost everywhere, a prevailing current, just as in the atmosphere prevailing winds exist, although large and frequent fluctuations can occur. Around the shores of the British Isles the prevailing currents are weak compared with the tidal streams, and careful observation is needed to reveal the resultant flow of water along the English Channel into the North Sea, and through the Irish Sea from south to north.

In some parts of the oceans, though, the average currents are more conspicuous. The Spaniards soon noticed the Gulf Stream in their exploration of the West Indies, and early in the sixteenth century Spanish ships were making good use of the prevailing currents to aid their passages, keeping well to the south in the Equatorial Current on the outward journey, and returning part of the way to Europe in the northeastward flowing Gulf Stream.

In deep water, far from land, a sailor can often detect a current only by the discrepancy between his observed position and that reckoned from his ship's course and estimated speed. Did Necho and his Phoenician sailors realize that they were being helped by the Agulhas Current, and later hindered by the Canaries Current, in their much-disputed circumnavigation of Africa? By the thirteenth century, the Agulhas Current must have been known, for Marco Polo had heard of it. With every improvement in the art of navigation, and better means of determining position at sea, men gained more and more knowledge about the surface currents, and the discrepancies between observed and estimated positions – which must have alarmed the sailor in unknown currents – could be turned to his advantage or avoided.

But it was a long time before this gradually accumulating knowledge was collected, put on charts, and made available to seafarers in general. Thus in 1770 we find the Board of Customs in Boston complaining to the Lords of the Treasury in London that the mail packets usually took two weeks longer to cross the Atlantic than did merchant ships. Benjamin Franklin, who at that time was Postmaster General, found that although many fishermen and merchant ships' captains were familiar with the Gulf Stream, the mail packet captains were not, and he had a chart of its course drawn up and printed for their benefit. Matthew Fontaine Maury, of the United States Navy, was the first to organize the systematic collection of current observations. About the middle of the nineteenth century he extracted from ships' logs the scattered observations of currents, winds, and weather and produced charts of the average values. He persuaded mariners to make better observations and rewarded those who co-operated with free copies of his charts and sailing directions. Their use by sailing ships shortened ocean passages by several days, or even weeks, and his charts and methods of compiling them are the immediate forerunners of those in use today.

At the same time as this increase in practical interest and use of currents, there was much scientific speculation about the causes of the great ocean current systems. Two rival hypotheses were the source of much controversy. Benjamin Franklin's view, adhered to by Rennell, James Croll and many others, was that the prevailing winds, by their drag on the sea surface, were the cause of most of the currents. Others, including Maury and Dr. W. B. Carpenter, believed that differences of density in the water, caused by unequal heating in different latitudes, provided the main driving force for the currents.

But the arguments put forward in support of these ideas were merely qualitative, and inadequate to establish which process was most important. Only in the last decade or two have quantitative theories of the circulation of the ocean been devised.

Our knowledge and charts of the surface currents of the oceans have been built up gradually, over a period of several decades, from many thousands of observations of drift experienced by ships. When a chart of surface currents is made in this way, the *average* currents stand out clearly.

In general, the ocean currents form a pattern of nearly closed loops which turn clockwise in the Northern Hemisphere and counterclockwise in the Southern Hemisphere. These circulating systems correspond roughly to the pattern of the prevailing winds. Exactly how the winds drive the currents along is not so easy to see, though. The most obvious effect of the wind, when it blows over the sea surface, is to raise waves; part of the energy transferred

A scientist empties a water sampling device aboard the Challenger *during the expedition of 1872-76. This particular instrument was used for taking water samples immediately above the sea floor.*

The currents and surface temperature chart on the following pages shows the direction of movement of surface water over the world ocean. Winds, sea surface currents, and sea surface temperatures are all interrelated. Over much of the ocean winds drive the surface waters from one climatic zone to another, so that heat transferred from the atmosphere to the water is sometimes transported by currents from one area to another. In turn the air above the water may be warmed and this heat transported again by the winds. This chart shows conditions during the month of February. (See page 261 for prevailing winds chart.)

ARCTIC CIRCLE

60°

0°

5° C

10° C

15° C

20° C

TROPIC OF CANCER

25° C

NORTH PACIFIC CURRENT

OYASHIO

KUROSHIO

NORTH EQUATORIAL CURRENT

EQUATORIAL COUNTER CURRENT

EQUATOR 0°

SOUTH EQUATORIAL CURRENT

25° C

NORTH EQUATORIAL CURRENT

EQUATORIAL COUNTER CURRENT

SOUTH EQUATORIAL CURRENT

25° C

20° C

15° C

10° C

5° C

WEST WIND DRIFT

0° C

TROPIC OF CAPRICORN 25° C

20° C

15° C

10° C

5° C

60°

0° C

ANTARCTIC CIRCLE

AGULHAS CURRENT

60°   120°   180°

190°   180°

Below 0° C   0° C   5° C   10° C   15° C   20° C   25° C   Above 25° C

to the water from the air drags the water along as a current. Despite the tremendous power of storms and large waves, the forces acting on a particular stretch of water and creating a current are quite small, perhaps only one millionth of the weight of that particular piece of water.

When something is moving under the action of such weak forces, it turns out that an effect due to the Earth's rotation has to be taken into account. In our ordinary everyday experience – walking about or driving in a car – we can ignore the fact that all our activities take place on a rotating body. But with the sea it is different. Because the forces that create a current are so small, the effect of the Earth's rotation cannot be ignored. This effect is known as the "Coriolis force" and varies with latitude, being zero at the Equator and maximum at the poles. At first sight its effect is rather surprising: a surface current set up by the wind does not flow *directly* downwind, but is deflected to the right in the Northern Hemisphere, and to the left in the Southern Hemisphere.

The winds, as well as producing currents by their drag on the surface of the sea, have another effect on the water. They set up slopes in the sea surface by piling up water against some coasts and in places where converging currents are driven by different wind systems. Then other currents flow in consequence of the pressure gradients in the water which arise from these slopes of the sea surface. When a whole ocean basin such as the North Atlantic is considered – taking into account the regional variations of the stress of the wind, the Coriolis force varying with latitude, and the presence of continental boundaries – it is possible to calculate a pattern of currents that is a fair approximation to the observed pattern. In particular, it can be shown that the currents *should* be stronger and narrower on the western sides of ocean basins, and as it turns out, this is just what observations reveal. For instance, the three strongest of the major ocean currents are all on the western sides of their oceans – the Gulf Stream on the western side of the North Atlantic; the Kuro Shio on the western side of the northern Pacific Ocean; and the Agulhas Current on the western side of the Indian Ocean.

One of the most striking features of the surface current chart is the equatorial circulation of the oceans. In each of the three oceans extending across the Equator – the Atlantic, Pacific, and Indian oceans – two westward-flowing currents are found, and sandwiched between them is an eastward-flowing countercurrent. It is natural to suppose that the North and South Equatorial currents, as they are called, are drift currents driven by the Trade winds; and to regard the middle countercurrent as a compensating flow resulting from the piling up of water at the western boundaries of these three oceans. However, we now know that in the case of the Pacific Ocean, at least, this simple explanation seems inadequate. The observed currents can be accounted for better by a careful consideration of the varying wind stress and the Coriolis effect.

The equatorial currents are not symmetrically arranged about the geographical Equator, but follow the wind systems. In the Indian Ocean, for instance, the equatorial currents are complicated by the seasonal changes of the monsoon. When the southwest monsoon is blowing from August to October, the westward-flowing North Equatorial Current disappears and is replaced by

Convinced that the wind and current systems of the South Pacific Ocean would carry a raft from the west coast of South America to the Polynesian Islands, Thor Heyerdahl and five companions set out in 1947 in the raft Kon-Tiki. They made a voyage of 4300 miles in 101 days, and proved that it was possible for South Americans of prehistoric times to have populated the Pacific islands.

the eastward-flowing Monsoon Current. The result is that, together with the Equatorial Countercurrent, all the currents in the Indian Ocean north of lat. 2°S. have a strong easterly trend. With the reversal of the monsoon during the Northern Hemisphere winter, the northeast monsoon reinforces the westward-flowing North Equatorial Current. The picture, then, is similar to that in the Pacific Ocean, with an easterly Equatorial Countercurrent sandwiched between the westerly North and South Equatorial currents.

In the Southern Ocean the west wind drift causes a great and continuous eastward-flowing current encircling Antarctica.

Over most of the ocean surface the currents are fairly weak, with speeds of around half a knot. However, in the more clearly defined currents, such as the equatorial system of ocean currents, speeds may reach one or two knots; and in the strongest currents, such as the Gulf Stream, speeds as high as four or five knots may be found. Most of the surface currents are not very deep; except in the case of the strongest ones, their strength has almost disappeared at a depth of a few hundred feet. The Gulf Stream's high speeds are not found much deeper than 1200 feet.

The weaker currents often vary their direction because they may be radically changed by local weather. Yet even within the stronger currents we find variety; fast-moving, narrow streaks alternating with weaker countercurrents produce quite a different picture from the broad, average currents shown on the charts. So a sailor may often find himself in a current that is far from constant, either in direction or speed, but in the long run he will gain by making use of the *average* current shown on the charts.

Perhaps the most important consequence of ocean currents is their effect on climate. Because the currents carry great masses of water from one place to another, large quantities of heat and cold are transported from one latitude to another. The harbors along the coast of Norway are free from ice because of the flow of relatively warm Atlantic water into the Norwegian Sea. Yet the harbors on the coast of Labrador – located farther south than Norway – do not benefit from such a flow of warm water and are consequently frozen for many months of the year. However, the popular notion of the Gulf Stream as a river of warm water flowing toward the western coast of Europe is incorrect. We should regard the Gulf Stream as a boundary current between the warm, blue waters of the Sargasso Sea in the central North Atlantic and the cold, green waters to the north and northwest. Because of its rapid flow, the Gulf Stream prevents the lighter, warm water from spreading out over the denser cold water.

What climatic changes would be brought about if the Gulf Stream became stronger or weaker? If it weakened, the climate of Europe would possibly become warmer, because the warm Sargasso Sea water would be less confined and would be free to spread farther north and east. But we have too little knowledge to answer such questions about the relationship between the changes of currents and changes of climate. The interactions of ocean and atmosphere are so complex that any attempts at prediction seem purely speculative.

The cold water to the northwest of the Gulf Stream is brought south by the Labrador Current, and with it comes a march of icebergs which cause such a notorious hazard to ships off the Grand

Hundreds of icebergs, some more than two hundred yards long, are brought south from Baffin Bay by the Labrador Current. They are carried into the North Atlantic, where they are a menace in shipping lanes.

The chart on page 208 shows the salt content of Atlantic Ocean water above a depth of 1250 meters (684 fathoms). The lines are isohalines (lines of equal salinity), expressed in parts per thousand. The cold but less saline Antarctic Intermediate Water spreading northward sinks from the surface at about lat. 50°S., and is shown on this chart extending northward from about lat. 45°S. This body of water lies above the more saline southward-flowing North Atlantic Deep Water, which sinks past this depth in the extreme North Atlantic and rises again to this depth in the extreme South Atlantic. Highly saline Mediterranean water spreads westward and northward at this intermediate depth. (This chart is taken from the atlas of the Meteor Expedition of 1926–27.)

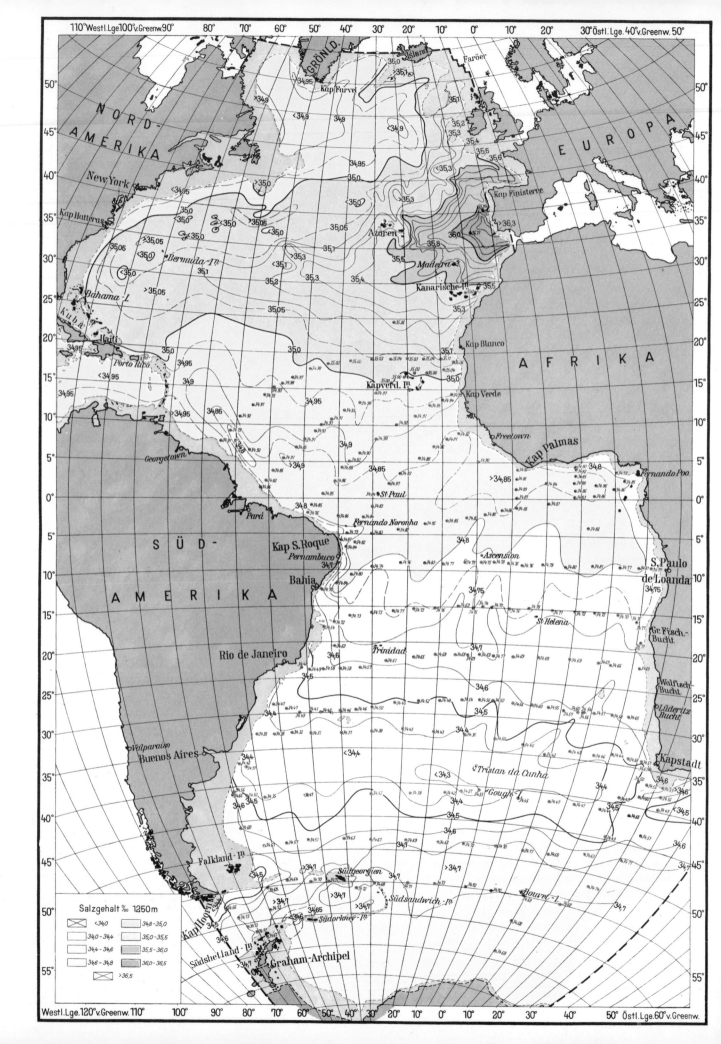

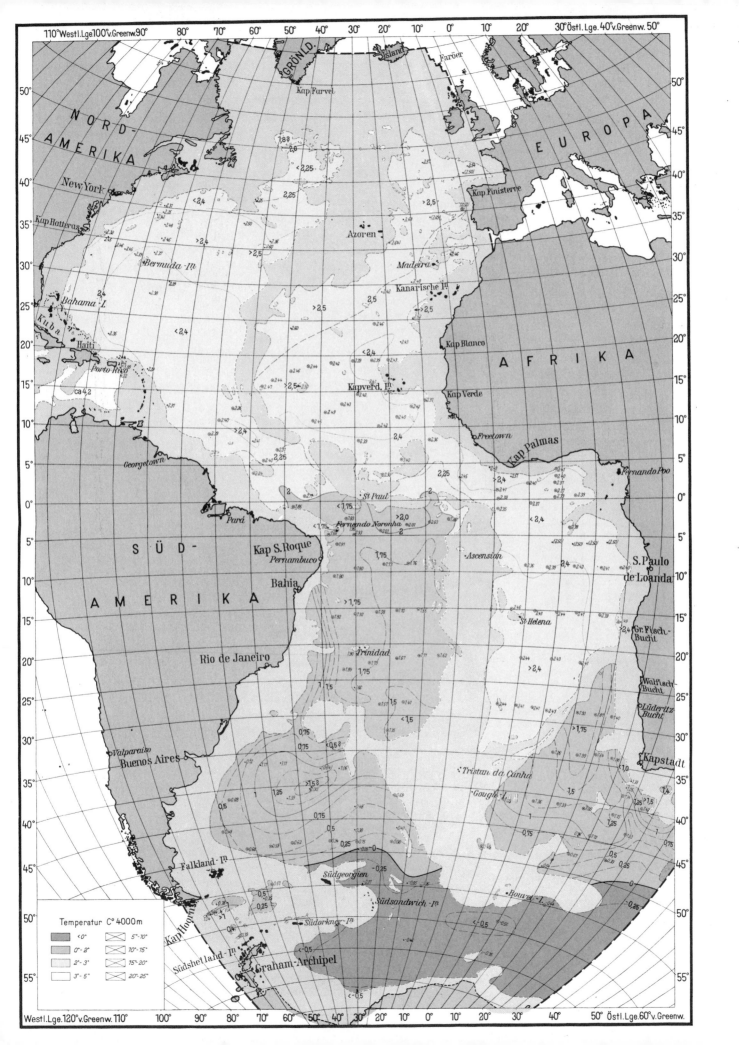

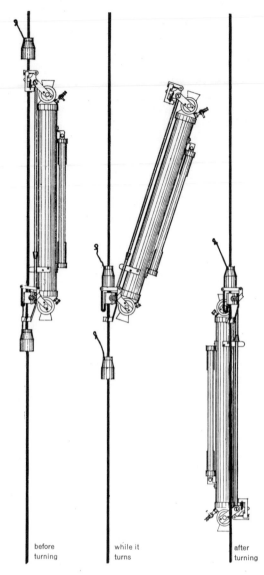

This Nansen water-sampling bottle is essentially a metal tube with valves at each end. It is fitted with reversing thermometers (see p. 257). As many as 20 bottles in a series are lowered on a wire. A "messenger" weight released from the ship travels down the wire and trips the first bottle. As it reverses, valves at each end close and trap a water sample; another messenger is released which trips the second bottle, and so on down the line.

The temperature chart on page 209 is taken from the atlas of the Meteor Expedition to the Atlantic in 1925–27. The chart shows temperatures at a depth of 4000 meters (2187 fathoms) in the deep basins east and west of the Mid-Atlantic Ridge, which rises well above this level. The cold Antarctic Bottom Water from the Weddell Sea spreads northward, particularly in the western basins. In the far north is the deepest part of the cold North Atlantic Deep Current which flows southward. The isotherms shown are lines joining places of equal temperature (in degrees centigrade).

Banks of Newfoundland. At the same time, dense fog is liable to be formed in the same area when the warm winds from the Sargasso Sea meet the cold water of the Labrador Current. After the *Titanic* disaster in 1911, the International Ice Patrol was set up to keep watch on icebergs and warn ships of their movements. Observation of the water masses and the currents of the Labrador Sea has made it possible to predict ice movements with some success, a good example of the practical use of the study of currents.

As well as influencing climate, currents have a direct effect on the fertility of the oceans. Where there is a steady upwelling of water from below, the water brought to the surface may be colder than usual for a given latitude. This happens most noticeably near the coasts of southwest Africa and western South America, off Peru. In these regions the prevailing winds, which are all offshore, tend to drive the coastal surface water out to sea, and colder water wells up from depths of a few hundred feet to replace the water driven away. This deep water is rich in nutrients needed for the growth of plankton, and when it rises to the sunlit upper layers there is a tremendous outburst of growth of both marine plants and animals. Regions of upwelling are, therefore, particularly fertile and may support large populations of fish. In turn, this means there is food for large numbers of sea birds living along the coasts. As a result, thriving fishing and guano industries have grown up, especially on the Peruvian coast. In certain years, though, the winds (and therefore the currents) may shift so that the upwelling is weaker, or the area may be invaded by less fertile water. Whenever this happens there are disastrous mortalities of fish and sea birds; for miles the beaches have been covered thickly with dead fish.

Less violent, but none the less serious for fisheries, are the longer term fluctuations of water movements. The decay of the herring fishery in the English Channel and the fall in catches of sardines off the coast of California have both been ascribed to gradual changes in the water circulation. These changes have resulted in less nutrient material being brought into the areas than is needed to support an economically worthwhile population of fish.

So far only the surface currents have been mentioned. Over most of the deep ocean basins they do not extend downward more than a few hundred feet. The total depth of water in the oceans, though, is usually between two and three miles. There is movement even in these deeper layers. Here, though, the average currents are much slower than those on the surface. In the shallow seas, where much of the world's fishing is done, a knowledge of the bottom currents and the subsurface water movements can be useful to fishermen. Sometimes these bottom currents may run quite differently from those on the surface, although in shallow water the tidal streams predominate. One example of a contrary undercurrent in the shallow seas is found in the Bosporus. Here the surface water of the Black Sea flows out into the Sea of Marmara, but underneath there is an opposing flow of saltier water (from the Mediterranean) into the Black Sea. At times this undercurrent is so strong that if fishing nets were lowered into it, a boat would be towed against the surface current.

In most parts of the oceans, there is no obvious "profit" to be gained from a study of the deep currents; we cannot, for instance, enable ships to make a faster passage. Knowledge of the deep-water movements has come about only with the scientific study of the oceans.

Nearly everything we know about the deep water we have found out by taking samples of the water, then by measuring its properties – temperature, salinity, the dissolved oxygen content, and so on.

To collect water from great depths, many kinds of samplers have been designed, the Nansen bottle being typical. Usually, samples are taken at chosen depths at each of a number of selected positions along a line or spread over an area. Each position is called a "station". At a station where the water is more than ten thousand feet deep, it may take as long as three or four hours to collect samples from twenty or more different levels. After the samples have been analyzed, charts showing the distribution of the different properties of the water can be prepared. From the way these properties vary from one place to another, we can infer something about the way the deep water is moving.

Even though we cannot see directly how fast the deep currents are moving, we can learn something about them by studying the distribution of water density. Density, which is the mass of water per unit volume, can be calculated from the temperature and salt content – the colder water being heavier than the warm, and the saltier water being heavier than the less salty. Once the density distribution is known, then the pressure distribution (force per unit area) can be found. Then by taking into account the effect of the Earth's rotation we can calculate the currents that *should* be there to balance the observed pressure gradients. The meteorologist follows a very similar process to find the speed of the winds from the spacing of the isobars on a weather map. But in the sea the height of the surface cannot be measured accurately, as it can be on land. This means that there is no convenient reference level from which to measure the pressure, and so only differences between currents at different depths can be calculated in this way. To obtain an over-all picture of the currents at all depths we must know, or assume, something about the current at one particular depth.

Despite all these uncertainties, oceanographers have built up a fairly consistent picture of the deep-water circulation, mainly from extensive systematic surveys made during the 1920s and 1930s. Although temperature soundings had been taken more than a hundred years earlier, and the *Challenger* expedition and others of the late nineteenth century had brought back information about temperature and chemical composition of sea water, it was not until deliberate surveys were made of particular areas that charts and profiles showing in detail the distribution of the various properties of sea water at all depths could be constructed. Such surveys include the *Meteor* survey of the South Atlantic in 1925–27, and the *Discovery* investigations in the Southern Ocean from 1925–51. Since then, interest in the deep water has grown and many more samples of water at all depths have been collected.

During the International Geophysical Year (1957–58) there was a great deal of activity in deep-water investigation. In the Atlantic, for instance, east-west lines of stations were worked at every eight degrees of latitude, providing information about temperature, salinity, and dissolved oxygen content at varying depths; in addition, intensive studies of more limited areas were made. Similar investigations were carried out in the Pacific and Southern oceans.

A scientist aboard a research ship stands on the hydrographic platform to remove a reversing water bottle from the wire.

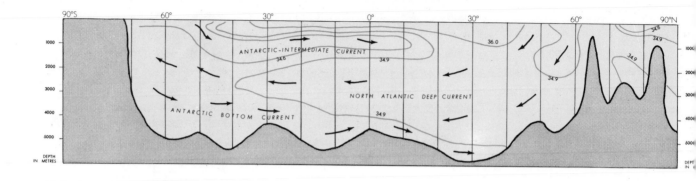

One reassuring result of this continuing study is that there have been no signs of large changes in the distribution of temperature, salinity, and other properties in the deep water over a period of a few decades. Work on a similar scale is planned for the forthcoming International Indian Ocean Expedition.

The earliest observations on the deep water showed that, even in equatorial latitudes, the temperature at great depths was very near to freezing point. Recently, more detailed surveys have shown that in the moderate latitudes of all oceans there is a more or less steady fall in temperature with depth for about the first half mile or more. Below this the temperature decreases more slowly. At a depth of a mile the temperature nearly everywhere is down to 4°C.; and the bottom half of the water in all of the oceans has temperatures lower than 4°C. Because salt water (unlike fresh water) becomes denser as the water is cooled below 4°C., there is a more or less steady increase in density with depth in the oceans.

This vast reservoir of surprisingly uniform cold water appears to be formed from two sources – one in the extreme north of the Atlantic, the other in the Weddell Sea on the borders of Antarctica. In these two regions the surface waters may be cooled sufficiently to make them heavy enough to sink and mix with the deep water, setting up a density-driven deep circulation. The North Atlantic Deep water can be traced as a distinct water mass throughout the entire length of the Atlantic Ocean; it is slightly warmer and saltier than the Antarctic Bottom water coming from the Weddell Sea, which is found underlying it in the South Atlantic. The deep layers of the Pacific and Indian oceans appear to be made up of a mixture of these two kinds of deep water.

Overlying the deep water in much of the Southern Hemisphere there is the Antarctic Intermediate water. This water mass – colder than the North Atlantic Deep water but much less salty, so that it has a lower density – is formed from the northward-drifting Antarctic surface water which sinks at the Antarctic Convergence (roughly about lat. 50°s.), where it meets warmer water.

In the northern Atlantic Ocean the Deep water is overlaid by a much warmer and saltier water mass originating in the Mediterranean Sea. Evaporation of the surface water of the Mediterranean greatly exceeds rainfall and river runoff around the Mediterranean seaboard. This means that the salt content of the surface water is increased. In the winter some of the surface water is cooled sufficiently so that it sinks and forms a dense deep layer of highly saline water which, as an undercurrent, overflows from the Mediterranean into the Atlantic. Here the water quickly sinks to a depth of more

This vertical section of the Atlantic from the Antarctic to the Arctic shows the Antarctic Bottom Current flowing beneath the less dense water of the North Atlantic Deep Current. (Salinity of the water is given in parts per thousand by weight.)

This chart illustrates Stommel's theory of deep water circulation of the oceans. Dots mark the two main sources of deep water – in the extreme North Atlantic and in the Weddell Sea. Thick lines along western sides of the major oceans show the strong, deep currents. Thinner lines show horizontal movement of deep water that should be everywhere directed toward the poles.

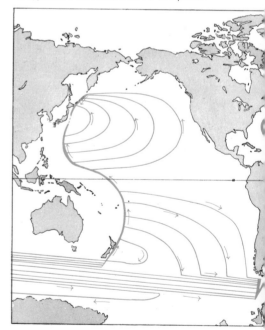

The neutrally-buoyant float measures deep currents. Each free-floating tube is weighted so that it will stabilize itself at a chosen depth. As it is carried along by a current, a battery-powered transmitter sends out sound pulses. By observing these "pings" with ship-borne hydrophones, the movement of deep water can be traced.

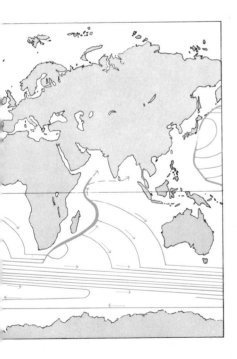

than half a mile, where it finds its own density level and spreads out across the North Atlantic, easily recognized by its relatively high temperature and high salinity.

Although water sampling gives us a clear picture of the spreading of different water masses over the oceans, it is more difficult to assign speeds to these movements. Calculations from the density distributions which, in a few cases, can be supported by direct measurements, indicate speeds of about a mile a day in some of the deep-water masses; but these speeds are variable and uncertain, and the average movements of these deep-water currents may be much slower.

One way in which the average rate of movement of deep water masses can be found is by measuring radiocarbon concentration. When the surface waters sink in high latitudes to form new deep water, they carry down traces of radiocarbon from the atmosphere. Thereafter this radioactive isotope of carbon decays at a known rate. Despite the difficulties in applying this method, more and more measurements suggest that the deep waters spend, on an average, several hundreds of years below the surface. Assuming that, in this time, a typical particle of North Atlantic Deep water travels southward through the whole length of the Atlantic, its average speed must be about one mile per month — much less than the currents observed directly over a period of a few days or weeks.

How certain can we be of any particular pattern of movement we may infer for the deep waters? The real pattern may, in fact, be quite different from the simplest pattern suggested by our readings of temperatures, salinities, and other properties. Recent theoretical work on the dynamics of the deep-water circulation suggests that the flow may be more complicated. If we start with the two main sources of deep water (the extreme North Atlantic and the Weddell Sea, where the water is sinking) and suppose that everywhere else the deep water is very slowly moving upward, it can be shown that the horizontal movements of the deep water *should* be everywhere directed slowly toward the poles — except at the western boundaries of the oceans where strong deep currents should be found. This is, of course, quite a different picture from the slow southward drift of the North Atlantic Deep water that can be inferred from observations of its temperature and salinity. There is some evidence for the existence of the predicted southward deep current along the western side of the Atlantic, but other details of this theoretical model still await confirmation.

In two recent discoveries, though, the observations were ahead of the theoretical predictions. Only a few years ago a remarkable undercurrent was found flowing eastward along the Equator under the westward-flowing South Equatorial Current in the Pacific. At a depth of only two or three hundred feet below the surface, this undercurrent flows at a speed of two or three knots for at least 3500 miles along the Equator.

Even more recently a similar undercurrent has been found flowing under the South Equatorial Current in the central Atlantic. To date we do not know what kind of current flows under the equatorial current in the Indian Ocean. With the changing surface currents brought on by the monsoons, the pattern may be quite different there.

The Restless Tides
K. F. Bowden

*Fishing by horse and cart in the Bay of Fundy
is made possible by the great tidal range.
When the tide ebbs, pollack, flounder, and
bass are left hanging on the nets.*

The rise and fall of the sea twice a day is such an obvious thing
that it must have been well known to people living along the coasts
of tidal seas from very early times. These people also must have
noticed that the tides came later and later each day – fifty minutes
on the average – as did the rising of the Moon. And possibly there
were some who associated this celestial event with the rhythmical
rise and fall of the sea.

Most early written records of the tides were made by people
living on the shores of the Mediterranean, but in nearly all parts of
this sea tidal rise and fall is negligible. It was not until Phoenician,
Greek, and Roman navigators ventured beyond the Mediterranean
– west into the Atlantic and east into the Indian Ocean – that they
saw impressively high tides, sometimes to their great surprise and
fear. When the army of Alexander the Great approached the mouth
of the Indus from the north in 325 B.C., his men were alarmed and
confused by the effects of the tides on their moored ships. And
when Caesar's legions invaded Britain in 55 B.C., his ships were
left high and dry by a twenty-foot spring tide reinforced by a
strong wind.

Much of our evidence of Greek and Roman knowledge of the tides comes from Strabo (born *c.* 63 B.C.) who, in his *Geography*, referred to the observations and writings of men before him. Pytheas, who sailed to Britain and the North Sea around 325 B.C., is credited with making the first systematic observations of the tides, and being the first to relate the alternation of spring and neap tides to phases of the Moon. Strabo knew that in certain places the morning tides on successive days tended to resemble one another more closely than morning and afternoon tides of the same day (known as diurnal inequality). He also described the dangers of tidal bores which regularly and dramatically invade certain rivers. Pliny the Elder (A.D. 23 – 79), in his *Natural History*, correctly explained that spring and neap tides are raised by the combined effects associated with the Sun and Moon; and that diurnal inequality is related to their positions north or south of the Equator.

The tides vary greatly from place to place, often within a surprisingly short distance. Only forty miles separate the Atlantic and Pacific oceans along the Panama Canal, yet at the Atlantic end the tidal range is about two feet while at the Pacific end it is about fourteen feet. Around the British Isles the tidal range is greatest in the Bristol Channel where, at Avonmouth, the spring range reaches forty feet. At Portland Bill, near the center of the English Channel coast, the spring range is only seven feet. The largest range in the world is at the head of the Bay of Fundy, between New Brunswick and Nova Scotia, where the spring range reaches fifty feet at the head of the Minas Basin. Yet a few hundred miles south, around Cape Cod, the range is less than three feet, although it increases again farther south along the United States coast.

As tidal ranges vary from place to place, so do tidal rhythms. Along the shores of the Gulf of Mexico, where the range is no more than a foot or two, the rhythm of the tides would seem remarkable to anyone accustomed to two high waters and two low waters a day. Here the tides are diurnal, with only one high water and one low water each lunar day of twenty-four hours and fifty minutes. On the other hand, the Pacific coasts of North America have mixed tides – two highs and two lows a day, but usually of markedly unequal heights. In fact, the tides everywhere are made up of the oscillations of both diurnal and semidiurnal periods. Where the semidiurnal oscillations predominate, as around the European coasts, there are two tides a day. In areas such as the Gulf of Mexico the semidiurnal oscillations are much weaker, and it is the diurnal ones that govern the rhythms of the tides.

The simplest way to measure the rise and fall of the tide is to erect a vertical pole marked in feet, and then watch the change in water level at regular intervals of time. But a more common practice nowadays is to use a tide gauge which records the height of water automatically (see diagram). The coastal tide gauge gives the oceanographer a "cardiogram," as it were, of tidal height measured against time. In principle, gauges used in the open sea are pressure gauges that are laid on the bottom and record the changing pressure of the water brought about by the changing depth. With their positions marked by buoys, these gauges are left at sea for several weeks and give oceanographers a continuous record of tidal change.

Since Greek and Roman times men have known that the rhythm of the tides was somehow related to the apparent motion of the

Tide gauges located at various points along a coast provide records which can be analyzed to form a basis for predicting future tides. The gauge shown here consists of a float which transmits the rise and fall of the water to the paper on a recording drum. Above, a U. S. Coast Guard officer reads a portable tide gauge.

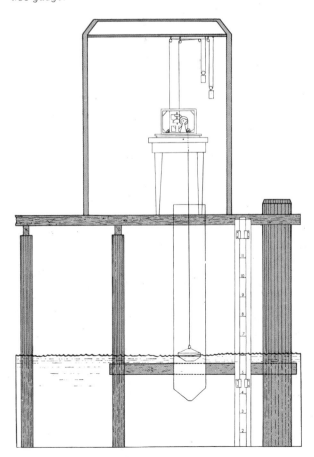

Moon and Sun, but it was not until Newton's time that we were given a rational explanation of the link. In his *Principia*, published in 1687, Newton showed that the tides are one of the consequences of the laws of gravitation. Every particle of matter on the Earth is attracted by the Moon, and the force of attraction is directed toward the Moon's center; also, the farther away from the Moon's center the particle is, the weaker the attracting force. So the force varies slightly in both direction and in strength, depending on the position of the particle on the Earth. It is this variation in the attracting force that causes the ocean waters to move to and fro over the Earth's crust and so produce the tides. As we might expect, the tidal forces tend to cause the water on the side of the Earth facing the Moon to be heaped up, but a similar bulge also forms on the opposite side of the Earth.

Because the ocean waters on the far side of the Earth (most distant from the Moon) are the least affected by the Moon's gravitational attraction, they tend, in a sense, to be left behind and so form a far-side bulge.

We know that the Sun also exerts a tide-generating force on the Earth's waters. It may seem surprising that the Sun, nearly twenty-five million times more massive than the Moon, does not have a greater effect. But mass is not the only key to the explanation. Although tidal force is directly proportional to the mass of the heavenly body concerned, it is also inversely proportional to the cube of its distance. The Sun's greater distance from us, then, is the dominating fact, with the result that its ability to raise tides on Earth is less than half that of the Moon.

Although we can calculate exactly the tide-generating forces at every point on the Earth's surface, we have yet to reach a complete understanding of the movements of the waters of the oceans and seas in response to these forces. Newton himself found a solution of sorts: he imagined an ideal ocean that covered the whole earth and he assumed that its water could respond instantly to the changing tidal forces. According to this solution, known as the equilibrium tide, the surface of the world ocean would rise in a bulge reaching its maximum height at the point directly below the Moon. At the same time a similar bulge would form on the opposite side of the Earth. As the Earth rotated on its axis, each point on the surface would have two high waters and two low waters each lunar day.

With the same hypothetical ocean, the Sun would tend to produce its own equilibrium tide. Now if we consider the combined action of both Moon and Sun, we can see how the alternation of spring and neap tides occurs. When the Earth, Moon, and Sun are in line (at either new or full Moon) the high waters produced individually by solar and lunar attraction reinforce one another, so a tide of maximum range occurs. When the Sun and Moon form a right angle with the Earth (at the first or third quarter of the Moon), the solar and lunar tides oppose one another, resulting in a tide of minimum range.

Newton's imaginary world ocean with its equilibrium tide, although greatly oversimplified, explains many of the features of the tides. But there are other influences at work. In 1775 the French mathematician Laplace showed that the tidal picture is made much more complex because of the inertia of the ocean waters and the

Sir Isaac Newton.

Earth's rotation. And the complexity is added to by the irregular shape of the coast lines and the varying depth of the sea floor. The oceans may be regarded as forming natural basins, in each of which the water — once disturbed — would continue to move back and forth, each basin having its own period of oscillation. If the period of oscillation happens to be close to the tidal period, then the response of the water is much increased. The large semidiurnal tides in the North Atlantic are produced this way.

While the tides in the deep oceans ebb and flow in accordance with the changing positions of the Moon and Sun, the tides in coastal seas, such as the English Channel and the Red Sea, are secondary effects and depend on the oceanic tides. If these seas were cut off from the oceans, the tides in them would be almost imperceptible; it is the tidal waves coming in from the ocean that set them oscillating. But here too resonance plays an important part and is responsible for large ranges of tides, as in the Bay of Fundy, Bristol Channel, and the Sea of Okhotsk. Wherever we find a large vertical rise and fall of tidal water we know that enormous quantities of sea are also flowing horizontally from one place to another; in the Bay of Fundy tidal currents twice daily move 100,000,000,000 tons of water. In restricted passages and straits these tidal currents sometimes attain speeds of more than ten knots, as they do in Discovery Passage and in Seymour Narrows, British Columbia. In coastal seas tidal currents frequently attain speeds of two or three knots, but in the open oceans they are rarely more than a quarter of a

Mont St. Michel, the fortified abbey off Brittany, at low tide is surrounded by miles of sand flats. At high tide the sea floods the surrounding plain, leaving the fortress an island linked to the mainland only by a causeway.

A sixteenth-century circular tide table.

Ports located in areas having a tidal range of fifteen feet or more require a system of closed docks. The water level is kept more or less constant by one or more locks. The Royal Docks, Woolwich, part of the great dock area of London, are shown here.

knot. Wherever tidal currents are strong, there is danger for ships. One of the more notorious tidal current areas of the world is around the Aleutians, where ships have been cast up on the rocks as they attempted to work their way through the Akutan Pass and the Unalga Pass.

Most of the great ports of the world are situated in tidal waters. The tidal regime not only affects their everyday working but determines the character of the port's layout and installations. Where the range of tide is not more than about fifteen feet, the open quay system can be used, as in New York and Southampton, but the depth of water at the quayside must be great enough to keep the ships afloat at low water.

Where the tidal range is greater than fifteen feet, port engineers have to plan an elaborate system of closed docks like those at Liverpool and London. A ship passes through a lock and into the dock basin, where the water is kept at a more or less constant level. When the approach channel to a port is not deep enough at low tide for large ships of deep draft, the ships' movements to and from the port are dependent entirely on the tides. The importance of accurate tidal predictions – of heights as well as the times of high and low water – is obvious in such cases.

Today we have tide-predicting machines that can quickly work out the times of high water and low water at a given place for any future date. The basic information needed is a continuous set of observations – preferably over a year – of the tides at the place in question. This information is analyzed and the results used together with our knowledge of the positions of the Sun and Moon at any given moment to predict future tides.

To a ship's pilot and to a navigator, a knowledge of tidal currents is as important as that of the tidal rise and fall. Before a pilot brings

his ship into or out of port he must know exactly how the tidal current is flowing. Large ships such as the *United States* must wait for slack water before attempting to tie up at their piers in New York; if they did not, the strong tidal current could swing them against the pier with crushing force. Charts of tidal currents are, therefore, as indispensable to the mariner as his tide tables are.

It is not only those who have a professional interest in the sea who find their activities dependent on the tides. In many seaside resorts the holidaymaker soon learns that he has to arrange his bathing, sailing, fishing, or building of sand castles according to the tide.

When tides flow into an estuary they become distorted and slowed down by the restricting effect of shallow water. What usually happens is that the water level rises more rapidly than it falls, and the flood stream flows faster than the ebb, although for a shorter length of time. In extreme cases the flood stream rushes up the river in the form of a tidal bore – a turbulent mass of water with an almost vertical wave front, followed by a series of choppy waves. There are some half dozen or more well-known tidal bores in the world. In the British Isles, bores occur in the River Trent, a tributary of the Humber, in the River Severn, and in the Solway Firth. One of the most striking bores is in the Chien-Tang Kiang,

The map on the following pages shows tidal systems of the main oceans (based on Dietrich, 1944). The cotidal lines – lines joining places which have high tides simultaneously – are based on semidiurnal tides due to the Moon and do not include the Sun. Numbers on the lines indicate the time of high water, in "lunar hours," after the Moon has crossed the prime meridian. Every twelve lunar hours there is one tidal period (equal to 12 hours, 25 minutes of mean sun time). The cotidal lines shown on the map are for the oceans only; cotidal lines for the enclosed and peripheral seas are too complex to be shown on a small scale map.

This nineteenth-century drawing shows a tidal bore rushing up the Chien-Tang Kiang, a river that empties into the Bay of Hangchow. The wall of tidal water forming the bore reaches a height of about eleven feet and moves up the river at a speed of about twelve knots. There are a half dozen or more well-known tidal bores in the world.

翠樓前其高致可想至今若以陵

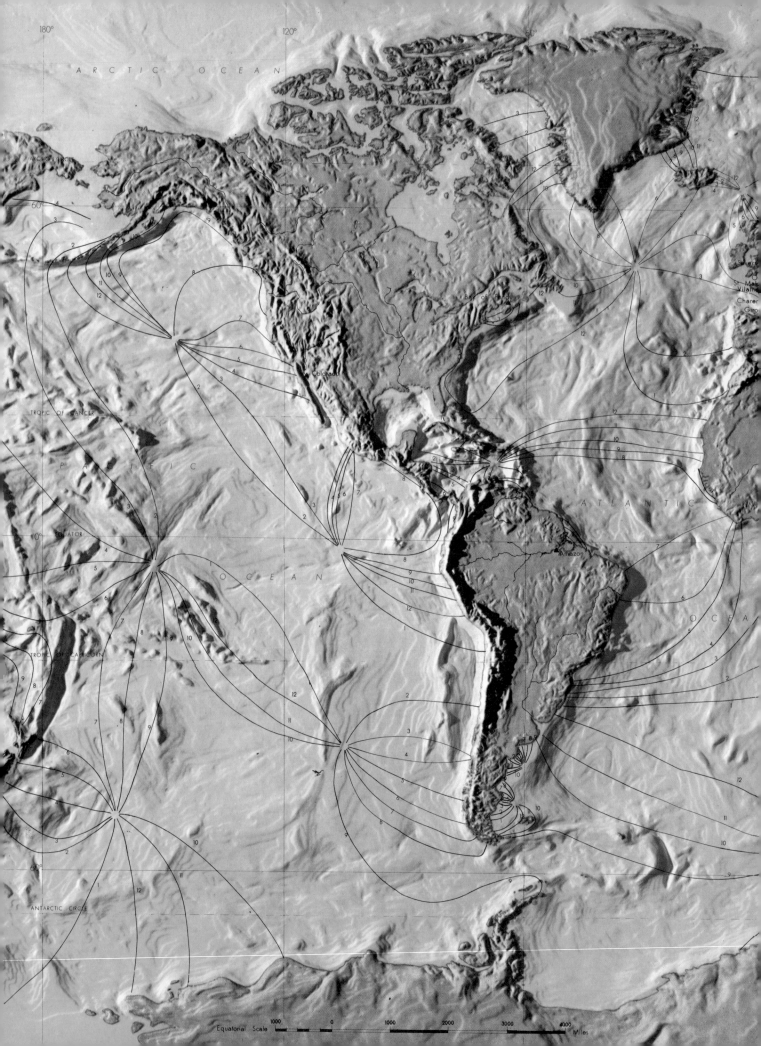

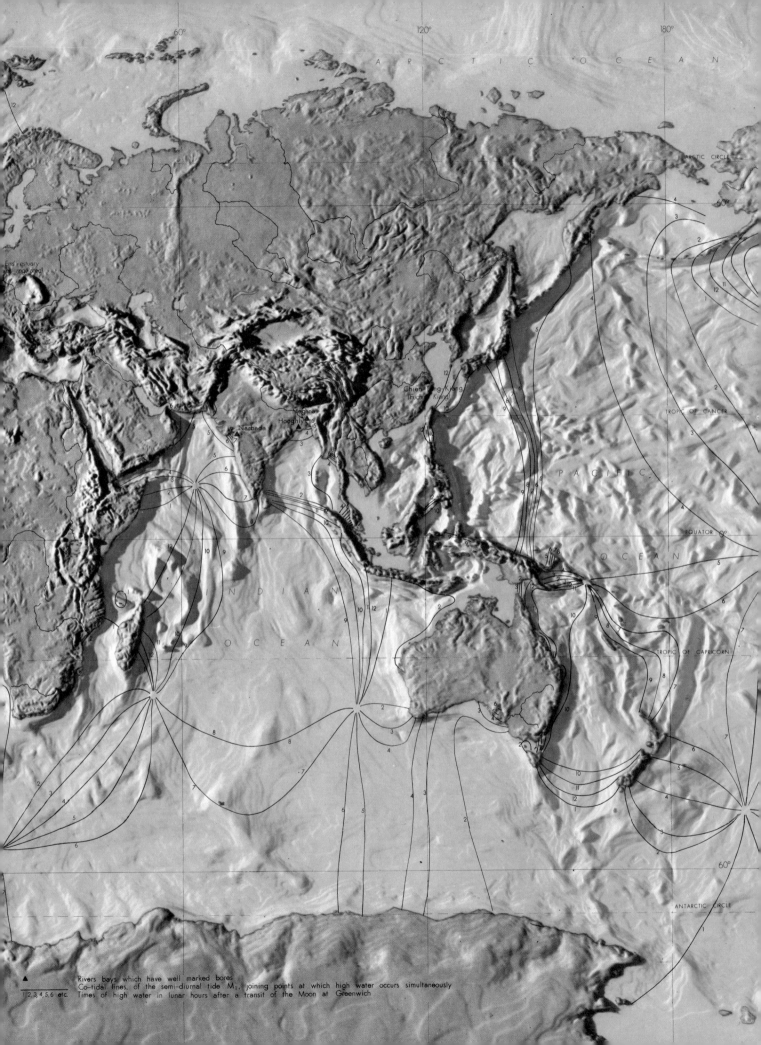

Rivers bays which have well marked bores
Co-tidal lines, of the semi-diurnal tide M₂, joining points at which high water occurs simultaneously
1,2,3,4,5,6 etc.   Times of high water in lunar hours after a transit of the Moon at Greenwich

Broken dykes, such as this one near Rotterdam, caused areas of Holland to be flooded during the storm surge of 1953. This tidal storm occurred when high winds, reinforced by spring tides, caused a piling up of water at the southern end of the North Sea.

which flows into China's Bay of Hangchow. There, at high tide, the bore surges upriver as a wave up to eleven feet high with a speed up to twelve knots or more. Within a period of ten minutes the river rises nine feet, and about one and three-quarter million tons of water flow upstream per minute. The Chinese boatmen take advantage of the great rush of water following the bore by allowing it to carry their junks up the river.

Since the tides depend on the motions of the Moon and Sun, normally we can predict them rather accurately – the times of high and low water to within a few minutes, and the heights of the water itself to within a few inches. But from time to time our predictions are thrown off by meteorological disturbances. The water may be several feet higher or lower than we predicted, and it may come earlier or later than we expected.

These disturbances are known as storm surges, and they can be disastrous over a large area. The most destructive surge occurring in northwest Europe in recent years was the one of January 31 and February 1, 1953, when strong northerly winds caused a piling up of water in the southern part of the North Sea. Because the peak of the surge came very near the time of high water of a spring tide, this storm tide inundated the coasts of Holland and eastern England at levels up to ten feet higher than were predicted; and high waves generated by the gale added to the destructive force of the water. In Holland more than eighteen hundred people were killed, while England lost more than three hundred, and in both countries there was extensive damage to property. This disaster made it obvious that some sort of flood warning service should be set up in Britain. Such a service is now operated jointly by the Admiralty and the Meteorological Office, and by methods based on a study of previous surges we can forecast the probable height of a surge about twelve hours before it strikes.

The surges born of hurricanes in the Gulf of Mexico and along the Atlantic coast of the United States, and those brought on by typhoons in the China seas, have a special character. The wind piles up the water in the storm region, as it did in the 1953 North Sea surge, but at the same time the low pressure area of the storm causes a temporary rise in sea level. And a third effect – resonance – may build up the surge to even greater heights if the cyclone or hurricane happens to be moving at almost the same speed as that at which a tidal wave, once set up, would travel freely.

Destructive surges of still different character can be produced by submarine earthquakes. These surges are popularly known as "tidal waves," although they have nothing to do with the tides. Scientists prefer to call them by their Japanese name, *tsunamis*. When an earthquake jars the ocean floor, the resulting disturbance in sea level sets up a wave that fans out for hundreds or thousands of miles in all directions at a speed of about five hundred miles an hour. In the deep ocean the height of a tsunami is only one or two feet, and a ship overtaken by one may not even detect it. But on entering shallow water, although the wave's speed is greatly reduced, its height may build up to thirty or forty feet before it overwhelms the shore and rushes inland. These waves do not occur singly but in a long train, and in deep water a hundred miles or more may separate them from crest to crest. On reaching the shore the third or fourth wave in the train is usually the highest and most destructive, after which waves of decreasing height follow one another at intervals of ten to twenty minutes for some hours.

There have been many highly destructive tsunamis throughout history. When a series of violent shocks shook the west coast of South America in 1868, the sea withdrew ominously from the coast, but shortly afterward returned as a great wave that swept boats a quarter of a mile inland. When the volcanic island of Krakatoa exploded in 1883, the resulting tsunamis swept a gunboat inland for two miles. Tsunamis announce themselves indirectly, their messengers being the earthquakes that touch them off. As soon as the seismologist has detected and fixed the position of a submarine earthquake, he can send out a tsunami warning to people in the path of the wave, usually several hours in advance.

Whether we are concerned with surges or simply with normal tides, there are enormous amounts of energy locked up in the movement of the water. Tidal energy enters the western end of the English Channel from the Atlantic Ocean at the rate of about 240 million horsepower, but eighty-seven per cent of this energy is dissipated by bottom friction with the channel floor. On a global scale this tidal friction acts as a kind of brake that is slowly but decisively slowing down the rate of the Earth's rotation, with the result that the length of our days is increasing at a rate of about $\frac{1}{1000}$ second in a hundred years. At the same time, the tidal friction is slowly pushing the Moon farther away from the Earth, which means that the Moon is taking longer and longer to circle the Earth – which in turn means that the length of our months is also increasing. Small as these effects are, their consequences in the course of many millions of years are considerable.

In its early life the Moon rotated rapidly on its own axis, but tidal friction on its surface gradually slowed it down until it became "frozen." Today we see only one side of the Moon as it revolves about us. Its far-side face is forever turned away. Astronomers tell us that, if other conditions continue as at present, a similar fate awaits the Earth 50,000 million years from now. Our days will continue increasing in length and the Moon will continue spiraling away from the Earth until the length of a day and a month will eventually be the same – equal to about forty-seven of our present days. At that time, tides as we presently know them would have ceased to exist, but the astrophysicists tell us that long before this state of affairs could come about the Sun will become so much brighter and radiate such intense heat that all our oceans will be boiled dry.

Among many proposals to harness the tides for power generation the French plan now being developed at the Rance Estuary at St. Malo is the most promising. A system of two-way turbines will be operated by both the incoming and outgoing tides. Twenty-four hydroelectric generators are expected to produce an average of 567.5 million kilowatt hours per year.

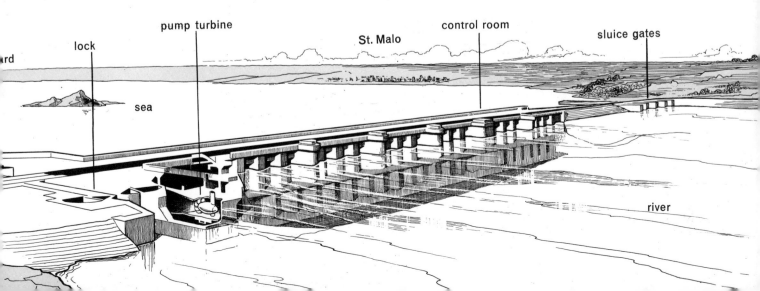

Edge of the Sea
C. A. M. King

The destructive forces of waves year by year eat away many coasts. Building breakwaters is one way to diminish the destructive forces of the waves, but, like the coast itself, breakwaters are in time worn away by the endless train of waves.

If we go down to the edge of the sea from the land, the rocks or beach at the shore line first command our attention. But beyond the shore are the waves of the sea, waves born of the wind and which travel effortlessly for hundreds and thousands of miles until they break upon the beach and help shape the coast. To understand the changing nature of the edge of the sea, we must first understand the nature of waves, for the two are inexorably linked.

From a small boat out in the open ocean the sea appears to be in a state of chaos, especially if there is a strong wind. Waves of different lengths, different heights, and traveling at different speeds and in different directions interlace and engulf each other. Away from the land, where waves are being formed by wind, they are known as sea. Here they build in height (distance from trough to crest) and in length (distance from crest to crest). They build as the wind strength rises, as its duration lengthens, and as the distance across which it blows increases — called its fetch. Although we can make generalizations about waves, we still do not know *exactly* how they grow, exactly how the energy that forms them is transferred from the air to the water. Waves that are growing are usually fairly short in length compared with their height, and we describe them as being steep. Scientists working at England's National Institute of Oceanography, located in Surrey, have invented a ship-borne instrument that measures the height of waves in the open ocean. This has helped bring some order out of the apparent chaos. Mounted in the weather ship anchored at lat. 61°N., long. 15°20′W. in the Atlantic, the instrument has shown that fifty-foot waves are not uncommon in winter (the average height for February 1954 being twenty-three feet), but in summer the average height falls to about ten feet. The larger the steep waves are, the more work they can do when eventually they crash against the coast. Along the shore the waves are lower but longer. Off Cornwall, in England, even in winter, waves higher than twenty feet are rare.

As the storm which forms a steep, high sea dies down or moves away, the waves do not suddenly disappear. They travel away from their generating area at various speeds – the longer the wave, the faster it travels. And so the waves, once generated, spread out and begin their long march toward the coast, the longer ones overtaking the shorter ones and becoming symmetrical to form swells. Long, low waves can travel hundreds of miles and more before they lose their energy, but gradually their height diminishes as they move shoreward. This explains why waves at the coast tend to be longer and lower than those in the open ocean; the short waves become attenuated and the long ones become lower. The ability of waves to travel over great distances is impressive, even to the oceanographer. We know that waves that have broken on the Cornish coast were formed by a hurricane off the east coast of the United States, about three thousand miles away; similarly, waves measured off California were traced to a storm about seven thousand miles away in the South Pacific. These waves were more than a thousand feet long in the open ocean and up to ten feet high when they reached the coast.

Waves in the open ocean move independently of the bottom, but as they march toward the shore the shallowing water begins to slow them down. The depth at which a particular wave begins to feel the influence of the bottom depends on the length of the wave. We may say that a wave is in "deep" water if the water's depth is greater than the wave's length. The long, low swells are, therefore, affected soonest. As they near the coast they lose their rounded tops and develop a pointed crest instead, then gradually the crest becomes more and more unstable until the wave begins to curl over with a foaming top, ideal for surf riding. The particles of water within the wave crest are now moving forward as fast as the wave form itself, so they carry the surf rider with them toward the shore. In deeper water the wave form moves much more rapidly than the water making up the wave. The water itself merely rotates in open circular orbits. This is why a boat or other floating object is left very much in the same place as it bobs on the waves, although a floating object does move along very slowly in the direction of wave motion.

While the shape of a wave changes as the wave advances toward the shore, its length becomes shorter and its speed slower, although it builds in height. The best waves for surf riding are called spilling breakers. Because these waves usually pass over a gently sloping sandy beach, they advance smoothly without losing their foaming crest for some distance. But where the beach is steep the waves usually break up entirely as plunging breakers.

When waves enter shallow water and begin to feel the effect of

In the open sea during a gale, waves build up to twenty feet or more. Giant waves like the one shown above are less common. Rarer still are forty-foot waves like those shown on the wave record below, made aboard the Weather Explorer in the North Atlantic. The highest wave recorded so far measures about seventy feet from crest to trough.

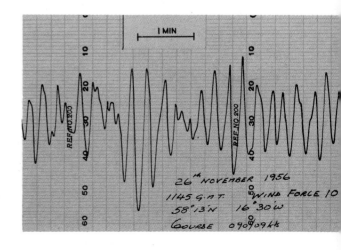

the bottom, the movement of water within each wave changes pattern. As the wave form begins to lose its symmetry on the surface, the circular motion of water making up the wave becomes elliptical, and along the bottom the water moves to and fro. The water directly under each wave crest moves forward toward the beach, accelerating as each crest becomes shorter and steeper; but under each trough there is a slower, seaward movement of water before the wave breaks. It is the bottom movement of the water beneath the wave crest that pushes sand and gravel-like material called shingle up toward the coast and high onto a beach. Shingle, easy for the water to move, is usually found near the top of a mixed beach.

If we look at an aerial photograph of long waves moving in toward the coast it is easy to see that they bend around and become nearly parallel to the shore. This is because the waves travel more slowly where the water becomes shallower, so that part of a wave entering shallow water first gets held back, while the parts still in deeper water sweep forward faster. This bending of the wave crests, called wave refraction, concentrates the energy of waves on certain parts of the coast, particularly on promontories and where land ridges extend into the sea. The waves tend to build higher here and set up the longshore currents that run along the coast to more sheltered areas where the waves are lower. As a result, an excess of water builds up and tries to escape seaward, as a rip current, through the breakers. Longshore currents may also be set up by waves approaching the shore obliquely, especially when the waves are short and, therefore, not seriously affected by refraction.

The effects of the wind on coastal waves, and so on the coasts themselves, can be destructive or constructive at the edge of the sea. An onshore wind, by creating an undertow along the sea floor, helps to make waves destructive, while an offshore wind has the opposite effect. But waves are not the only force affecting the edge of the sea, although they are the most important one. The tides, described on page 214, also set up local currents that influence the movement of material in the sea. Sandbanks, such as the Goodwin

As waves sweep in toward the coast and enter shallow water, they slow down and curve into the shape of the bay they may be entering. The photograph here shows waves breaking on the beach at Angus Point, Ireland.

Since the last ice age Scotland has been slowly rising out of the sea. A raised beach partly obscured by sand can be seen in the middle background of this photograph of the Sands at Gairloch, western Scotland.

Sands off the Thames estuary, and other similar banks in the North Sea have been formed by tidal currents and are a threat to ships.

Imperceptibly, year by year, world-wide changes in sea level are taking place and affecting nature's work where the sea meets the land. As world climate seems to be growing milder, glaciers are melting and returning water to the oceans, with the result that sea level is rising at about one to two millimeters a year in many places. In some regions, such as Holland, which have a tendency to sink, the rate is greater and all the more menacing because the land is already below high tide level. In other regions, the Baltic Sea, for example, where the land has been steadily rising since it was freed of its load of ice from the most recent ice age, the sea level is falling and more land is appearing. Scotland, too, is recovering, and has well-marked raised beaches on the west coast. The east and south coasts of England, however, are sinking, and the rising sea level is shown by the submerged forests found on many beaches. In the North Sea the sea level has risen by about 180 feet or more during the last ten thousand years. The present shore line, then, is very recent geologically.

Having looked briefly at the character of the waves, it is now time to follow them onto the shore — together with the wind and tide — to see how they attack and alter the coast, eroding some areas and building up others.

The sea, in its fiercer moods, can be an awe-inspiring sight, especially when it hurls itself against cliffs and sea walls. The destruction it causes depends partly on the rocks themselves and partly on how the sea breaks against them. If the rocks have many cracks, each time the sea breaks against them the air trapped inside

At Beachy Head, on England's south coast, sections of the soft chalk cliffs tumble into the sea each year; but in Cornwall (above), on the west coast, slate cliffs stand up to the endless pounding of the waves.

the cracks is compressed and so helps break them up. Whenever the waves enclose a pocket of air as they break against the cliff, great pressures may be built up within the pockets, then with an explosive force these pressures send spray high into the air, spray capable of carrying pebbles and rocks. In the United States, off the coast of Oregon, the roof of Tillamook lighthouse, ninety-one feet above low water, was broken by a spray-propelled rock weighing 135 pounds. On the other hand, cliffs made of hard rock, or that slope gently into the water, can stand up to the sea for long periods and show few signs of change. The coastal cliffs of Cornwall, for example, show traces of beaches cut during an interglacial period about a hundred thousand years ago, but we must remember that sea level was higher then, and it has not been at its present level for long.

Where the rocks are soft, as in Holderness and East Anglia, England, erosion carves the edge of the sea much more rapidly. We have only to look along the Holderness coast to see that the cliffs are retreating at an average rate of nearly six feet a year in places; several villages once lining the coast were completely swept away by the sea. Old records show that farther south, in Lincolnshire, in 1287, St. Peter's church at Mablethorpe was "rent asunder by the waves of the sea." More recently, at the end of January 1953, strong northerly winds caused a piling up of water in the southern part of the North Sea, and at high tide the effect was devastating in Lincolnshire and Essex. The flooding here was particularly serious because the land behind the sea walls, even in normal times, is well below high-tide level. Several centuries ago this land was reclaimed from the sea when sea level was about three feet lower, but today the coastal area is entirely dependent for its defense against the sea on sea walls, except where the natural protection of a wide, high beach and well vegetated dunes survive. During the 1953 storm surge these walls were overtopped and breached by the power of the storm waves. The sea rushed in at a level 7.8 feet higher than the predicted high tide, sweeping far inland and carrying along tons of beach sand. Where there were high dunes and a lot of sand on the beach, the storm waves spent their energy by moving the sand instead of attacking the sea walls.

In some areas erosion has been caused artificially. Leeward of the breakwater built in 1929 at Santa Barbara, California, serious loss of land, extending ten miles down the coast in a few years, resulted from the interception of the normal beach drift. The cutting of an artificial channel through a barrier at Thyboroen in west Jutland in 1825 also resulted in prolonged erosion. Natural erosion is severe along part of the Baltic coast of Poland. Here longshore drift removes sand in both directions from the beach, and the weak cliffs, no longer protected from the waves, are driven back at a rate of up to six feet a year; only one wall of a monastery built in the fourteenth century, about one and a quarter miles from the sea, now remains. Erosion in this area is speeded up by extra high sea levels raised during periods of storm.

Along the Suffolk coast, where there are low cliffs of sand and gravel, erosion during the night of storm cut a forty-foot-high cliff back forty feet, while another cliff only six feet high was driven back ninety feet. But such rates of erosion occur only under very unusual conditions. Even so, parts of the coast of East Anglia are

The sea encroaches on the land. On November 30, 1936, high tides caused cliffs of glacial sands and clay on the east coast of England, near Lowestoft, to crumble and collapse into the sea. Abandoned houses near the edge were left in shambles.

being eaten away by erosion with alarming regularity; at Covehithe the land is retreating at the rate of about seventeen feet a year.

Although many coasts seem to have a "permanent" beach, sometimes the beach is maintained only at the expense of cliff erosion. Where a coast curves smoothly "longshore" movement continually washes material away. Flamborough Head off England's east coast, for example, prevents the replenishment of Holderness beaches. Although waves are constantly moving beach material south in this area, new beach material, won from the cliffs by erosion, replaces the old. But we should remember that these "permanent" beaches continually change – sometimes they build up when they reclaim material from the sea; other times they are lowered as their sands are washed out to sea. The steep storm waves are the chief force that robs the beaches of their sand. When these waves reach their break point, they are called destructive waves, and whenever they are reinforced by an onshore wind their powers of destruction are greatly increased. The excess water pushed shoreward by the wind must flow back to the sea, and does so as an undertow that scours the bottom. This is the reason why after stormy periods the level of a beach is lower than normal.

While carrying on their destructive work, these storm waves can also be constructive by throwing coarse gravel, called shingle, high up the beach, higher than normal waves ever reach. It is the storm wave, then, that helps make the familiar shingle ridges that line many beaches high above the normal high-water mark. Chesil beach in Dorset, which has large shingle deposits, reaches up to forty-three feet above high-tide level near Portland.

Destructive waves do not move material very far offshore, and it is usually returned to the beach in time. Permanent loss of material results from its being carried along the beach and eventually deposited outside the beach area. This longshore movement can be devastating to areas suffering from erosion. For this reason coastal engineers build groynes on beaches from which the material is liable to be swept away and carried along the coast. If you look at a groyned beach, you will usually find that the sand is piled much higher along one side of the groynes – from the direction of longshore movement. Inadvertently, in our attempts to preserve one section of beach or coast, we may destroy another. While groynes can protect a windward beach, they can be dangerous to the leeward beaches by starving them of sand, and so making conditions right for erosion. In the United States, along the west coast near Los Angeles, where some beaches have been lost for this reason, or where a breakwater has acted as a large groyne, large quantities of sand have been artificially dumped on the leeward beach in an attempt to maintain its height.

The coastal engineer wants to know exactly how much material is being carried along the shore by longshore movement. One of the techniques developed recently is to follow the movement of radioactive material with Geiger or scintillation counters. Along the Suffolk coast at Orford Ness, where this technique was used, scientists found that the movement of material between the offshore zone and the beach was very limited. Even strong currents seem unable to move shingle against waves approaching from a different direction. On the other hand, waves reinforced by northerly winds were able to move great quantities of shingle in a southerly direc-

Groynes, like these along the beach at Brighton, England, prevent beach material from being washed away by longshore movement of the water. Evidence of the longshore movement can be seen by the way sand and pebbles have been piled up along one side of the groynes.

The land may gain temporarily over the sea when sand dunes formed above the high-tide line are held in place by dune plants, such as these in Loch Inchard, Scotland.

Caves like this one on the Cornish coast of England are hollowed out of soft cliff faces by continuous pounding of the waves.

tion. The waves, then, appear to be the chief force that wears away and builds up our beaches. Off Dungeness, divers have studied the underwater movement of shingle by an even newer method, one that makes sand fluorescent under ultraviolet light. So the amount of sand or shingle moved along the coast in a given time and under given conditions can be measured. Now that we have seen the destructive forces of the waves, let us turn to their constructive forces, and to the endless variety of the edge of the sea.

In some areas the land is gaining at the expense of the sea as constructive waves add to the material making up a beach, but the gain may be only a temporary one. Unlike the short and steep destructive storm waves, constructive waves are long and flat. They build up the beach by moving material onto the shore from both inside and outside their break point. In some areas, such as southern California, where the weather pattern is fairly regular, the beaches always build up at the shore line in summer when the waves tend to be low. But in winter, when storms lash the coast, the beaches are eaten away at the top, although the material is deposited just offshore where the water is fifteen to twenty feet deep.

Beaches, built by the waves, show a multitude of variety, depending on the character of the waves washing up on them, the tide, the nature of their material, and their exposure. Anyone who knows the beaches at Blackpool in England, or Le Touquet in northern France, would notice that the beach profile is not smooth, as are those of Devon, Cornwall, and South Wales. Beaches like the one at Blackpool have ridges that can become traps for the unwary as the rising tide floods into the runnel and cuts off escape. Similar ridges on the beaches of Normandy caused trouble during the invasion landings of World War II. They occur on coasts where the tidal range is fairly large, where the exposure is not too great, and where there is much sand. They may be built up by constructive waves, in front of their break point, where there is an overabundance of sand. Although the ridges tend to be flattened by storm waves, they soon build up again when the low waves return. The beaches exposed to the long Atlantic swells – along Cornwall and the west coasts of Ireland and the Cherbourg Peninsula – have

High chalk cliffs of Flamborough, fairly static due to resistant rocks

0°

0° 30'

Flamborough Head

Scale at 53° 30'N   1 0 1 2 3 4 5 6 7 8 9 10   Miles

Bridlington
Old cliff line of interglacial times, running inland

54°   54°

Hornsea

Hornsea
Mere

Boulder clay cliffs of Holderness, an area of rapid recession due to erosion of the soft clay

N O R T H

Hull

S E A

Immingham

DIMLINGTON
CLIFFS

Grimsby

Area of accretion

Humber Channel

Cleethorpes

Spurn Head

Cliff line in interglacial times, old chalk cliffs, their lower part buried by glacial deposits

53° 30'   53° 30'

Silver Pit
(possibly a sub-glacial drainage channel)

LINCOLNSHIRE WOLDS

Mablethorpe
Outmarsh of Lincolnshire

Coast protected by sea walls & erosion fairly static now except in storm surges

INNER DOWSING
(possibly remains of old morainic barrier)

Ingoldmells Point
Relatively steep gradient of modern shore

Skegness

STICKNEY MORAINE
Probable limit of the Newer Drift ice advance in Lincolnshire

Area of accretion
Gibraltar Point

Offshore banks dry at low water with possible ebb and flood tidal channels between them

Area of marsh reclamation

Lynn Deep
The Well

53°   53°

Witham

Boston

Tidal channels

Hunstanton

Welland

Fenland bank

T H E   W A S H

T h e   F e n s

Welland

Nene

Ouse

0°   0° 30'   King's Lynn

Built up by the long breakers sweeping in from the Atlantic, this beach at Cap Breton in the Bay of Biscay is composed of long stretches of sand. Its ridged profile, gradually built up by the long waves, is worn smooth each year by winter storms

Part of the east coast of England is shown on this map at a large scale and in detail. This particularly interesting area has been chosen because it has both cliffs and artificially reenforced coast lines, low coast lines and also areas of erosion and deposition. In some areas where the Pleistocene glaciation has left marked features, these have been indicated.

a flat gradient and their sandy slopes are usually smooth at low water. The finer the sand of these beaches, the flatter their slope and the less the waves will be likely to change them.

When landings were taking place in the Mediterranean during World War II, many of the landing craft suddenly found themselves grounded on sand bars hidden beneath the water, with deep water left between them and the shore. These bars, common in tideless seas such as the Mediterranean, Baltic, and the Great Lakes, move about as the waves change in height: high waves move the bars offshore, but as the waves grow smaller the bars gradually move back toward the shore. These shifting bars are not formed by constructive waves, as are those found on tidal beaches, but by storm waves. The higher the storm waves, the deeper the water they break in, and it is at the break point of the waves that the bars form. Here sand is pushed landward outside the break point, but inside it nearer the shore the steeper waves carry sand seaward, back to the break point where it accumulates from two sides and so builds the break point bar. These bars form only in the tideless seas because it is only in such seas that the break point of the waves can remain constant enough – free from the tides – for the sand to accumulate.

The interplay of waves, loose sand, shingle, and solid rock all contribute to the limitless variety of the coast. As the waves break against bare rock they loosen tiny pieces which become abrasives that help wear away the cliff. So the waves gradually eat into the coast, sometimes cutting a platform across which they advance on their endless attack. Or they carve out caves which over centuries may unite and form a natural arch, and centuries later the arch may collapse and leave a stack, such as the Needles off the Isle of Wight, or Old Harry in Dorset.

Cliffs are constantly being reshaped by the waves, the reshaping depending on the kinds of rock making up the cliff. Rocks composed of chalk make spectacular cliffs such as Beachy Head and the white cliffs of Dover. Nearly all rocks that are hard can stand as vertical cliffs, such as the cliffs on the north coast of Scotland where the Old Red Sandstone forms the cliffs of Duncansby Head. In other areas the cliffs may be composed of soft rocks, clays, or loose sands. When the cliffs are made of soft rocks they become waterlogged, and parts of them collapse in landslides when the foot of the cliff is washed away by the sea. Loose material such as sand and gravel cannot stand so steeply to the sea and is more likely to be washed away. People living on the east coast of England are lucky that the waves are not fierce, for the east coast rocks are soft. On the other hand, people living on the exposed southwest shores, where the waves violently attack the coast, are protected from the sea's encroachment by the hardness of the rocks.

Some of the material washed down by the rivers and worn from the cliffs remains at the edge of the sea and builds new land. One place where the land seems to be gaining over the sea is Dungeness foreland. This promontory has grown out into the sea since Neolithic men lived there. In its shelter are the rich pastures of Romney Marsh, reclaimed probably by the Romans, since the Rhee Wall running across them is Roman in date. The stretches of shingle ridges protecting the marshes were formed by the storm waves that have long been throwing the shingle high onto the beach and well out of the reach of normal waves. The

"Stacks", like this one off the coast of Orkney, are left after erosive forces of the sea have crumbled the arch that once joined the stone column to the mainland.

sharp point of Dungeness is constantly protected from wave action by the French coast close across the Channel. Although the south coast of the Ness is now being eroded, new ridges are being built up on the east coast.

Some spits, such as Spurn Head at the mouth of the Humber, are predominantly sandy in character. They are built up largely by the long, flat constructive waves that carry sand up the beach from offshore. But sand cannot be brought in quantity from depths greater than about thirty feet, so much of it must come along the shore, carried by oblique waves and currents from a coast that is being eroded, or from a river mouth.

The sandy shore line features born of waves and wind can be raised further by wind alone. As the desert sands are piled into dunes, so are the sands along our beaches, but the beach dunes are different because of the part vegetation plays. Their sand is held – and more is trapped – by the growth of sand-loving plants such as the dune plant known as marram grass that thrives only where it is being continually buried by fresh sand. Because the plant cannot stand salt water it cannot get a foothold on the dunes until the wind has raised them above the limits of the highest tides. Today vast quantities of sand are trapped in some of the larger dune areas around Britain's coasts—the dunes of Braunton Burrows in the southwest, Newborough Warren in Anglesey, and the Culbin Sands in east Scotland. This sand has come mainly from the sea, first washed onto the beaches by waves, then blown inshore at low tide.

In some places estuaries or bays are almost entirely shut off from the sea by the growth of spits or other barriers. In the sheltered lagoons behind the barriers the land, with the help of salt marsh plants, can reclaim part of its loss from the sea. Capable of growing in salt water, these plants trap the silt and mud carried into the lagoons by the tidal inundations. Year by year the land level is raised, until eventually the marshes are covered only at the highest tides; this is the time when they are ripe for reclamation, for their rich silt makes fertile land. In the Norfolk marshes nature's reclamation goes on at a rate of up to one centimeter a year, but elsewhere the rate can be rather quicker – particularly if it is aided by man, as it is in Holland.

Although the loss of land to the sea may be more spectacular than land reclamation, in 1911 the Royal Commission on Coast Erosion estimated that on the whole Britain has gained more from the sea than she has lost. Reclamation is also taking place in the Danish Wadden Sea, where man is helping nature along by artificial means. Active outbuilding is also extending the land seaward around part of the coast of the Gulf of Mexico, particularly near the big river mouths, and off the coast of northern Brazil. In such places the rivers bring down great quantities of sand and clay. While the sand is built into ridges by the waves, the clay fills the hollows between them and forms a wide, low coastal belt of accretion called a chenier plain.

In the seemingly endless battle between sea and land, there is no winner, there is only change, and in the large scale of things man can only stand by and watch and attempt to understand the forces great and small that change the edge of the sea before his eyes. As in the past, the seas have swept over the continents and flooded the land, then retreated, and so they will again and again.

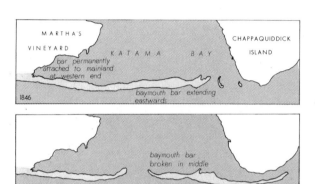

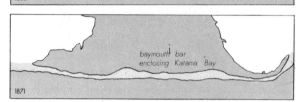

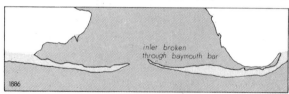

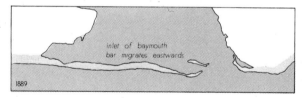

The five diagrams above show how the sand bar at the mouth of Katama Bay, Martha's Vineyard, was changed by wave action from 1846 to 1889. Submarine sand bars form at the break point of waves and are built up from both sides – some of the sand being carried onto the bar from the seaward side, some carried by the backwash of water from the beach.

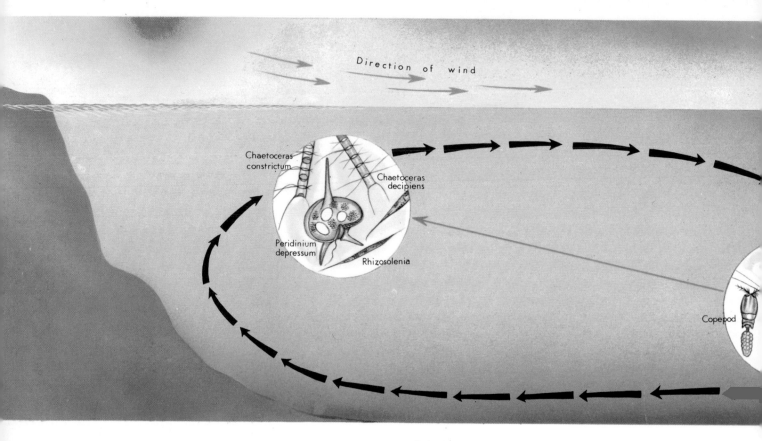

Direction of wind

Chaetoceras
constrictum

Chaetoceras
decipiens

Peridinium
depressum

Rhizosolenia

Copepod

Future of the Sea
Ronald I. Currie

Organic matter in the sea is first produced by the photosynthesis of microscopic algae. These plants are the food of small animals, which in turn are eaten by progressively larger creatures. Here, typical food chains in coastal and oceanic waters are shown. During their growth the algae make use of certain salts, mainly nitrates and phosphates, which are gradually transported to deeper waters as the organisms sink, die, and decompose. Upwelling of deep water returns these salts to the surface, making them available once more for plant growth. In coastal waters there are generally more algae but they are confined to shallower layers; light needed for their photosynthesis does not penetrate so deeply as in oceanic waters. Much of the material that sinks to the bottom in coastal waters supports an abundant fauna of bottom-living animals, which in turn are the food supply of many commercially important fishes. Creatures shown at the bottom of the illustration: 1. Pterygoteuthis, 2. Gigantactis, 3. Pachystomias, 4. Gastrostomus, 5. Bathothauma lyromma, 6. Aulastomatomorpha, 7. Vinciguerria.

Since the time of Pytheas and his voyage beyond the Habitable World we have come a long way. Present-day techniques enable us to explore and chart the sea with an accuracy and mechanical advantage undreamed of even in Magellan's time. Bathyscaphes, electronic flash photography, seismic sounding, and other devices are constantly helping us refine our knowledge of the sea's archaeological treasures, its plant and animal life, the chemistry and dynamics of its waters, and the geography and geophysics of its vast floor. But what of the future of the seas? In what ways can man harvest them for food, mine them for minerals, and harness them for power?

Since early times man has turned to the sea for food as good and as plentiful as he could find on the land, although for the most part the land has been his chief supplier. However, as we have come to face the fact that somewhat more than half of the world's population is undernourished, and that our population is increasing each year at a rate of about one per cent, we are thinking more and more of turning to the sea to help solve the problem of future food supplies. But to what extent can the sea help us? According to some specialists, the amount of organic matter produced in the sea is about the same as the yield of good agricultural land. But what, exactly, does this mean? And what bearing does it have on the food we can take from the sea for direct consumption?

All organic matter in the sea begins its production cycle by the photosynthesis of plants — the tiny single-celled algae that float

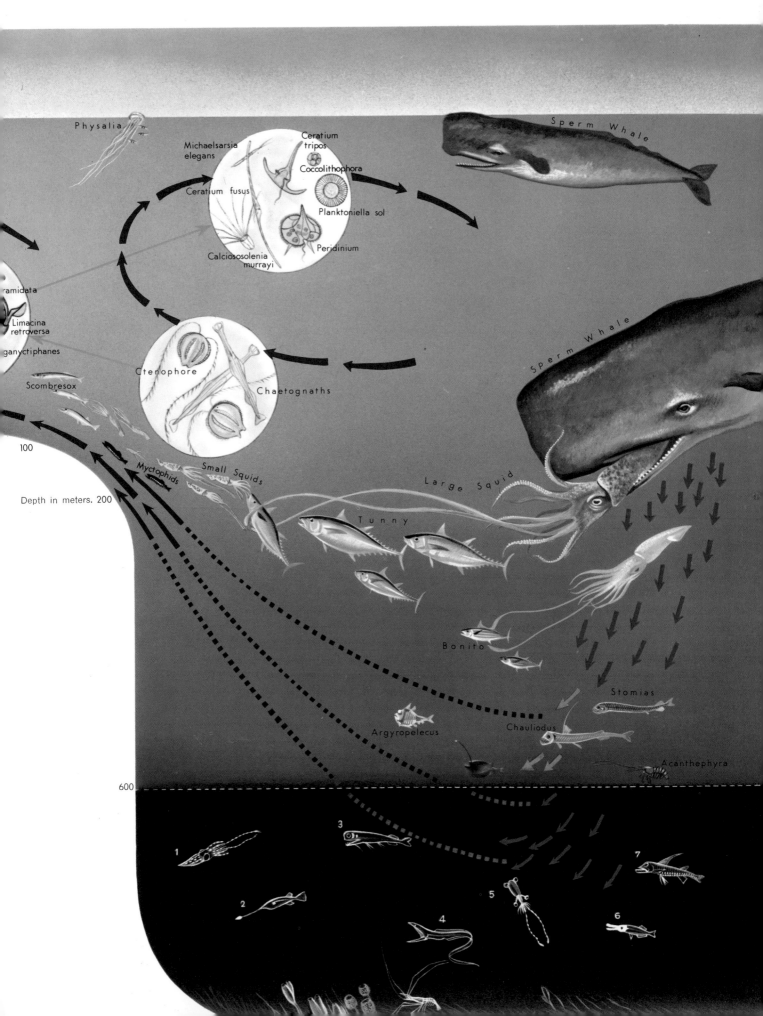

Physalia

Michaelsarsia
elegans

Ceratium
tripos

Coccolithophora

Ceratium fusus

Planktoniella sol

Calciososolenia
murrayi

Peridinium

...ramidata

Limacina
retroversa

...ganyctiphanes

Scombresox

Ctenophore

Chaetognaths

100

Depth in meters. 200

Myctophids

Small Squids

Sperm Whale

Sperm Whale

Large Squid

Tunny

Bonito

Stomias

Argyropelecus

Chauliodus

Acanthephyra

600

1

3

2

4

5

7

6

Because we know so little about the movement of deep currents, we cannot say to what extent radioactive wastes deposited in the deep sea might contaminate fish and plant life. Here, a Japanese uses a Geiger counter to test fish for radioactivity in a Tokyo market.

about in the surface layers of the ocean. These algae, most of them invisible to the naked eye, are the "grass" of the sea. They provide the food for a host of small herbivorous, or plant-eating, plankton animals which in turn provide food for small carnivorous creatures, and eventually for fish and whales. At every stage of this food chain – when one animal eats another – great amounts of organic matter are lost, partly because animals are unable to assimilate all they eat, and partly because much of their food is "wasted" through respiration and excretion. So the fish we catch represent only a small part of the original production of organic matter by photosynthesis.

The quantity of plants or animals present in any place is always changing as an animal eats a plant or one animal eats another. It is only a momentary point of balance between the rates at which they are produced and at which they are destroyed. So when we want to compare the fertility of one part of the sea with another, we compare their rates of production—either gross production (the rate of production of all organic matter), or net production (the rate of production of plant tissue alone). It is these figures that are usually presented when we compare the yield of the sea with that of agricultural land. In practice this is a misleading comparison, for while we can harvest a field of corn directly, the plants of the sea have to pass through many mouths before we can harvest them as fish, and in the food chain considerable losses may take place before the product is of any use to us.

The number of fish in any area depends largely on the amount of food available, and so in general we find rich fisheries where there is a rich supply of plankton, and desert areas of the sea where conditions do not encourage a high rate of plankton production. But this is only part of the story. Many of our important food fishes feed on bottom-living animals, so they are confined to the shallower waters where these animals thrive. There are few large fisheries in the Southern Hemisphere because there are few extensive areas of relatively shallow water; also the great successful group of gadoid fishes (cod and haddock among them), which are the basis of the great northern fisheries, are very poorly represented in the Southern Hemisphere.

Fishing as a method of obtaining food is still primitive compared with agriculture. In several respects, for centuries fishing has remained on a level with hunting. Although we are now developing electronic means of finding fish and electrical methods for catching them, these are only marginal improvements; they do not go to the heart of the problem. The whole principle of fishing would be vastly improved if we were able to apply some of the lessons we have learned from agriculture. But just how far can we go in applying the principles of farming to fishing? Essentially, we have brought about our vastly increased agricultural yields in four ways: 1. by the use of fertilizers; 2. by the removal of weeds; 3. by the control of insect parasites; 4. by selective breeding.

Although experiments with sea fertilizers have been tried, they are not very encouraging. If we fertilize an enclosed arm of the sea we may be successful in, say, increasing the size of fish, but at the same time we may also be stimulating weed growth and feeding unwanted animals, and so defeat the purpose of the fertilizer. On account of this, the addition of fertilizer is hardly an economical proposition.

Like a farmer, the fisheries biologist can try to protect his "crop" by removing predatory animals that take a heavy toll of the food needed by fish. Starfish, for example, feed on molluscs which are the food for many bottom-feeding fish, so if we could devise an economical means of controlling the starfish in a given area we could probably increase our yield of the fish we want to market.

While some regions have too many fish for the amount of food available, others have too few fish to make full use of the abundance of food. Why not, then, transplant certain fish to such underpopulated regions? The Dutch have tried a similar method in the culture of mussels with great success. Mussels growing around the Friesian Islands are transplanted to the rich waters of the western delta of southwest Holland for fattening, and then after being cleaned in fresh sea water are ready for marketing.

The success of plant and animal breeding in agriculture has encouraged the fisheries biologist to try to develop new hybrids

In Southeast Asian countries farmers combine rice culture with fish culture. The mature carp these Malayan farmers have just taken from their rice field was placed in the water as a young fish at the same time that the rice was planted.

A Portuguese boat at Aveiro, south of Oporto, gathers seaweed. Seaweeds are rich in iodine and are used for medicinal purposes and as fertilizer.

Guano deposits, rich in nitrogen and phosphates, have been valuable fertilizers since prehistoric times. Islands off the coast of Peru, such as the Chincha Islands shown here, are the most important source, yielding guano up to 150 feet thick, laid down by cormorants, boobies, and pelicans. The dark areas in the photograph are massed guano birds.

of fish, and to experiment in the intensive culture of fish in fish ponds, a centuries-old practice in Asian countries.

Fish ponds range from what one might call kitchen gardening to full-scale farming covering many square miles. In principle the ponds are fertilized and stocked with fast-growing species which do not compete for food but make use of all the available food. There might be one species feeding on surface weeds, one feeding in mid-water on plankton, and another on bottom weeds. One of the most interesting examples of fish ponds is found in southeast Asian countries where farmers combine rice culture with fish culture. After flooding their paddy fields and planting the young rice plants, the farmers place young carp in the water, and while the rice is growing the carp feed on the plankton. By the time the fields are drained to harvest the rice, the carp are also marketable.

Because the quantity of plankton produced in the sea is greater than the quantity of fish, experts have proposed using plankton themselves as a protein-rich food source. But the difficulty is catching them. On the whole, planktonic plants and animals are very small. Even with fine-mesh filters we could expect an average catch of not much more than one gram of plankton animals for each ton of water filtered, even in the richest areas. This does not mean that plankton as a food source is out of the question. We can grow large-scale cultures of planktonic plants. One gigantic culture covering an area the size of Kent and Sussex combined (two million acres, an area smaller than the island of Hawaii) would provide nearly enough protein to satisfy the requirements of the present world population!

Century after century water washing off the land has been flowing into the oceans and depositing every mineral known to man. Many of them, including certain salts, are accumulating as the water that originally brought them to the sea evaporates, condenses over the land, and brings a fresh supply down to the sea again and again. Yet other minerals seem not to be accumulating. Although the rivers wash down great quantities of calcium salts, we find proportionally fewer of them in the seas than in the rivers. We know that a variety of marine creatures — snails, oysters, and shelled animals of microscopic size — extract calcium from the sea to make their shells, and the tiny coral polyp uses calcium to build the vast reefs in tropical seas. Some species of ascidians even manage to extract and concentrate a rare element, vanadium, in their blood.

Man has been less successful in tapping the mineral wealth of the sea than the creatures who make the sea their home, yet he has tried in two ways: by taking from the plants and animals the chemicals they have extracted from the sea, and by "mining" the ocean waters directly.

Seaweeds have long been an important source of iodine, yet iodine is one of the scarcest nonmetallic elements in the sea. Although there is only about one gram in every twenty tons of sea water, some seaweeds contain one gram of iodine in only 200 grams of the dry seaweed. Today we obtain some iodine from the ashes of burned seaweed, but about two-thirds of the world's production comes from "fossilized" seaweed deposits, chiefly in the desert regions of Chile. Apart from their use as a source of iodine and fire-resistant textiles, seaweeds are a traditional source of fertilizer for the land, but by far the greatest supplies of fertilizers which come indirectly from the sea are in the more concentrated form of guano, which is rich with phosphates and nitrates.

While the quantities of many elements in the sea are dependent on the plants and animals which alternately extract them and return them to the sea on their death, the sea is a storehouse for many other elements and compounds that are not influenced materially by biological processes, and since nature has not already concentrated them for us, it is these that man has attempted to take directly from the oceans.

The value of the sea as a source of chemicals must depend on the economics of the process of extraction. What is the point in mining silver from the sea when we can mine it less expensively from the land? Even though there is a vast abundance of elements suspended in the sea – about 50 of the 103 known elements – they generally occur in low concentrations. As a result, large quantities of water have to be processed for a relatively small return. So it is not unusual that substances we might expect to obtain easily from the sea are more economically obtained from the land.

Common salt, so familiar and essential to our lives, and the basic substance of our chemical industry, is an interesting exception. It makes up by far the greatest part of the solids in sea water – it has been estimated that one cubic mile of sea water contains about 166 million tons of salts. For centuries men have obtained common salt by simple evaporation, relying on the heat of the Sun to drive off the water until only salt remains. In many parts of the world –

These three settling tanks at a magnesium factory at Hartlepool, England, show one stage in the extraction of magnesium from the sea. The magnesium salt is treated with lime, producing magnesia which settles in great tanks. The metal magnesium can then be extracted from the magnesia by a chemical and electrical process.

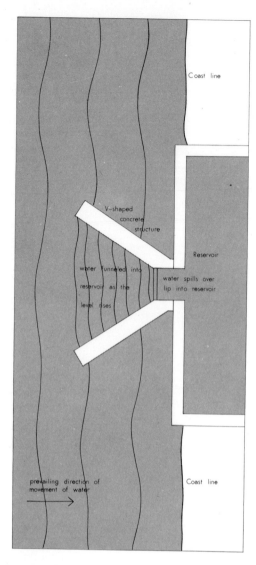

In the illustration, the following labels appear:

Coast line

V-shaped concrete structure

Reservoir

water funneled into reservoir as the level rises

water spills over lip into reservoir

prevailing direction of movement of water

Coast line

In an attempt to harness the energy of waves a V-shaped concrete structure was set up on the Algerian coast. Waves are funneled into the open end of the V, the water then spilling over the narrow end into a reservoir. The steady outflow of water from the reservoir operates a turbine from which power can be generated.

Britain, the United States, and the Middle East, for instance – this process has already been done for us by nature. Extensive deposits of rock salt – the remains of seas of a distant geological age – have been laid down by nature, and it is more economical to mine them directly than it is to process sea water. In some countries, on the other hand, where there are no rock salt deposits, imported salt is expensive, so the production of salt by evaporation becomes an attractive proposition.

A more recently exploited chemical product of the sea is magnesium, the demand for which has increased rapidly ever since the aircraft industry has required lighter and stronger alloys. Because the sea has large supplies of magnesium – about four million tons in a cubic mile of water – processes have been devised by which it can be extracted at a competitive cost.

Although the sea contains a great store of elements, its future as a source of supply must depend on demand, and on the competitive cost of extracting them from the land. At present potassium, for example, is obtained mainly from salt deposits or from the Dead Sea, which has an unusually high potassium content compared with sea water. In spite of this, the prospect of extracting potassium directly from the sea appears promising as a result of the development of a new extraction process.

Men have long been tempted by the possibility of extracting gold and silver from the sea. After the First World War, Germany sponsored an expedition – the Meteor Expedition – to attempt to extract enough gold to pay the German war debt, but the concentration of gold found was less than a tenth of the expected amount. At present it would cost more to extract the gold and silver from the sea than these metals are worth. In time, however, as man exhausts the land supply of certain chemicals, he may be forced to turn to the sea as his major supplier.

While the sea is a vast storehouse of food and minerals, it is also a gigantic source of energy. Even in these days of atomic energy, engineers are considering means of producing power from the sea. One method that has been proposed is the generation of power from the thermal energy of the sea. It is based on the principle that the change of heat into energy requires a hot source and a cold source. In driving a steam engine, for example, we boil water (hot source) to make steam which passes through the cylinders then is cooled in the condensers (cold source). In tropical and subtropical latitudes there is a substantial difference in temperature between the surface water and deep water. Because water boils at progressively lower temperatures as the atmospheric pressure is reduced, it would be possible to boil the warm surface water by piping it into low pressure containers, then introduce the steam into a turbine. For a cold source, to convert the steam back into water, the cold, deep water which lies close to the shore could be used. To pump this cold water to the surface would require little energy, for the effective height it would have to be raised is merely that from the sea surface to the power station. French scientists have tried to assess the practical possibilities of such a scheme, and after pilot trials plans have been drawn up for a full scale generating station at Abijan on the Ivory Coast.

The most obvious source of power would seem to be the endless train of waves that wash against the shore. There is a wide spectrum of sea waves, as there is a spectrum of electromagnetic waves. They range from the shortest of ripples to the very long waves which we call tides.

Although it is mainly the long waves of the tides that are of interest for power generation, there have been many attempts to harness the energy of the shorter waves. The most promising scheme to date, one tested on the Algerian coast, is a relatively simple device consisting of a V-shaped concrete structure open to the sea. The waves approaching the coast are funneled into the open end of the V, and as the water is crowded by the tapering sides, the level rises until it becomes high enough to spill over a dam at the apex and flow into a reservoir. Power can then be derived from turbines operated by the steady outflow of water from the reservoir. Although sound in principle, to be economically sound the device must have large enough waves of a sufficiently uniform size throughout the year to keep it running continuously, and this has been the difficulty.

The tides, which are much longer waves, can be relied upon throughout the year. Their amplitude varies with the relative positions of the Sun and Moon, but in contrast to the short waves tides exhibit a fairly regular fluctuation and can be harnessed during given periods of the tidal cycle. Coastal areas with high tides obviously are the best sites. Because some of the highest tides in the world occur in European waters near highly industrialized areas that could well make use of the power developed, it was in Europe that the first large schemes were thought out.

In 1933 British engineers proposed a plan for the River Severn estuary which has a tidal range of some forty feet, the so-called Severn Barrage, but the project was abandoned. Since then it has been reviewed from time to time. Initially the plan was to trap water of the incoming tide in a single basin, the power being generated on the outflowing tide. Later, two basins were proposed to give continuous power output, but this project, like the first, was not approved, and now it seems doubtful that anything will ever be done. The general opinion seems to be that if the scheme had been undertaken when it was first proposed, it would have been successful, but expensive labor costs today make it unattractive financially. However, when the British come to appreciate the irreplaceable nature of the coal they so happily burn today, tidal energy projects may again be considered in Great Britain to supplement the demand with which nuclear power production will be hard put to keep pace.

In contrast to the fate of the Severn Barrage, the French have begun construction of a plant to harness the tides in the Rance estuary at St. Malo. In principle the power station consists of a dam with two-way turbines capable of being worked by both the incoming and outgoing tides. In addition, the turbines can operate as pumps. The critical point about this scheme is that turbine generators require a certain head of water to operate them efficiently, so by virtue of their ability to pump, the turbines can also quickly adjust the water levels in the estuary and behind the dam at the end of each tidal period so that power generation can be resumed quickly. When completed, the Rance project will feed about 565 million kilowatt hours annually into France's electricity system, yet the Rance scheme is looked upon as a pilot experiment for a much

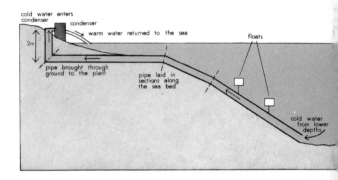

A scheme proposed by the French to utilize the thermal energy of the sea depends on availability of deep, cold water near the coast. This diagram shows details of the system to be used for raising cold water to the surface. It is then pumped to a generating station, where it is used to condense low-pressure steam coming from turbines.

more extensive project – the Isles des Chaussey Project which involves building a dam across the bay of Mont St. Michel. The output of this scheme would supply a half of France's present electricity consumption.

From time to time there has been talk of reclaiming land from the sea, on a scale far greater than that achieved by the Dutch. In 1928 the German engineer Herrmann Sörgel proposed his Atlantropa Project, without doubt the greatest engineering venture ever contemplated by man. His idea was to alter the geography of much of the continent of Africa. Setting aside all political and technical implications, the basis of the plan lay in building dams across the Strait of Gibraltar and the Dardanelles, isolating the Mediterranean.

At present the water exchange through the Strait of Gibraltar results in a net inflow of water from the Atlantic into the Mediterranean. Together with inflowing water from rain and other sources, there is a total annual inflow of about three and a half million, million tons of water, but all of it is lost by the intense evaporation over the Mediterranean. By building two dams the inflow would be cut down by about sixty-five per cent and the level of the Mediterranean would fall. Sörgel calculated that the level would drop about five feet a year, but more recent estimates suggest a rate only half as much, so it would take more than a hundred years for the level to drop the 330 feet he envisaged, thereby exposing new land for cultivation. In addition, vast amounts of power would be generated at all the river mouths.

At present, while surface water of the Atlantic flows into the Mediterranean, the very salty, and consequently heavier, water of the Mediterranean flows at deep levels into the Atlantic, joining the great deep currents of that ocean. These deep currents are important to man in many ways. For one, they are a tempting repository for radioactive wastes that are accumulating at an alarming rate from atomic energy plants. At the moment, however, we know very little about the speed of these deep currents, and in particular the rate of vertical exchange of water, so we are unable to say just how quickly waste deposited at the bottom of the sea might rise to the surface and pollute our fish.

The deep currents contain great quantities of the nutritive salts needed by plant plankton, but these currents do not mix easily with the shallower waters where the plankton thrive. If we could bring this rich, deeper water to the surface in certain areas we would enrich the surface layers with a ready-made fertilizer for the plant plankton. The temperature and salinity structure of some parts of the ocean are of such a nature that we might use them to achieve this end.

In many parts of the tropical and subtropical oceans the salinity of the warm surface waters is higher than that of the deeper, colder waters. If, therefore, a long thin-walled tube were lowered into the deep water, and then by means of a pump the deep waters were started flowing up the tube, they would continue flowing up even after the pump were taken away. The reason for this is simple. As the deep water flowed slowly up the tube it would be warmed by conduction of heat through the thin wall of the tube, and so at the same level inside and outside the tube the water would be at the same temperature. Because the water inside the tube is less salty – and therefore less dense – than the outside water, the water

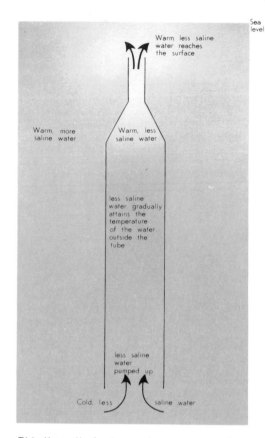

This theoretical scheme shows one way of bringing nutrient-rich deep water up to the surface to provide a fertilizer for the plant plankton. Once started by a pump, the deep water rising up the tube would continue flowing up to the surface forever, even after the pump were taken away (for explanation, see text).

inside would continue to rise up. But even if this process could be realized as a practical proposition, it is doubtful if the quantities of water which could be raised could ever be great enough to have more than a purely local effect. It would also have to operate for several years to produce any effect in terms of fish we could catch.

An ability to forecast the "weather" of the sea would bring enormous savings to merchant shipping of all kinds, including fisheries. For instance, the success of the Arctic cod fishery around Bear Island depends largely on the climatic functions of both the sea and air. Far more than the land, the oceans absorb and retain great quantities of heat, which the currents carry from one part of the earth to another. Most of the radiant energy from the Sun is in the form of short-wave radiation absorbed only in small amounts by the atmosphere, but in large amounts by the land and sea. The sea and land reflect this energy into the atmosphere as long-wave radiation which the air can absorb; so much of the heating of the atmosphere is directly dependent on the sea. The ocean currents are, therefore, an important factor in climate. As we come to learn more about the movements of currents, and about the interchange of energy between air and sea, we will inevitably come to a better understanding of climate change.

Considering that the sea covers the greater part of the earth's surface, it would be difficult to overstate its future use to men. In this brief conclusion it has been possible to mention only a few of the ways the sea can be made to serve us. Our present knowledge of large parts of the oceans is hopelessly inadequate, and it is only within the last decade or so that we have begun to understand some of the processes taking place in the sea.

Map on the following pages shows relative fertility of different parts of the oceans. In general the most fertile areas are found in higher latitudes, but one exception is found along the west coasts of continents in tropical latitudes. Here deep water rises to the surface, bringing with it nutritive salts for the plankton population. The deep shadows along the eastern sides of the continents, and on the eastern slopes of rises on the sea floor, are related to topography, as are the deep shadows indicating mountains on the land. These darker areas are not intended to represent regions of greater fertility.

Since 1932 the Dutch have reclaimed from the sea thousands of acres of land. These photographs show what was once the Isle of Schokland, but which is today a long, low hill surrounded by cultivated land. When the reclamation plan is completed the Dutch will have won from the sea more than a half million acres of new land.

ARCTIC OCEAN

ARCTIC CIRCLE

180°

120°

60°

60°

TROPIC OF CANCER

ATLANTIC

P A C I F I C

0° EQUATOR

O C E A

TROPIC OF CAPRICORN

O C E A N

60°

ANTARCTIC CIRCLE

Average minimum limit of pack ice

Equatorial scale

1000   0   1000   2000   3000   4000

Miles

A R C T I C   O C E A N

Average minimum limit of pack ice

ARCTIC CIRCLE

60°

P A C I F I C

TROPIC OF CANCER

EQUATOR 0°

O C E A N

I N D I A N

TROPIC OF CAPRICORN

O C E A N

60°

ANTARCTIC CIRCLE

Average minimum limit of pack ice

180°

Least fertile   Most fertile

Facts about the Sea

The Earth and its Oceans

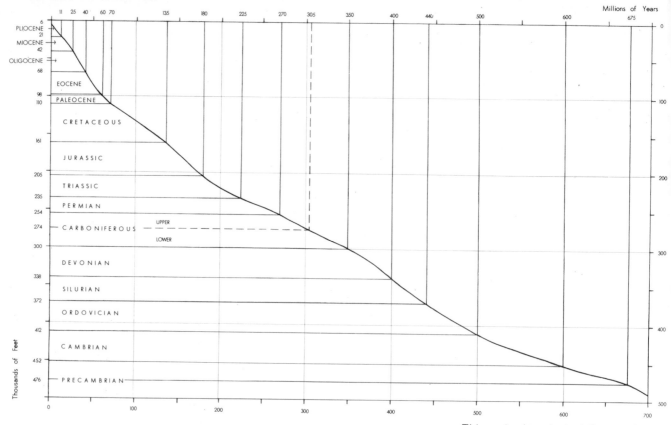

This revised geological time scale shows age of rocks plotted against cumulative thickness (after Holmes).

Centigrade-Fahrenheit Conversion Table

FAHRENHEIT	CENTIGRADE or CELSIUS	FAHRENHEIT	CENTIGRADE or CELSIUS
104	40.0	50	10.0
102	38.9	48	8.9
100	37.8	46	7.8
98	36.7	44	6.7
96	35.6	42	5.6
94	34.4	40	4.4
92	33.3	38	3.3
90	32.2	36	2.2
88	31.1	34	+ 1.1
86	30.0	32	0.0
84	28.9	30	— 1.1
82	27.8	28	2.2
80	26.7	26	3.3
78	25.6	24	4.4
76	24.4	22	5.6
74	23.3	20	6.7
72	22.2	18	7.8
70	21.1	16	8.9
68	20.0	14	10.0
66	18.9	12	11.1
64	17.8	10	12.2
62	16.7	8	13.3
60	15.6	6	14.4
58	14.4	4	15.6
56	13.3	2	16.7
54	12.2	0	— 17.8
52	11.1		

Fathoms, Meters, Feet Equivalents

FATHOMS	METERS	FEET	FATHOMS	METERS	FEET	FATHOMS	METERS	FEET	FATHOMS	METERS	FEET
1	1.8	6	110	201.2	660	275	502.9	1650	1400	2560.3	8400
5	9.1	30	120	219.5	720	300	548.6	1800	1500	2743.2	9000
10	18.3	60	130	237.7	780	400	731.5	2400	1600	2926.1	9600
20	36.6	120	140	256.0	840	500	914.4	3000	1700	3109.0	10200
30	54.9	180	150	274.3	900	600	1097.3	3600	1800	3291.8	10800
40	73.2	240	160	292.6	960	700	1280.2	4200	1900	3474.7	11400
50	91.4	300	170	310.9	1020	800	1463.0	4800	2000	3657.6	12000
60	109.7	360	180	329.2	1080	900	1645.9	5400	3000	5486.4	18000
70	128.0	420	190	347.5	1140	1000	1828.8	6000	4000	7315.2	24000
80	146.3	480	200	365.8	1200	1100	2011.7	6600	5000	9144.0	30000
90	164.6	540	225	411.5	1350	1200	2194.6	7200	6000	10972.8	36000
100	182.9	600	250	457.2	1500	1300	2377.4	7800			

Nautical Miles, Kilometers, Statute Miles, Equivalents

NAUTICAL MILES	KILOMETERS	STATUTE MILES	NAUTICAL MILES	KILOMETERS	STATUTE MILES
1	1.9	1.2	20	37	23.0
2	3.7	2.3	30	56	34.5
3	5.6	3.5	40	74	46.1
4	7.4	4.6	50	93	57.6
5	9.3	5.8	60	111	69.1
6	11.1	6.9	70	130	80.6
7	13.0	8.1	80	148	92.1
8	14.8	9.2	90	167	103.6
9	16.7	10.4	100	185	115.2
10	18.5	11.5			

A knot is a nautical measurement of speed. One knot equals one nautical mile per hour. 0.8684 knots equals one statute mile per hour. 0.5396 knots equals one kilometer per hour.

Continental Drift – Snider (1858)

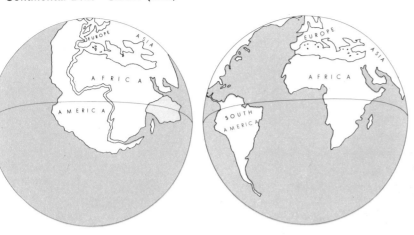

Continental Drift – Du Toit (1927)

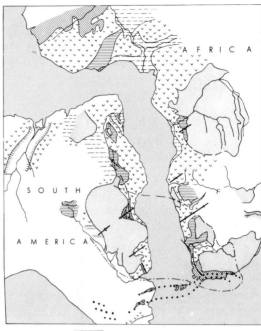

--- Cretaceous-Eocene
Gondwana
Pre-Silurian
Old Granite
v v v Silurian-Carboniferous
v v v Post-Triassic uplifts
••••••• Cape foldings
•--•--• Limit of Mesosaurus
– – – Post-Nama foldings

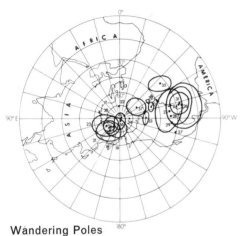

Wandering Poles

Interest in theories of continental drift has been recently aroused by modern paleomagnetic measurements giving estimates of possible different positions of the poles in past geological periods. When rocks are laid down they are magnetized in the direction of the Earth's magnetic field. By measuring the direction of magnetization of rocks of different ages, we can determine past positions of the Earth's axis, assuming, as is most probable, that the magnetic poles have always been aligned with the Earth's axes of rotation.

Gondwanaland

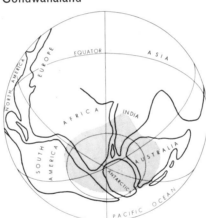

Wandering Continents

There are a number of controversial theories of continental drift. Taylor considered the land masses as having moved away from the poles toward the Equator. Wegener described the westward drift of continents as "ships of sial ploughing through a sea of sima." Du Toit based the fitting together of the east coast of South America and the west coast of Africa on evidence provided by the shapes of the coast lines. In 1944 Holmes investigated glacial climates in the Southern Hemisphere, particularly in the late Carboniferous, and came to the conclusion that the continents had moved.

Extent of Carboniferous Glaciation

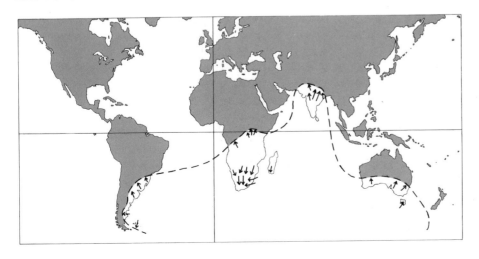

Evidence of glaciation, particularly during Carboniferous times, shows that during this period similar ice sheets spread across Argentina, south and east Africa, India, and south Australia. This is difficult to account for unless we suppose that the regions were once joined together – far south of their present position – forming "Gondwanaland." When the land masses separated, the South Atlantic Ocean, Indian Ocean, and that part of the Southern Ocean lying to the south of them were formed. The periphery of Gondwanaland is indicated by fold mountain ranges, some with associated oceanic deeps – including the Andes of South America, the Himalayas, and the Southern Alps of New Zealand.

249

Men Against the Sea

Pytheas

A sundial of the late Roman period. This was one of the earliest known methods of determining position possibly available to Pytheas during his voyage.

The thick and sluggish "curdled sea" described by Pytheas on his voyage to "Thule" possibly owed its appearance to ice of the type shown right.

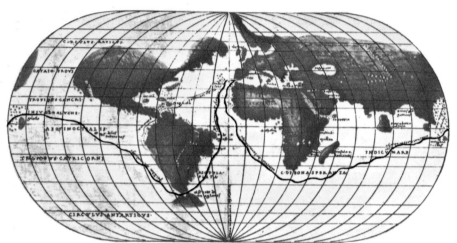

Ferdinand Magellan

This map of 1536 by Battista Agnese shows the route of Magellan's ship *Victoria*, the first ship to circumnavigate the world. The trade route from Spain to Peru by way of the Isthmus of Panama is also marked.

Earliest recorded European astrolabe dated *c.* 1185. The astronomers' astrolabe in mediaeval times was an instrument designed to observe the altitude of the Sun and stars and to plot their positions. Basically it was a brass disc engraved with a projection of the sky as seen by the observer, graduated around the perimeter and fitted with an alidade. Mariners used a simplified version.

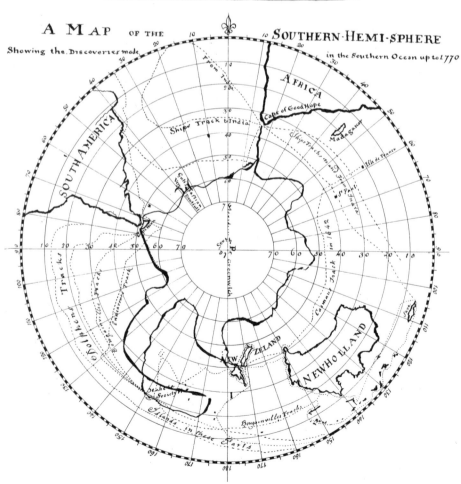

Captain James Cook

This map of the Southern Hemisphere was made by Cook in 1772, showing by dotted lines the tracks of earlier navigators. It also shows Cook's proposed route for his second voyage – to be taken by the *Resolution* and *Adventure* – as a continuous line.

Before he set out on his Pacific voyages Cook spent several years making excellent surveys of eastern Canadian and Newfoundland coasts. His chart of the St. Lawrence was made before the fleet took General Wolfe's men up the river to Quebec.

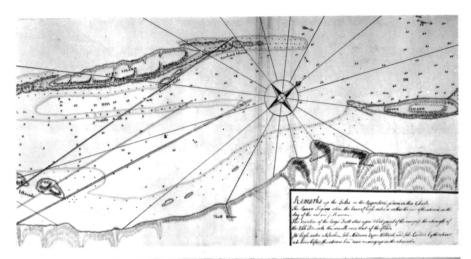

James Clark Ross

This pocket sun compass was used by Sir James Clark Ross during his Arctic and Antarctic expeditions.

This map of the North Polar regions by Sir John Barrow shows the state of knowledge when Admiralty rewards were offered for achievements in Arctic exploration.

Enormous tabular bergs like these are formed by the breaking of the shelf ice around the Antarctic continent. Such icebergs would have been seen by Sir James Clark Ross during his voyage to the Antarctic.

The "Nautilus"

A certain amount of open water in the form of leads appears in recent photographs of the area near the North Pole under which the *Nautilus* passed. This condition is rather different from the very heavy pack in which the *Fram* drifted somewhat to the south.

Fridtjof Nansen

This illustration from *Farthest North* shows Nansen taking temperature measurements of deep water on July 12, 1894. Samples were taken at different depths from the surface to the sea bottom. Among other unexpected discoveries, Nansen found that the Arctic Ocean was much deeper than previously thought, and that warmer, saltier layers of water were under the cold surface waters.

This illustration of the control room of the *Nautilus* gives some idea of the complexity of the instruments used in navigation under the ice. From the time of Cook until 1900 instruments of navigation changed little; but with the impetus of two great wars the art of navigation has been greatly aided by radar, the gyro-compass, echo sounder, and inertial navigation systems.

Life in the Sea

CLASSIFICATION OF MARINE PLANTS

This subject is complex and still under discussion; the following sets out what is currently accepted:

SCHIZOPHYTA
Bacteria
Blue-green algae
RHODOPHYTA
Red algae
PYRROPHYTA
Dinoflagellates
CHRYSOPHYTA
Yellow-green algae
Diatoms
PHAEOPHYTA
Brown algae
CHLOROPHYTA
Green algae
FUNGI
CORMOPHYTA

ANGIOSPERMS: There are about 30 species of these flowering plants present in the sea. They did not originate in the sea but have colonized it by way of fresh water. They are found mainly in estuaries or in water of low salinity.

MARINE PHYTOPLANKTON consists of microscopic members of the divisions PYRROPHYTA, CHRYSOPHYTA, and CHLOROPHYTA. Its chief constituents are dinoflagellates, yellow-green algae, especially coccolithophores, and diatoms.

CLASSIFICATION OF MARINE ANIMALS

Phylum PROTOZOA

Mastigophora – dinoflagellata
Sarcodina – foraminifera
Actinopoda – radiolaria
Ciliata
PARAZOA (Sponges)

Phylum COELENTERATA

Hydrozoa – hydroids and medusae
Scyphozoa – jellyfishes

Anthozoa – Subclass Alcyonaria includes black corals, sea fans, gorgonia, and sea pens. Subclass Zoantharia includes sea anemones, true corals, and stony corals.

Phylum CTENOPHORA

comb jellies

Phylum PLATYHELMINTHES

flatworms

Phylum NEMATHELMINTHES

roundworms

Phylum TROCHELMINTHES

Rotifera – wheel animalcules
Kinorhyncha

Phylum POLYZOA or BRYOZOA

moss animals

Phylum BRACHIOPODA

lamp shells

Phylum CHAETOGNATHA

arrow worms

Phylum ANNELIDA

true or ring worms

Phylum MOLLUSCA

Amphineura – chitons
Gastropoda – many with spiral shells, and limpets.
Scaphopoda – tusk shells
Pelecypoda (Bivalvia) – mussels, scallops, oysters, and clams.
Cephalopoda – squid, octopus, cuttlefish, and nautilus.

Phylum ARTHROPODA

Crustacea – includes Ostracoda, Copepoda, Cirripedia (barnacles).
Malacostraca – includes Euphausiacea (krill), prawns, lobsters, crayfish, crabs (the last four being known as decapod Crustacea).
Pycnogonida (sea spiders)
Insecta

Phylum ECHINODERMATA

Holothuroidea (sea cucumbers)
Echinoidea (sea urchins)
Asteroidea (starfishes)
Ophiuroidea (brittle stars)
Crinoidea (sea lilies, feather stars).

Phylum CHORDATA

Pogonophora – beard worms
Phoronida
Ascidiacea – sea squirts
Thaliacea – includes salps
Larvacea
Enteropneusta
Pterobranchia
Cephalochordata (amphioxus or Branchiostoma)

Subphylum VERTEBRATA

Cyclostomata – lampreys, hag fishes.
Euselachii – sharks, dogfishes, angelfishes, skates, and rays.
Bradyodonti – rabbit fishes
Pisces – true or bony fishes
Crossopterygii – coelacanth and lung fishes.
Reptilia – sea snakes and turtles.
Aves – few birds are truly marine, but some are dependent on the sea for food.
Mammalia – Cetacea include whales, dolphins, and porpoises; Pinnipedia include walrus, sea lions, and seals; Sirenia include dugong and manatee.

ZOOPLANKTON includes all of the animals which drift about passively with the currents, as distinct from those animals which can make extensive movements and migrations by their own efforts. It is composed of many groups of animals including Protozoa, smaller Crustacea, Medusae, Fishes, Molluscs, and the eggs and larvae of many other groups.

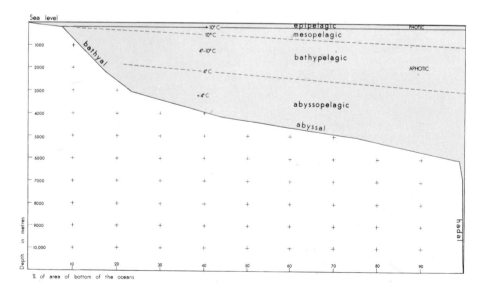

Zones of Marine Environment

The marine environment can be divided into several ecological zones based on physical-chemical factors, or the nature of the fauna and flora. While the boundary between the zones may sometimes be well defined, usually there is overlapping because the zones are interdependent. The organisms in a deep trench, for instance, are dependent on biological conditions of the overlying water masses up to the very surface, where the primary production of organic matter takes place. The two primary zones of the sea are the "photic" and "aphotic." In the photic zone light is the dominant factor during the day. In the aphotic zone there is virtually no light.

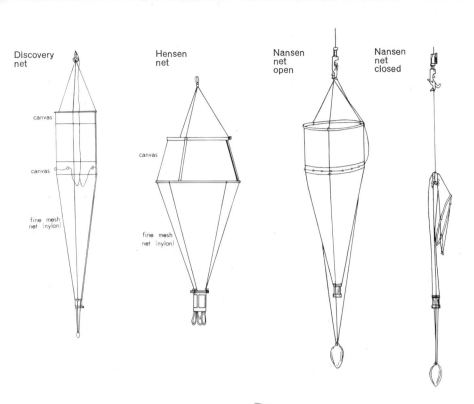

Discovery net
- canvas
- canvas
- fine mesh net (nylon)

Hensen net
- canvas
- fine mesh net (nylon)

Nansen net open

Nansen net closed

Tow Nets

Because no single device can sample the diverse forms of plankton, the oceanographer must use a variety of nets and instruments, each designed for a particular type of sampling. Collectively these provide a cross section of the pelagic plant and animal life. One of the most effective qualitative samplers is the tow net, which filters large volumes of water and strains off small organisms. The area of the mouth opening, size of mesh, and over-all shape of the net are varied to suit requirements. The nets may be towed horizontally, obliquely, or vertically. Because the plankton is distributed unevenly horizontally and vertically, it is important that these variations are expressed quantitatively. The nets usually are fitted with meters that register the volume of water filtered; they also may have closing devices which permit any desired depth range to be sampled.

Isaacs-Kidd Midwater Trawl

To capture the larger marine organisms a net larger than the tow net is needed. The Isaacs-Kidd midwater trawl (right), which can be towed at speeds up to six knots, has a mouth opening so arranged that animals in its path are not disturbed.

towing cable
bridle
spreader bar
mouth of trawl
cod end
net, extends whole length from mouth to cod end
tow point
vane area
tension member
hinged side arms
compression snout

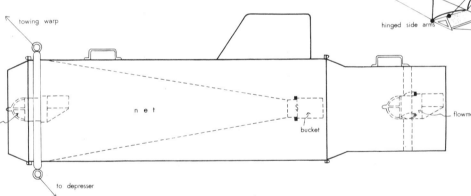

- towing warp
- flowmeter
- net
- bucket
- flowmeter
- to depresser

Hardy Plankton Recorder

This continuous recorder (below) is designed to be towed by merchant ships without interfering with their normal routine. The plankton is collected on a continuous roll of silk gauze that moves across the sampler's mouth at a rate proportional to the ship's speed. As the sample is collected, it is preserved automatically in formalin.

High-Speed Plankton Sampler

High-speed samplers (above) are rigid nets of metal mesh mounted in stream-lined metal or plastic containers having small mouth openings. Unlike conventional tow nets, these high-speed samplers can be towed at or near normal cruising speed.

Petersen Grab

The Petersen type "grab" is used for quantitative studies of bottom-living (benthos) organisms. The heavy metal jaws of the sampler remain open until it strikes bottom; when the grab is hauled the jaws come together and trap a sample from a standard area. The animals are then sieved, washed, identified, counted, and weighed.

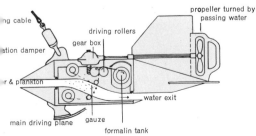

- ng cable
- driving rollers
- propeller turned by passing water
- ation damper
- gear box
- r & plankton
- main driving plane
- gauze
- water exit
- formalin tank

Sunken Cities and Forgotten Wrecks

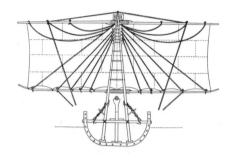

Ships

The earliest known ships were those of Egypt. From about 3000 B.C. to 1000 B.C. they were built of short planks (above) held by dowels. The midship section (above right) shows the double mast of an Egyptian ship of about 1500 B.C. Greek warships were about 150 feet long and had a pointed ram at the bow. Such ships built of unseasoned planking must have had a short life. The fighting ships of the Romans (right) were copied from Carthaginian ships and were manned by slaves. The Roman warships were designed chiefly as troop transport carriers which enabled the soldiers to grapple and board an enemy ship. Roman merchant ships of the first century A.D. were two-masted. A large center mainmast carried one large sail and possibly a topsail. In the bows a small foremast carried a smaller sail set at an angle.

Early Anchor Stock

Later Development of an Anchor Stock

Classical Anchor

Anchors

Ships of the Mediterranean probably began carrying anchors about the seventh century B.C. The earliest anchors were most likely blocks of stone. Later lead and wood, and iron were used. One first-century A.D. Roman anchor had a lead stock weighing 900 pounds and a shank of wood.

Amphorae

Amphorae, jars made of baked clay, were used to store wine, oil, fish, and other products. Amphorae can be classified to provide chronological evidence of the age of wrecks. The classification shown here is based on that of Paul Eydoux: I. Etruscan amphora, 6th century B.C.; 2. Ionian amphora, 5th to 3rd century B.C.; 3. amphora from Rhodes, 2nd century B.C.; 4. Greek; 5. Italian amphora, 2nd century B.C., of cylindrical form with long neck; 6. Italian amphora – from Campania and called the "Punic" type because of the similarity to those from Carthage.

1.

2.

3.

4.

5.

6.

Harbor Plans

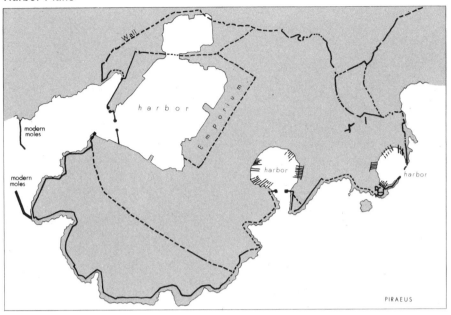

PIRAEUS

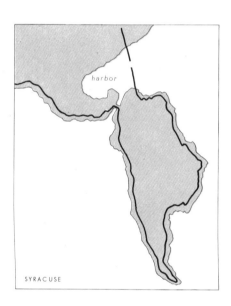

SYRACUSE

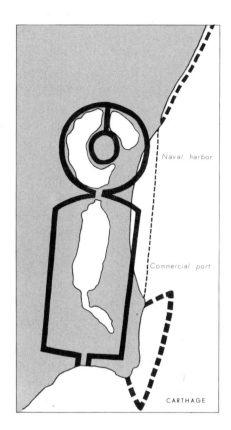

CARTHAGE

HALICARNASSUS

Classical Harbors

As maritime trade developed in the ancient world, the history of ports became the history of Mediterranean civilization. Many ancient ports were located strategically in relation to trade routes, such as the Phoenician cities where the Mediterranean touched the Fertile Crescent, the Cretan cities located on cross-routes, and the Greek and Roman ports that controlled various straits. Principal ports which where free of silting – such as Massilia, Carthage, and Alexandria – could be developed; but in the Adriatic and Asia Minor the rivers silted up the harbors. Promontories and islands in other ports provided shelter from wind and waves, but many such natural harbors still required help from man. Stonework remains found today show that port works ranged from simple quays and moles (such as those at Halicarnassus and Syracuse) to the sophisticated structure of the "cothon" harbor at Carthage. With their invention of hydraulic cement the Romans greatly advanced harbor engineering.

Rebikoff's Underwater Camera

Rebikoff's Torpille is a flash unit housed in a streamlined casing. It can be used by free divers. (right) The self-contained submarine vehicle (below) is capable of carrying one diver. It is possible to photograph rapidly underwater sequences in a short time and in a constant position.

1. Instrument panel in water-tight housing
2. Magnetic compass
3. Chronometer
4. Gyrocompass
5. Depth gauge
6. Battery
7. Body of vehicle
8. 1-1/2 HP electric motor
9. Directional rudder control bar
10. Turbo propeller
11. Directional rudder
12. Diving rudder
13. Propeller shroud
14. Control stick
15. Motor control stick
16. Differential aileron controlling pitch & roll
17. Bumper

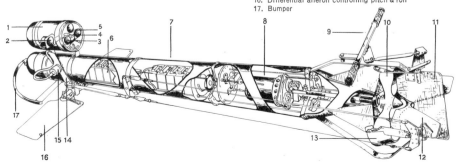

The Endless Search

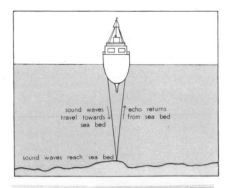

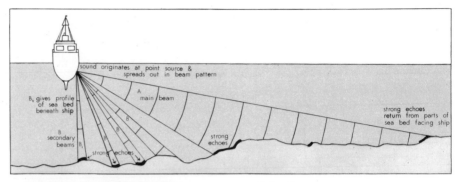

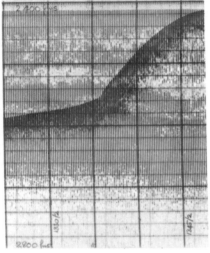

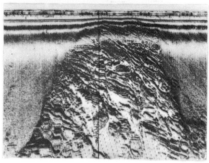

Echo Ranging

An acoustic picture of details of the sea floor can be obtained by the echo ranger. When a fan-shaped acoustic signal is sent out obliquely from the ship a strong echo is returned by any part of the sea floor facing the ship. The acoustic picture at left, which has been interpreted geologically, shows sand (even shading) surrounding a ridge of slates.

Echo Sounding

A continuous profile of the sea floor can be recorded aboard a moving ship by the echo sounder. The instrument sends out an acoustic signal which is received back as an echo from the sea floor. Depth at any place can be calculated since the velocity of sound in water of different temperature and salinity is known. On the echo sounding record shown left the horizontal lines are at 20-fathom intervals; vertical lines are time marks every 5 minutes.

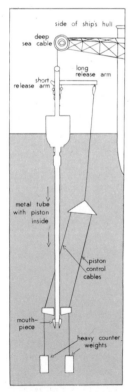

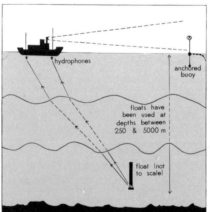

The Current Float

The neutrally-buoyant float, designed by J. C. Swallow, is used to measure deep currents. Made of aluminium, it is a free-floating tube sealed at both ends, which is less compressible than sea water. Loaded to sink to a predetermined depth, it drifts along with the deep currents. An acoustic transmitter operated by batteries sends out a sound pulse that can be picked up by hydrophones hung over the ship's side. The differences in times of arrival of the float's signal are measured, and, aided by radar bearings from buoys, the float can be tracked.

The Corer

The corer (above) is a hollow steel tube that can be forced into the sediments covering the sea floor. When the tube is withdrawn it brings up undisturbed samples of sand, clay, volcanic ash, and other deposits. Cores 70 feet long can be made with the Kullenberg corer.

Deep-sea Camera

The deep-sea camera, developed by A. S. Laughton, is designed to photograph the sea floor. Each time a weight suspended from the camera unit is allowed to touch bottom, a photograph is taken automatically. (Another illustration appears on page 201.)

Reversing Thermometers

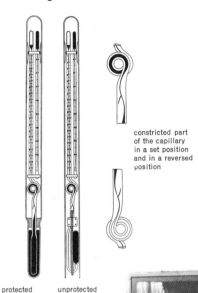

constricted part
of the capillary
in a set position
and in a reversed
position

protected
reversing
thermometer

unprotected
reversing
thermometer

To record temperature at any depth three thermometers are attached to a water sampling bottle (right) which closes, and reverses the thermometers, as required (page 210). When each protected thermometer is reversed (left), the mercury column breaks at the constriction between the large reservoir and the loop and runs down into the bulb and part of the graduated capillary. The loop traps any mercury forced past the constriction when the temperature rises after reversal. An auxiliary thermometer mounted alongside is used to correct for the effect of temperature change between the time of reversal and the time of reading. The thermometer is protected by being enclosed in a strong glass tube, of which the part around the reservoir is filled with mercury to help conduct heat. The reading of the unprotected reversing thermometer, which has no strong glass sheath, is increased by the pressure, but this is not so with the protected thermometer; so the difference between the readings of the two types, mounted and reversing together, can be used to determine the depth of reversal.

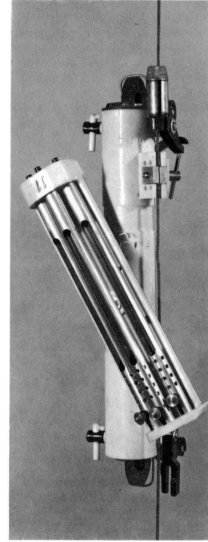

Thermostat Salinity Meter

Developed by R. A. Cox, this meter measures the salinity of sea water to an accuracy of one part in 10,000. It operates on the principle that electrical conductivity is proportional to salinity. The salinity of a sample of sea water is found by comparing its conductivity with that of "standard" sea water. To minimize temperature effects both samples of water are placed in the same thermostat bath (center in photo above).

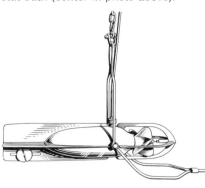

Current Meters

The Ekman current meter shown above consists of three main components: 1. a vane which orients the instrument so that it is kept heading into the current; 2. a propeller, the revolutions of which are recorded on a dial and measure the current's speed; 3. a special compass that reveals the current's direction. The modified Roberts current meter (at left) has propellers to measure speed, a magnetic compass to measure direction, and a pressure gauge to measure depth. Readings are sent to the ship electrically through the wire holding the current meter.

Floor of the Sea

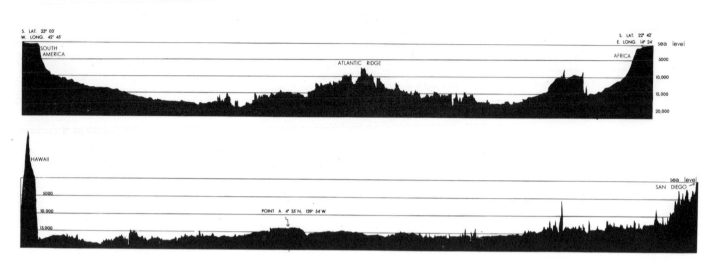

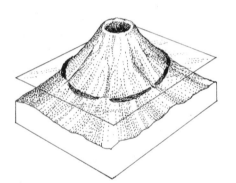

Comparative Profiles

These diagrams compare the profile across the United States with those of the Atlantic and eastern Pacific. The exaggerated vertical scale of 100:1 distorts the actual slope, which seldom exceeds 20°. The Atlantic section shows the mid-Atlantic Ridge to be comparable to, if not greater than, the western mountains of North America.

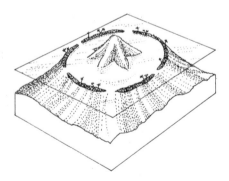

The Formation of Guyots

These diagrams show the formation of atolls and the flat-topped seamounts called "guyots." Their similarity to atolls gives a strong indication of how they are formed: 1. A volcano forms a seamount. 2. A volcanic island is built up. 3. The extra mass of the volcano depresses the Earth's crust and the volcano begins to sink. 4. Waves cut off the top of the island. 5. Coral growing on the fringes builds up as the volcano sinks, forming a barrier reef and lagoon. 6. In time nothing is seen of the volcano, which becomes covered with limestone. 7. If the sinking rate exceeds the rate of coral growth, the coral is dragged down and stops growing. 8. The guyot reaches equilibrium depth when its mass is supported by the displaced mantle material beneath the oceanic crust.

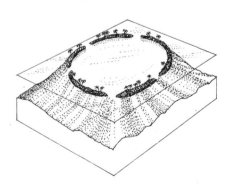

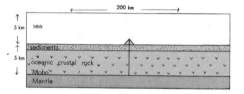

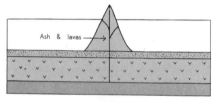

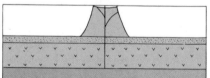

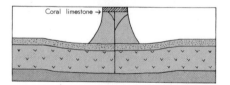

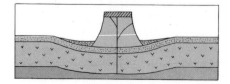

The Formation of Canyons

Submarine canyons are found cutting the continental shelves all over the world. Although they have been known for a long time, there is no one theory of their origin that is universally accepted. They usually have a V-shaped cross section and extend from the level of the continental shelf down into the deep ocean. Smaller canyons may join and form a single larger one. Occasionally they are associated with a well-defined river valley on shore, but more often they lead up to a coast that shows no indication of a valley, either now or earlier. At one time it was thought that submarine canyons were river valleys cut when the sea level was so low that the canyons were above water. Some scientists now believe that the canyons represent the locations of faults in the continental shelf edge. Others believe that the continental margins have been sinking by many thousands of feet and that the canyons may have originated as subaerially cut valleys progressively depressed beneath the sea and cut back. There is more agreement over the idea that they have been modified, enlarged, and kept scoured out by the frequent transport of sedimentary material from the shelf into deep water. These sediments are deposited as fans at the mouth of the canyons and spread out to form the abyssal plains.

Sea Floor and Coast of Central California.

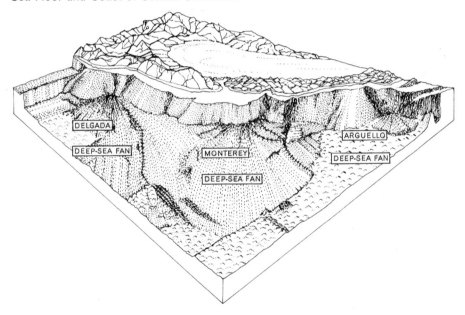

Mid-Oceanic Ridges

When the first trans-Atlantic cable was laid, an enormous mountain range was discovered in the mid-Atlantic. Subsequent surveys have shown that the mid-Atlantic Ridge (page 176) forms part of a world-wide system of mid-oceanic mountain ranges encircling the continents and having a total length of some 40,000 miles. The origin of this ridge system is still unknown, although much is being learned about its detailed structure and geophysical characteristics. In many places throughout its length, there is a pronounced valley near the crest of the ridge. This "rift valley," which is associated with intense earthquake activity, suggests that the oceanic crust is under severe tension.

The Currents

Temperature at 200 meters

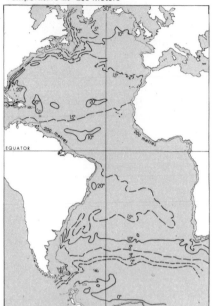

1000 meters

2000 meters   Temperature in °C.

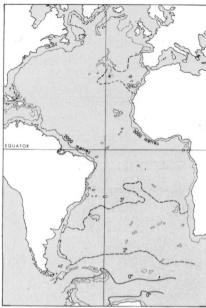

Salinity at 200 meters

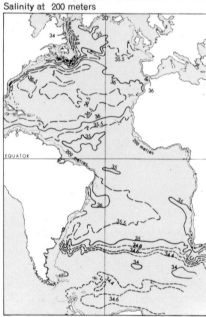

1000 meters

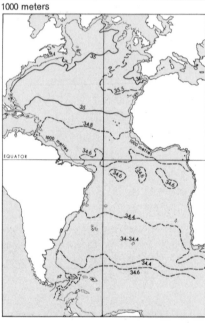

2000 meters   Salinity in parts per thousand by weight

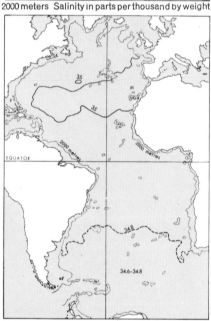

Meteor Tracks

The German Atlantic Expedition of the *Meteor* (1925–27) was a survey of the Atlantic Ocean from the Antarctic ice edge to lat. 20° N. The 14 transverse sections of the *Meteor* (see diagram left) plus more information collected later enabled comprehensive horizontal charts and vertical profiles to be constructed.

The immediate subsurface water (200 meters) in the two subtropical high pressure regions indicates the increased effect of the absorption of solar radiation and its storage in the upper layers of the oceans. Here the water temperature may reach 20°c. or more. These areas also have high salinity. The spread of warm water over the North Atlantic, bounded in the north by the meandering "wall" of the Gulf Stream, is also well marked at this depth. Other details to notice are the warm Agulhas Current rounding the southern tip of Africa and the cooler

upwelling water in the Benguela Current off the southwest coast of Africa.

The temperature chart at 200 meters shows the exceptional cooling to below 0°c. in the Weddell Sea and off the Labrador coast and Davis Strait. The coldest water in the southern Weddell Sea sinks to the ocean bottom and spreads northward as the Antarctic Bottom Water, as can be seen on the vertical temperature profile. The surface layers of the ocean around the Antarctic continent, cold but less saline because of melting ice, stretch northward and sink at the Antarctic Convergence as the Antarctic Intermediate Water. This is particularly noticeable on the vertical salinity profile. On the charts this mass of cold water is shown as a broad band of less saline water between about lat. 40°S. and lat. 55°S. at a depth of 200 meters and at a depth of 1000 meters. It does not appear at a

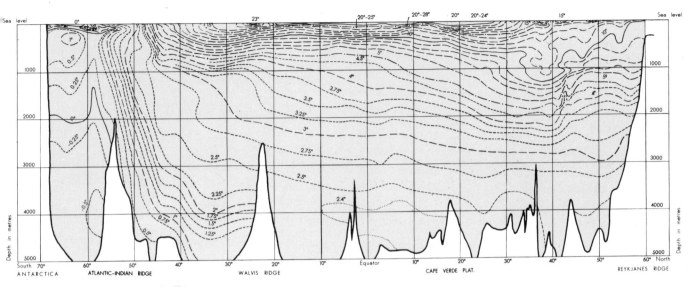

East Atlantic Ocean Temperature Profile

East Atlantic Ocean Salinity Profile

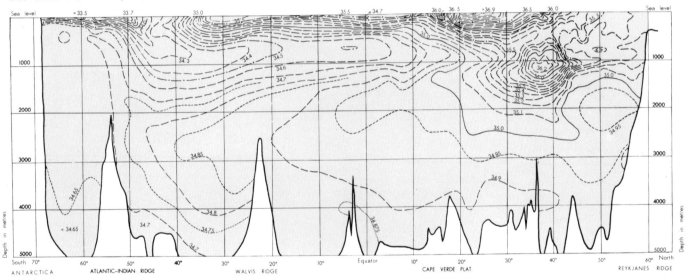

depth of 2000 meters where the North Atlantic Deep Water flows southward below the Antarctic Intermediate Water. This North Atlantic Deep Water forms in the extreme North Atlantic where cold water sinks to a depth of some 3000 meters and travels southward to the Antarctic where it rises over the colder Antarctic Bottom Water and yet remains below the Antarctic Surface Water. The chart of temperatures at 1000 meters shows that this North Atlantic Water, which has reached the Southern Ocean at this level, is less cold than water at 200 meters. Both the salinity and temperature charts at 1000 meters show the warm and highly saline water that flows out of the Mediterranean at a depth of about 300 meters. It travels down the continental slope and spreads westward and northward in the Atlantic at intermediate depths. The core of this distinctive Mediterranean water is particularly noticeable on both the vertical profiles of salinity and temperature.

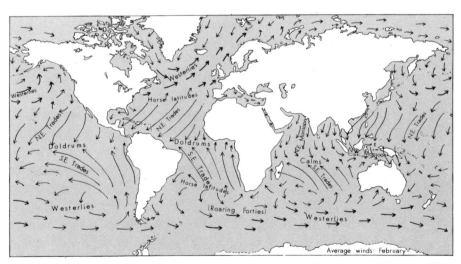

Compare this chart of the prevailing winds with the currents chart on pp. 204-05. In general, the main surface currents follow the winds.

The Restless Tides

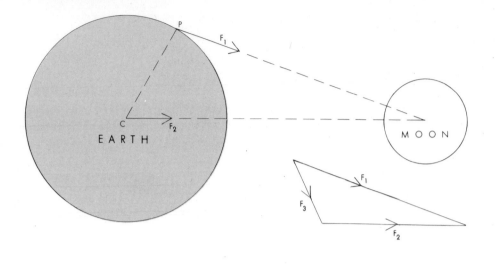

Water on the Earth's surface is rather like a loose skin on the fairly solid crust of the Earth. If the Moon's force of attraction on the water at a point P on the crust is greater or less than the force of attraction at the center of the more or less rigid Earth, the water tends to move toward or away from the Moon. When P is nearer to the Moon than C the force of attraction F_1 at P is greater than the force of attraction F_2 at C. The differential force F_3 (shown in the triangle of forces) acts toward the Moon. When P is on the side of the Earth farther from the Moon F_2 is greater than F_1, and F_3 acts away from the Moon. The differential force is greatest at the points nearest to the Moon and farthest from it, but at these places the Moon's pull is vertically upward, away from the Earth, and since it is only one ten-millionth of the opposite, vertically downward pull of the Earth it does not move the water. It is at points such as P, where the differential force has some horizontal pull along the Earth's surface, that the Moon's force of attraction becomes a tide-raising force. The Sun exerts a similar tide-raising force, but it is less than half as strong as that of the Moon. Although the Sun is more massive than the Moon it is much farther away, hence its weaker force of attraction.

The horizontal components of the Moon's force of attraction are least at the points nearest and farthest from the Moon. They are also zero, or very nearly so, around the great circle at right angles to the line joining Sun and Moon because there the attraction forces F_1 and F_2 are equal and there is no differential force. The tide-raising forces (horizontal attraction forces) are greatest halfway between this and the points nearest and farthest from the Moon, as shown here.

Because the Earth rotates around its own axis – the north-south line in the figure – water anywhere on the Earth's surface is pulled first one way and then the other twice every 24 hours, 50 minutes. If the Earth were covered entirely by water we should expect as an "equilibrium tide" two permanent "humps" of water on opposite sides of the Earth, as shown here; and the rotation of the Earth would mean that any point P would experience high water at P and again at P^1. Unless the Moon happened to be in the plane of the Earth's Equator the two tides at P and P^1 would not be the same height. At new and full moon, when the Sun and Moon pull in more or less the same direction, the tides are higher and are called spring tides. At the first and third quarters, when the Sun and Moon act at right angles, the tides are less and are called neap tides.

This diagram (right) shows the rotary tidal current at Nantucket Shoals Lightship. The lengths of the radiating lines represent the velocity of the current at the beginning of each hour, and their directions indicate the direction of the current. H denotes high water, L low water. The current has a maximum velocity toward the northeast 2½ hours before high water, and toward the southwest 2½ hours before low water.

Scale of knots

0   0.2   0.4   0.6   0.8   1.0

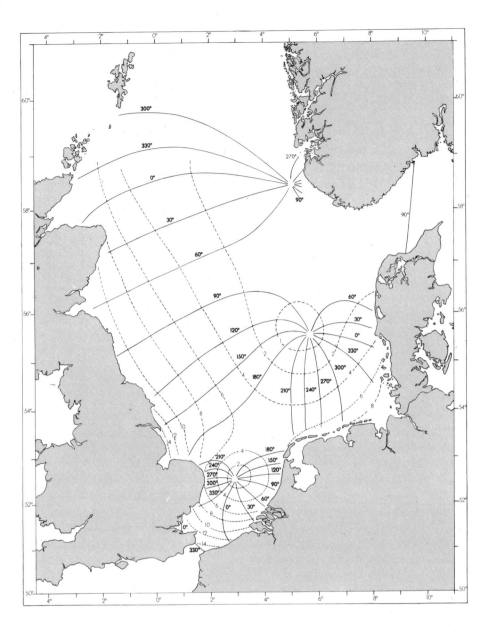

In 1922 Professor J. Proudman and Dr. A. T. Doodson collated many observations of tidal streams from a network of stations in the North Sea. The observations were made with the help of the International Council for the Exploration of the Sea and augmented by the Hydrographic Department of the Admiralty. Some of the tidal elevations in the open sea were measured by submarines. The dotted lines show the tidal range at intervals of 2 feet. The solid lines are cotidal lines and join places which have high water simultaneously at successive lunar hours. It is a complicated picture with several amphidromic points.

Actual tides in the oceans can be regarded as water swinging back and forth in a dish. A small force repeated at just the right timing will maintain a large oscillation. Ocean tides behave much as though the ocean had divided itself into a system of basins with natural periods of oscillation of about 12 or 24 hours. The oscillations are not simple movements from end-to-end or side-to-side because the geostrophic effect of the Earth's rotation introduces rotary movement. The figure here shows what is likely to happen in a large rectangular inlet. Without the effect of gyration the water would oscillate from end-to-end about a nodal line as in A and C. But at the intermediate times, as water is flowing from the high end to the low end, the gyration makes it move to the right in the Northern Hemisphere and the right hand side is higher than the other. The nodal line becomes a nodal point, called the amphidromic point, and the tide swings around it in a counterclockwise direction.

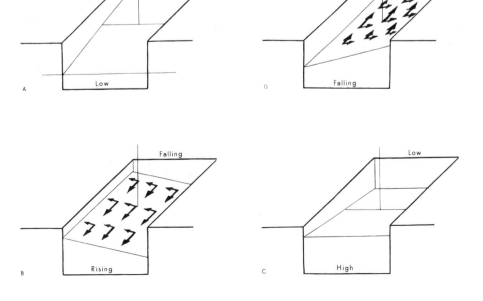

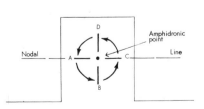

Edge of the Sea

Beach Nomenclature

A "beach" has three main zones (top right): 1. the "backshore" is above the swash of normal waves at high spring tides; 2. the "foreshore" is the zone between the high-water and low-water marks; 3. the "offshore" zone extends seaward from the low-water mark to a depth where appreciable movement of material ceases. Diagrammatic composite sand and shingle beach profiles (middle and lower right) illustrate the various "beach" terms.

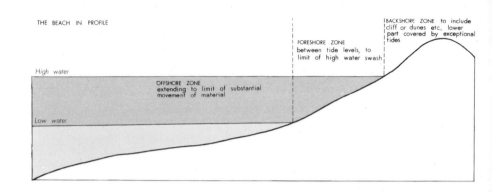

THE BEACH IN PROFILE

BACKSHORE ZONE to include cliff or dunes etc., lower part covered by exceptional tides

FORESHORE ZONE between tide levels, to limit of high water swash

OFFSHORE ZONE extending to limit of substantial movement of material

High water

Low water

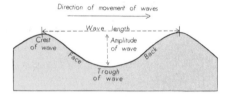

Direction of movement of waves

Wave length

Crest of wave

Amplitude of wave

Face

Back

Trough of wave

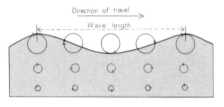

Direction of travel

Wave length

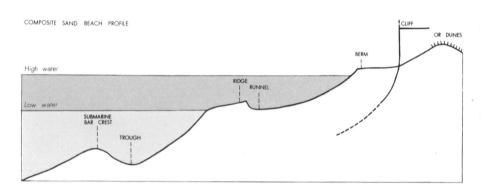

COMPOSITE SAND BEACH PROFILE

CLIFF

OR DUNES

High water

Low water

BERM

RIDGE

RUNNEL

SUBMARINE BAR CREST

TROUGH

"Wave length" is the distance from wave crest to wave crest. "Wave height," is the vertical distance from trough to crest. The particles of water in a wave do not move forward with the wave, but have an open circular motion. The radii of these paths decrease with depth.

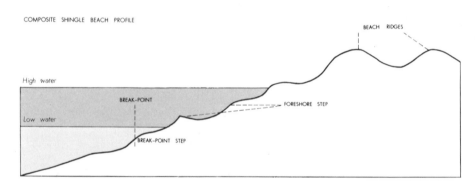

COMPOSITE SHINGLE BEACH PROFILE

BEACH RIDGES

High water

Low water

BREAK-POINT

FORESHORE STEP

BREAK-POINT STEP

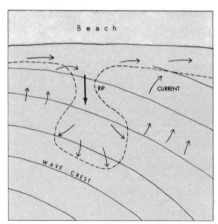

Beach

RIP

CURRENT

WAVE CREST

Above: A "rip current" is a strong narrow current moving away from the beach. It flows through the breakers and fans out beyond. These wave-induced currents seem to be associated with depressions or troughs in the beach.

Right: Weather chart for the North Atlantic shows conditions which are fairly typical in the winter months. Storm waves formed off the coast of Newfoundland began to break on the English coast midday, March 14.

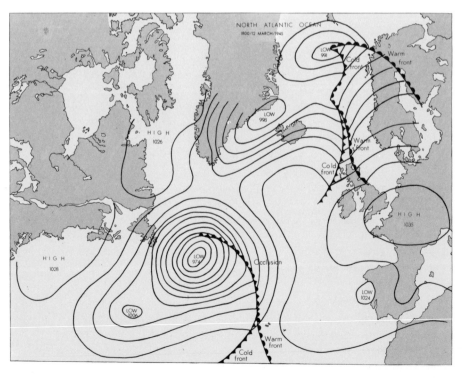

NORTH ATLANTIC OCEAN
1800/12 MARCH/1945

LOW 991

Cold front

Warm front

LOW 998

HIGH 1026

Warm front

Cold front

HIGH 1035

HIGH 1028

LOW 975

Occlusion

LOW 1005

LOW 1024

Warm front

Cold front

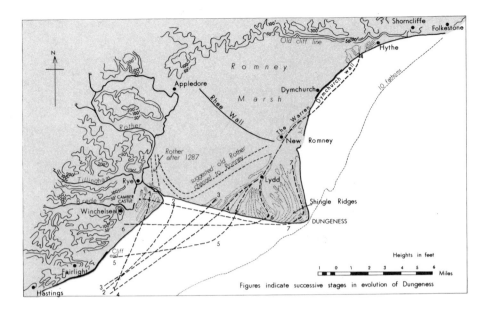

Dungeness Foreland Profile

Dungeness, England, is a large cuspate foreland which has been built out to sea ten miles to the east from the former coast line. The tip of the foreland is formed by shingle storm ridges. The waves that helped form Dungeness come from the southwest in the English Channel and from the east in the Strait of Dover. The accretion of Dungeness began possibly in Neolithic times. It started, probably, as a spit forming across a bay, from Fairlight to Hythe, then the spit gradually turned and built eastward to its present position. Today ridges on the southern side of the foreland are being eroded, and material is being redeposited on the eastern shore of the foreland.

Marsden Bay Profiles

On sandy beaches storm waves are nearly always destructive, removing sand from the foreshore – even from the backshore zone in severe storms – into deep water. Profiles at left illustrate the effect of destructive waves at Marsden Bay, County Durham. Recorded by C. A. M. King, they show that from December 2–12, 1950, about three feet of sand was removed from the north end of the bay; and that during an earlier period – October 18–28 – enough sand was removed above the high-water level of spring tides to leave a small vertical face. The profiles at far left illustrate the effects of constructive wave action at Marsden Bay at the end of 1949 and in 1950, showing the formation of berms.

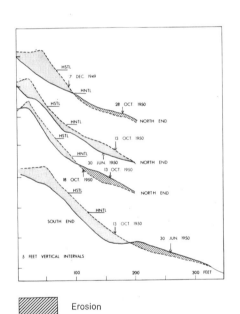

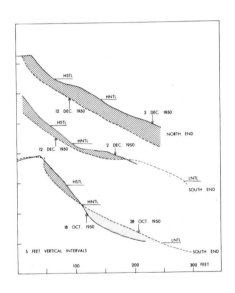

▨ Erosion

▨ Accretion

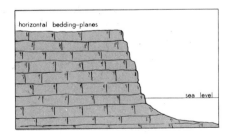

Erosion of Cliffs
A cliff formed of stratified and jointed rock is easily undercut by waves. It breaks along the bedding planes and weak lines called "joints."

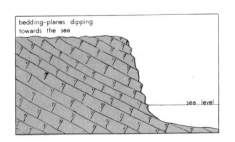

When the beds of rock dip seaward (and the joints landward) undercutting is more rapid. Large blocks may fall outward onto the beach, leaving an overhanging cliff.

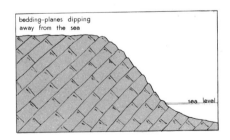

When the beds dip landward (and the joints seaward) the rock is less likely to fall onto the beach below. The result is that the cliff slopes toward the sea.

Future of the Sea

Salinity Profile of the Pacific Ocean

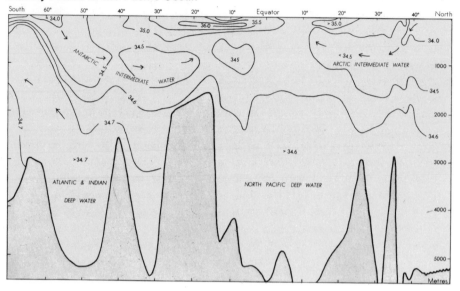

Salinity Profile of the Indian Ocean

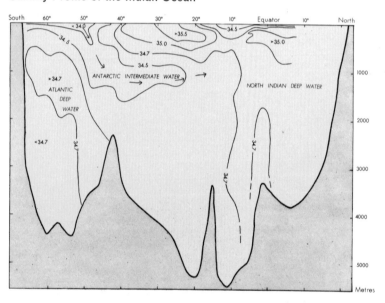

Salinity Profiles

These vertical sections through the Pacific Ocean and Indian Ocean show the distribution of salinity. From these sections the direction of movement of the deep currents can be deduced. Arctic and Antarctic Intermediate Currents converge towards the middle of the Pacific Ocean. There is a similar Antarctic Intermediate Current in the Indian Ocean and a source of more saline water in the north of the Indian Ocean. Highly saline water at the southern end of the sections can be traced back to the North Atlantic Ocean. The salt content along this path is reduced by mixing but there is an increase in the amount of phosphates (as shown in the map at the bottom) which accumulates as the result of biological processes. The highest salinity in the oceans is found in the Red Sea and in the Persian Gulf; the lowest in the Baltic Sea and Black Sea.

Concentration of Elements in Sea Water of salinity 34·33 parts per thousand

ELEMENT	CONCENTRATION IN MG./KG. (parts per million)
Chlorine	18980
Sodium	10561
Magnesium	1272
Sulphur	884
Calcium	400
Potassium	380
Bromine	65
Carbon	28
Strontium	13
Boron	4.6
Silicon	0-4.0
Fluorine	1.4
Nitrogen	0-0.7
Aluminium	0.5
Rubidium	0.2
Lithium	0.1
Phosphorus	0-0.1
Barium	0.05
Iodine	0.05

ELEMENT	CONCENTRATION IN MG./TON (parts per thousand million)
Arsenic	10-20
Iron	0-20
Manganese	0-10
Copper	0-10
Zinc	5
Lead	4
Selenium	4
Caesium	2
Uranium	1.5
Molybdenum	0.5
Thorium	0.5
Cerium	0.4
Silver	0.3
Vanadium	0.3
Lanthanum	0.3
Yttrium	0.3
Nickel	0.1
Scandium	0.04
Mercury	0.03
Gold	0.006
Radium	0.0000002

Distribution of Phosphates at 2000 Meters

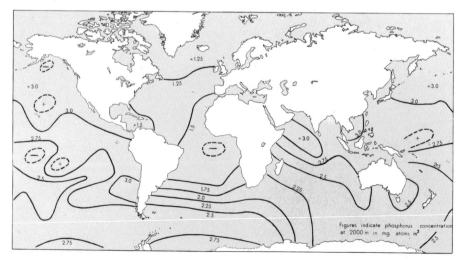

Figures indicate phosphorus concentration at 2000 m in mg. atoms m³

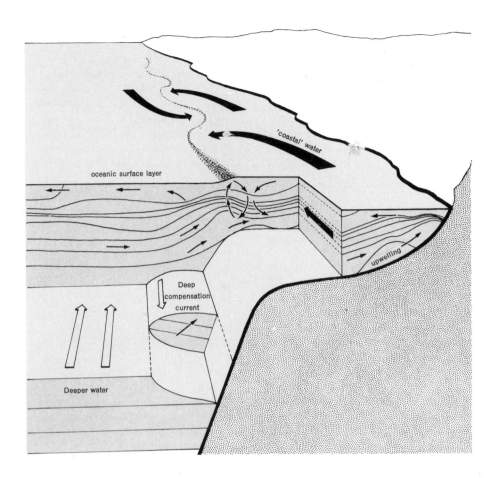

Upwelling of Water

This perspective diagram (looking northward in the Benguela Current) shows an idealized view of the principal horizontal and vertical water movements that take place during upwelling. The surfaces of equal density, shown by the thin lines on the vertical section, curve upward near the edge of the continental shelf and rise close to the surface in the coastal water. The shaded wavy line running north at the surface gives a rough indication of the boundary between the ocean surface water and the upwelled coastal water.

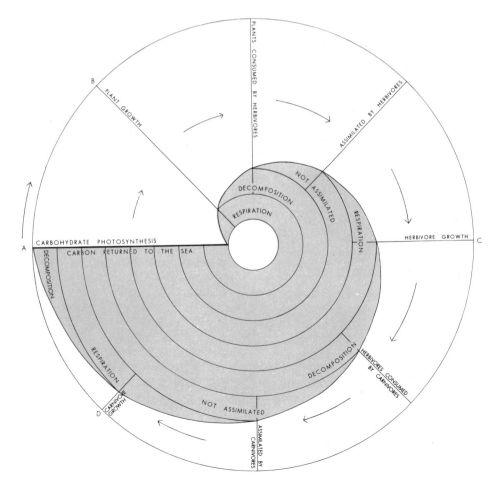

Organic Cycle of the Sea

This diagram illustrates the cycle of organic production in a part of the sea where equilibrium conditions are more or less maintained, and where there are no great losses to or introductions from neighboring areas. Initial photosynthesis and plant growth, which is consumed by herbivores (and these by carnivores), build up the large animals and fish. There is a lot of wastage in this chain and only a small part of the organic matter initially produced finds its way into the larger animals which we catch for our food. The material which is lost is returned to the sea (blue spiral).

Oceanographic Expeditions

EDMUND HALLEY (1657–1742)
British astronomer, Halley made probably the first primarily scientific voyage – to study the variation of the magnetic compass – sailing as far as lat. 52°S. in the Atlantic Ocean in 1698–1700. On a previous expedition to St. Helena, he made an important contribution to knowledge of the trade winds. He also wrote on tides. He realized more than anyone the value of Newton's *Principia* and arranged for it to be printed at his own expense.

JAMES COOK (1728–79)
On his three great voyages between 1768 and 1780, Cook carried naturalists in his ships and made careful observations of winds and currents. During the second voyage the Forster brothers measured subsurface temperature and found a warm deep layer below the Antarctic surface water.

FRANÇOIS PÉRON (1775–1810)
French naturalist and physicist, Péron accompanied a French circumnavigation of the globe in 1800–04. He was able to make only a few rather uncertain deep temperature measurements, but was much impressed by the importance of oceanic research and maintained that it had received too little attention.

IVAN F. KRUZENSTEIN (1770–1846)
He commanded a Russian circumnavigation in 1803–06 and was accompanied by Dr. J. C. Horner and with him made a number of deep sea temperature measurements in the tropical Pacific and the Sea of Okhotsk.

WILLIAM SCORESBY (Jun.) (1789–1857)
An English whaler and scientist, Scoresby made many surface and deep observations in the seas around Spitsbergen and off the coast of Greenland between 1810 and 1822.

FABION G. von BELLINGSHAUSEN (1779–1852)
He circumnavigated the Antarctic continent in 1819–21, much of the voyage being south of lat. 60°S. He was bitterly disappointed in having to sail without a naturalist. "In this way our hopes of making discoveries in the field of natural history were dashed to the ground," he wrote. Nevertheless he made many valuable observations, and his artist Paul Mikhailov painted a fine series of pictures of marine animals.

OTTO von KOTZEBUE (1787–1846)
This Russian admiral made two circumnavigations in 1815–18 and 1823–26, primarily for scientific purposes. Many deep-sea temperature observations were made, and Emil von Lenz, physicist on the second voyage, recognized that a surface flow of water from low to high latitudes must be supplied by a flow from the poles at great depths.

JEAN S. C. DUMONT d'URVILLE (1790–1842)
A French admiral, he made three circumnavigations in 1822–25, 1826–29, and 1837–40. He made many deep-sea temperature observations, but because of the effect of pressure on the thermometers he concluded that in the open oceans the temperature of the water below about 500 fathoms was uniform at nearly 4.4°c. He wrongly concluded that somewhere between lat. 40°S. and lat. 60°S., ocean water was at a uniform temperature of 4.4°c. from the surface to the bottom.

SIR JAMES CLARK ROSS (1800–62)
He made the first extensive series of deep sea soundings during his voyage to the Southern Seas in 1839–43 in H. M. S. *Erebus* and *Terror*. He made comprehensive studies of the Earth's magnetism, many deep-sea temperature measurements and extensive biological collections. Dr. J. D. Hooker, who went on the voyage as surgeon-naturalist, published his well-known *Botany of the Antarctic, voyage of the* Erebus *and* Terror. Ross also studied the effect of variations of atmospheric pressure on sea level. He had the same ideas as Dumont d'Urville about temperature of the deep water. Dredgings were made at depths down to 400 fathoms but the collections were subsequently neglected and lost to science.

CHARLES WILKES (1798–1877)
He commanded six ships taking part in the United States expedition of 1838–42. Although the scientific staff, under the direction of the famous naturalist, J. D. Dana, did not go south of Sydney, Australia, extensive natural history collections were made. Scientifically the expedition is best known for Dana's description of Crustacea. What must have been an enormous collection of fishes was never properly reported on.

ROBERT FITZROY (1805–65)
This British admiral commanded the *Beagle* during her famous voyages of 1826–36. Charles Darwin, who sailed in her from 1831–36, added much to our knowledge of natural history, especially on the structure and origin of coral reefs and islands. Only two sets of temperature observations were made.

MATTHEW F. MAURY (1806–73)
An officer in the United States Navy, he sailed around the world and his sea experience taught him the critical need to increase the efficiency of shipping through better navigation and safety at sea. He was successful in convincing the world of the value of more systematic study and charting of winds and currents. He also produced the first bathymetric chart of the North Atlantic Ocean.

EDWARD FORBES (1815–54)
He studied the fauna of the Aegean Sea and did much to stimulate interest in marine biology, partly,

perhaps, by promoting an active study of depths greater than 300 fathoms, below which he believed that animal life ceased to exist.

WILLIAM B. CARPENTER (1813–85)
SIR CHARLES WYVILLE THOMSON (1830–82)
GWYN JEFFREYS (1809–85)
They made dredging expeditions in H.M.S. *Lightning*, *Porcupine*, and *Shearwater* in the eastern North Atlantic and Mediterranean Sea. They found many new species of animals and made enough temperature observations to show that there was an active circulation of the water below the surface. They dredged at depths down to 2000 fathoms.

H. M. S. CHALLENGER (1872–76)
This research ship carried five scientists, under the direction of Wyville Thomson, and made extensive biological, chemical, geological, and physical observations, mainly in the Atlantic and Pacific oceans and across the Indian Ocean south of lat. 40°S. The extensive biological collections, together with soundings, bottom samples, and chemical and physical observations, presented the first broad view of the character of the oceans.

U. S. S. TUSCARORA (1874–75)
Commanded by Captain George E. Belknap. Scientists on this voyage studied the distribution of temperature in the northern Pacific Ocean, took a large number of soundings, and collected samples of bottom deposits. She was the first ship to use piano wire for a sounding line, although Sir William Thomson (Lord Kelvin) had used it in his yacht. The ship obtained a sounding more than five miles deep east of Japan. Her work was extended to the central Pacific Ocean in later years.

S. M. S. GAZELLE (1874–76)
This German corvette, like the *Challenger*, worked mainly in the Atlantic and Pacific oceans, adding especially to our knowledge of the physics of the oceans.

U. S. S. BLAKE (1877–80)
Scientists aboard this ship explored the Caribbean Sea, Gulf of Mexico, and the coast of Florida, under the direction of Alexander Agassiz. She was later commanded by John Elliot Pillsbury, who, beginning in 1885, made a remarkable series of current measurements. The current and temperature were measured at different depths along several sections across the Florida Strait and at a number of stations in the passages of the Windward Islands.

U. S. S. ALBATROSS (1888–1905)
This research ship, belonging to the United States Fish Commission, worked extensively in the eastern Pacific Ocean from Easter Island and Callao in Peru to the Bering Sea, and also in Japanese waters and in the Sea of Okhotsk.

Much of the work was under the direction of Alexander Agassiz.

H. M. I. S. INVESTIGATOR (1885–1905)
INVESTIGATOR II (1908–26)
These survey ships of the Royal Indian Marine over the years made extensive studies, primarily biological, of the Arabian Sea and the Bay of Bengal.

HIRONDELLE (1885–88)
PRINCESS ALICE (1892–97)
PRINCESS ALICE II (1898–1907)
HIRONDELLE II (1911–22)
From the year 1885, the Prince of Monaco made systematic oceanographic studies from the Cape Verde Islands to Spitsbergen, and from the Mediterranean to the coasts of New England and Newfoundland.

VITIAZ (1886–89)
This Russian research vessel circumnavigated the globe under Admiral S. O. Makarov who made many observations of sea temperature, specific gravity, currents, and tides. Makarov became well known for his oceanographic work and was one of the scientists who built up the International Council for the Exploration of the Sea.

S. S. NATIONAL (1889)
This German expedition worked in the North Atlantic under Professor Victor Hensen with the special object of studying the plankton and food cycles in the sea. Hensen was the first to use the name plankton, and it was called the Plankton Expedition.

FRAM (1893–96)
Fridtjof Nansen made his remarkable drift across the Arctic Basin in this ship. He made many valuable oceanographic, magnetic, astronomical, and meteorological observations. He showed that there was a large volume of relatively warm and highly saline subsurface water derived from lower latitudes.

INGOLF (1895–96)
This Danish ship made extensive biological and physical studies in the North Atlantic.

VALDIVIA (1898–99)
This German Deep Sea Expedition, under Professor Carl Chun, made extensive studies of the biology, physics, and bottom deposits of the Atlantic, Indian, and Antarctic oceans. She trawled successfully at great depths in high southern latitudes.

BELGICA (1897–99)
This Belgian Antarctic Expedition made biological collections and physical observations in the ocean west of Graham Sound and south of Peter I Island. She was the first ship to winter in the Antarctic.

SIBOGA (1899–1900)
The Netherlands Deep Sea Expedition principally studied the biology and also the hydrography of the waters of the East Indies and Malaya.

GAUSS (1901–04)
The German South Polar Expedition under E. von Drygalski made extensive studies of all aspects of oceanography, mainly south of the western Indian Ocean.

SCOTIA (1902–04)
This Scottish Antarctic Expedition was particularly successful in dredging and trawling at great depths in the Weddell Sea and off Coats Land.

S. M. S. PLANET (1906)
On this expedition German scientists worked in the Atlantic and Indian oceans, and discovered the remarkable double trench south of Java with depths of more than 7000 meters.

DEUTSCHLAND (1911–12)
This German Antarctic Expedition, under Wilhelm Filchner and the oceanographer W. Brennecke, made remarkable contributions to our knowledge of the physics and chemistry of the western half of the South Atlantic Ocean and the Weddell Sea. Professor Lohmann, also on the voyage, added much to our knowledge of plankton.

METEOR (1925–27)
This German Atlantic Expedition made repeated sections across the South Atlantic Ocean. The physical, chemical, geological, meteorological (and some biological) observations made during the voyage contributed more than any previous expedition to our basic understanding of the ocean.

DISCOVERY (1926–31)
WILLIAM SCORESBY (1926–39)
DISCOVERY II (1929–)
These ships of the Discovery Investigations made soundings, physical and chemical observations, and quantitative plankton studies all around the Antarctic continent. The physical and chemical data have been published and much of the biological material has been reported on.

GALILEE (1905–09)
CARNEGIE (1909–29)
These ships of the Carnegie Institute of Washington made the most extensive studies of the Earth's magnetic field over the ocean. During the last voyage extensive oceanographic observations, mainly in the tropical Pacific Ocean, were also made.

NORWEGIA (1927–31)
The Norwegian Antarctic Expedition under Professor Haakon Mosby and Gunnar Isachsen added a great deal to our knowledge of the Antarctic Ocean.

DANA (1928–30)
The Carlsberg Foundation Oceanographical Expedition around the world was the largest of a series of Danish expeditions directed by Johannes Schmidt.

WILLEBRORD SNELLIUS (1929–31)
A Netherlands expedition made a very detailed oceanographic survey of the waters of the East Indian Archipelago.

ATLANTIS (1930–)
Since 1930 the principal research ship of the Woods Hole Oceanographic Institution, the *Atlantis*, has carried out extensive oceanographic programs in the North Atlantic.

MABAHISS (1933)
This ship carried the John Murray Expedition to the Arabian and Red seas. Extensive soundings, physical and chemical studies, and biological and geological collections were made.

While this list calls attention to large oceanographic expeditions, it makes no mention of the steady and continuing work of many smaller research ships, warships, cable ships, and fishing ships that have maintained continuous observations in ocean waters nearer home.
The *Michael Sars* is an outstanding example. From 1900 to 1910 she made observations all over the Norwegian Sea and northern North Sea, and in 1910 she went on an extended cruise (described by Sir John Murray and Johan Hjort in their classical work *Depths of the Ocean*) to the Mediterranean, the Canary Islands, the Azores, and Newfoundland.
Since the second world war most of the principal maritime countries have expanded their oceanographic surveys; researches and the list of ships and men employed far outweigh all previous efforts. Two rather special expeditions of smaller countries are outstanding: The Albatross Expedition (1947–48), led by Professor Hans Pettersson, added much to our knowledge of the physics and geology of the Atlantic, Indian, and Pacific oceans; and the Galathea Expedition (1950–52), led by Dr. Anton Brunn, made a special study of marine life at the greatest depths and trawled successfully at a depth of 10,190 meters in the Philippine Trench. From the U.S.A. one of the most spectacular research ships is the *Vema* which has made extensive geophysical observations as far away as the Antarctic and Indian Oceans.

269

Books About the Sea

GENERAL

Biography of the Earth, *by George Gamow (Viking)*

Biography of the Sea, A, *by Richard Carrington (Chatto & Windus)*

Climate Through the Ages, *by C. E. P. Brooks (McGraw-Hill)*

Creation of the Universe, The, *by George Gamow (Viking)*

Fond de la Mer, Le, *by F. Sonrel (Hachette)*

Frontiers of the Sea, *by Robert C. Cowen (Doubleday)*

Half Mile Down, *by W. Beebe (The Bodley Head)*

Ice Ages, Recent and Ancient, *by A. P. Coleman (Macmillan, New York)*

Mer, La, *(Librairie Larousse.)*

Ocean, The, *by P. Gosse (S.P.C.K., 1849)*

Ocean, The, *by J. Murray (Williams and Norgate)*

Oceans, The, *their physics, chemistry, and general biology, by H. U. Sverdrup, M. W. Johnson, and R. H. Fleming (Prentice Hall)*

Ocean World, The, *by Louis Figuier (Chapman and Hall)*

Origin of the Continents and Oceans, The, *by A. L. Wegener (Methuen)*

Our Mobile Earth, *by Reginald A. Daly (Scribner's)*

Principles of Physical Geology, *by Arthur Holmes (Nelson)*

Sea, The, *by H. A. Marmer (Appleton)*

Sea and its Mysteries, The, *by John S. Colman (Norton)*

Sea Around Us, The, *by Rachel L. Carson (Oxford University Press)*

Story of Maps, The, *by Lloyd A. Brown (Little, Brown)*

20,000 Leagues Under the Sea, *by Jules Verne (James Nisbett)*

Universe Around Us, The, *by Sir Harold Spencer Jones (Cambridge University Press)*

Unrolling the Map, *by L. Outhwaite (Constable & Co. Ltd.)*

Voyage of Discovery and Research in the Southern and Antarctic Regions during the years 1839–43, *by Captain Sir J. C. Ross (John Murray)*

Voyage of the Challenger, *by Charles Wyville Thomson (Macmillan, London)*

Wissenschaftliche Ergebnisse der deutschen Atlantischen Expedition auf dem Forschungs- und Vermessungsschiff "Meteor" 1925-27 *(Walter de Gruyter & Co., Berlin)*

World is Round, The, *by Frank Debenham (Macdonald)*

MEN AGAINST THE SEA

Book of Discovery, A., *by M. B. Synge (Nelson)*

Carta Marina by Oleus Magnus, *by E. Lynam (Tall Tree Library)*

Conquest by Man, *by Paul Herrmann (Harper)*

Cruise of the Dolphin, The, *by F. Lallemand (Methuen)*

Discovery and Exploration, *by Frank Debenham (Doubleday, New York; Paul Hamlyn, London)*

Europe, a Visual History, *(Bodley Head)*

Explorers' Maps, *by R. A. Skelton (Routledge and Keegan Paul)*

Farthest North, *by Fridtjof Nansen (Constable & Co. Ltd.)*

Great Adventures and Explorations, *by V. Stefansson (Dial)*

Greek Geography, *by E. H. Warrington (Dent)*

Hawkesworth's Voyages, *(vols. 2 and 3) 1772–73*

History of Ancient Geography, A, *by H. F. Tozer (Cambridge University Press)*

History of Exploration from the Earliest Times to the Present Day, *by Sir Percy Sykes (George Routledge)*

History of Geographical Discovery and Exploration, *by J. N. L. Baker (Harrap)*

In Northern Mists, *by Fridtjof Nansen (A. H. Clark)*

Journals of Captain Cook, The, *ed. by J. C. Beaglehole (Cambridge University Press)*

Kon-Tiki Expedition, The, *by Thor Heyerdahl (Rand McNally)*

Legendary Islands of the Atlantic; a study of medieval geography, *by William H. Babcock (American Geographical Society)*

Life of Captain James Cook the Circumnavigator, *by Arthur Kitson (John Murray)*

Life of Ferdinand Magellan, The, *by S. H. H. Guillmard (Philip & Son)*

Magellan, *by Arthur S. Hildebrand (Harcourt)*

Magellan's Voyage Round the World, *by Antonio Pigafetta; translated by J. A. Robertson (A. H. Clark)*

Mappae Mundi, *by J. Leithauser (Safari Verlag)*

Nansen the Explorer, *by Edward Shackleton (Witherby)*

Journal of a Voyage for the Discovery of a North West Passage, *by Sir Edward Parry (John Murray)*

Narrative of a Second Voyage in Search of the North West Passage, *by Sir John Ross (John Murray)*

Nautilus 90 North, *by Commander William Anderson (Hodder and Stoughton; World)*

Pytheas, *by G. E. Broche (Societé Francais d'Imprimerie, Paris)*

So Noble a Captain, *by C. M. Parr (Hale)*

Submarines, *by W. P. S. Lawrence (Doubleday)*

Succini Prussica et Civilis Historia, *by P. J. Hartmann, 1677*

Ultima Thule, *by V. Stefansson (Harrap)*

Under the North Pole, *by Sir Hubert Wilkins (Ernest Benn)*

A Voyage of Discovery to the North Pacific Ocean and Round the World, *by G. Vancouver (Robinson)*

Voyages, *by Levinius Hulsius, 1603*

Voyages Indes Orientales, *by Theodore de Bry, 1607–12*

Voyages of Discovery and Research in the Southern and Antarctic Regions during the Years 1839–43, *by Captain Sir J. C. Ross (John Murray)*

LIFE IN THE SEA

Ancient Plants and the World They Lived In, *by H. N. Andrews, Jr. (Comstock)*

Animals Without Backbones, *by Ralph Buchsbaum (University of Chicago Press)*

Aquarium, The, *by P. H. Gosse (John van Voorst)*

Classification of Living Animals, *by Lord Rothschild (Longmans)*

Descent of Man, The, *by Charles Darwin (John Murray)*

Diary of the Voyage of the Beagle, *by Charles Darwin (Cambridge University Press)*

Fishes, their Ways of Life, *by Louis Roule (Norton)*

Fishing from the Earliest Times, *by W. Radcliffe (John Murray)*

Great Barrier Reef and the Adjacent Isles, The, *by Keith Gillett and Frank McNeill (Coral Press)*

Histoire Naturelle, *by Buffon (Dufart)*

History of British Starfishes, *by E. Forbes (John van Voorst)*

Island Life, *by Alfred Russell Wallace (Macmillan, London)*

Letters and Recollections of Alexander Agassiz, *by G. R. Agassiz (Constable & Co. Ltd.)*

Living Resources of the Sea, *by Lionel Walford (Ronald Press)*

Man and the Vertebrates, *by Alfred S. Romer (University of Chicago Press)*

Natural History of Marine Animals, *by G. E. (and Nettie) MacGinitie (McGraw-Hill)*

North American Game Fishes, *by Francesca La Monte (Doubleday)*

Ocean, The, *by F. D. Ommanney (Oxford University Press)*

Oceanic Birds of South America, The, *by Robert C. Murphy (Macmillan, New York)*

Ocean World, The, *by Louis Figuier (Chapman and Hall)*

Open Sea; its Natural History, The, *by Alister C. Hardy; Part 1, The World of Plankton; Part 2, Fish and Fisheries (Collins)*

Origin of Species, The, *by Charles Darwin (John Murray)*

Popular British Conchology, *by G. B. Sowerby (Lovell Reeve)*

Seas, The, *by F. S. Russell and C. M. Yonge (Warne)*

Seashore Animals of the Pacific Coast, *by Myrtle E. Johnson (Macmillan, New York)*

Seaside Book, The, *by W. Harvey (John van Voorst)*

Time's Arrow and Evolution, *by Harold F. Blum (Princeton University Press)*

Zoogeography of the Sea, *by S. Ekman (Sidgwick & Jackson)*

Zoology *(Vol. 2), by P. Gosse (S.P.C.K.)*

SUNKEN CITIES AND FORGOTTEN WRECKS

Atlas de la Provence Romaine d'Afrique, *by C. J. Tissot (Salomon Reinach)*

Atlas Historique de la Ville et des Ports d'Alexandrie, *by Gaston Jondet (Institut Francais d'Archaeologie Orientale)*

À Travers le Mond Romain, *by R. Cagnat (Fontmoing)*

Au fond des Mers en Bathyscaph, *by A. Piccard (Arthaud)*

Buccaneers of America, *by A. E. Exquemellin, 1684*

Contribution to the Study of Earth Movements in the Bay of Naples, *by R. T. Günther (J. B. Nichols)*

Deep diving and Submarine Operations, *by Sir R. H. Davis (St. Catherine Press)*

4,000 Years Under the Sea, *by Philippe Diolé (Sidgwick & Jackson)*

Free Diving, *by D. Rebikoff (Sidgwick & Jackson)*

Grand Port Disparu-Tyr, Un, *by A. Poidebard (Librairie Orientaliste Paul Geuthner)*

Greek Cities in Italy and Sicily, *by David Randall-MacIver (Clarendon Press)*

Hommes et Dieux de la Gaulle, *by Henri Paul Eydoux (Plon)*

Italia Antica sul Mare, *by L. A. Stella (U. Hoepli)*

Larousse Encyclopedia of Mythology, *by Robert Graves (Paul Hamlyn)*

Man and the Underwater World, *by P. de Latil and J. Rivoire (Jarrolds)*

Man Explores the Sea, *by James Dugan (Hamish Hamilton)*

Mission de Phoenicie, *by M. E. Renan (Imprimerie Imperiale, Paris, 1864)*

Plans des Ports de la Mediterranean, *by J. Roux, 1764*

Sicily, *by E. A. Freeman (T. Fisher Unwin)*

Silent World, The, *by J. Y. Cousteau (Hamish Hamilton)*

Sybaris, *by J. S. Callaway (John Hopkins Press)*

To Hidden Depths, *by P. Tailliez (William Kimber)*

2,000 Fathoms Down, *by G. Houot and P. Willm (Hamish Hamilton)*

Undersea Adventure, *by Philippe Diolé (Grosset)*

Warship Vasa, The, *by Anders Franzen (Norstedt and Bonnier)*

NEW ATTACK ON THE SEA

Apparatus and Methods of Oceanography, *by Harold Barnes (Interscience)*

Atlantic Ocean, The, *by F.G. Kay (Museum Press)*

Beaches and Coasts, *by C. A. M. King (Arnold)*

Between Pacific Tides, *by E. F. Ricketts and Jack Calvin (Stanford University Press)*

Campagnes Scientifiques de S. A. S. le Prince Albert 1e de Monaco, Les, *by Dr. Jules Richard (Monaco, 1910)*

Circulation of the Abyss, The, *by H. Stommel (Scientific American Co.)*

Coastal Changes, *by W. Williams (Routledge and Kegan Paul)*

Depths of the Ocean, The, *by Sir John Murray and Johan Hjort (Macmillan, London)*

Earth Beneath the Sea, The, *by Francis P. Shepard (Oxford University Press)*

Founders of Oceanography, *by Sir William Herdman (Arnold)*

Geographie des Atlantischen Ozeans, *by G. Schott (Boysen, Hamburg)*

Great and Wide Sea, This, *by R. E. Coker (University of North Carolina Press)*

Hydraulic and Nautical Observations, *by Benjamin Franklin, 1787*

International Aspects of Oceanography, *by Thomas Wayland Vaughan (National Academy of Science)*

Introduction to Physical Oceanography, *by William Stelling von Arx (Addison Wesley).*

Major J. Rennell and the Rise of Modern English Geography, *by Clements R. Markham (Cassell)*

Oceanography, *National Research Council, (Washington), Bulletin 85*

Oceanography and Marine Biology, *by Harold Barnes (Macmillan, New York)*

Physical Geography of the Sea, The, *by M. F. Maury (Harper)*

Physical Oceanography, *by A. Defant (Pergamon Press)*

Raw Materials from the Sea, *by E. F. Armstrong and L.M. Miall (Constructive Publications)*

Realms of Water, *by P. H. Kuenen (Cleaver-Hume Press)*

Report on the Scientific Results of the Exploring Voyage of H. M. S. Challenger *(32 volumes)*, *Challenger Staff*

Sea Shore, The, *by C. M. Yonge (Collins)*

Seven Miles Down, *by Jacques Piccard and Robert S. Dietz (Longmans)*

Shore Processes and Shoreline Development, *by Douglas W. Johnson (John Wiley)*

Submarine Geology, *by Francis P. Shepard (Harper)*

Sun, the Sea, and Tomorrow, The, *by F. G. W. Smith and H. Chapin (Hurst and Blackett)*

Surveyor of the Sea *by Bern Anderson (University of Toronto Press)*

Tide, The, *by H. A. Marmer (Appleton)*

Treatise of Marine Ecology, *ed. by Joel W. Hedgpeth (Geological Society of America)*

Voyage in the Antarctic Regions, *by Captain Sir J. C. Ross (John Murray)*

Wealth of the Sea, The, *by T. Douglas (J. Gifford & Son)*

Wind Waves at Sea, Breakers and Surf, *by Henry B. Bigelow and W. T. Edmondson (U.S. Government Printing Office)*

Index

Page numbers in bold figures refer to maps. When they are marked with an asterisk, it indicates that the information to which refence is made may be inferred from the map.

Index

Facts about the Sea

Illustrations credits

t-top; b-below; l-left;
r-right; m-middle.

294

Illustration Credits
Facts about the Sea

Unless otherwise stated, diagrams are by
GEOGRAPHICAL PROJECTS LTD.
photographs by MICHAEL HOLFORD.

248 Geological time scale
"A Revised Geological Time Scale" by
A. Holmes (Oliver & Boyd, 1960).

249 Theory of Continental drift Snider,
Extents of carboniferous glaciation,
Gondwanaland theory,
all *"Principles of Physical Geology"* by
A. Holmes (Nelson).
Theory of Continental Drift du Toit,
"Our Wandering Continents" by A. du
Toit, (Oliver & Boyd).
Polar wanderings,
"Geophysical Journal" vol. 2, 1959
(Royal Astronomical Society).

250 Roman sundial and Mediaeval astrolabe,
courtesy Trustees of the British Museum.
Pancake ice,
photograph Planet News Ltd.
Map by Battista Agnese, 1545,
*courtesy John Carter Brown Library,
Brown University, Rhode Island.*
Cook's proposed route,
*"Journals of Captain James Cook on his
Voyage of Discovery"* ed. by J. C. Beagle-
hole (published for the Hakluyt Society by
Cambridge University Press)
painting PETER SULLIVAN.

251 Cook's survey of the St. Lawrence,
*by permission of the Hydrographer of the
Navy* (chart on loan to the National
Maritime Museum, England.
Ross iceberg,
photograph ALFRED SAUNDERS.
Barrow's map,
"A Study of the Oceans" by J. Johnstone
(Edward Arnold),
drawing PETER SULLIVAN.
Ross Compass,
*courtesy Scott Polar Research Institute,
Cambridge.*
Nansen taking water temperature,
*original photograph from H. Aschehoug
and Co., Oslo.*
Nautilus control room,
Official U.S. Navy Photo.
Lead in ice,
photograph WILLIAM J. CAMPBELL.

252 Zones of environment,
*"The Ecological Zoneation of the Deep
Sea"* by A. F. Bruun, Tokyo, 1955 (Unesco
symposium on physical oceanography).

253 Townets,
"Ozeanologie" by Erich Bruns
(Deutscher Verlag der Wissenschaften).
Isaacs-Kidd mid water trawl,
*courtesy University of California,
Scripps Institution of Oceanography.*
High speed plankton sampler,
*courtesy U.S. Department of the interior,
Fish and Wildlife Service.*
Hardy plankton recorder,
"Oceanography and Marine Biology"
by H. Barnes (George Allen & Unwin).
Petersen grab,
*catalogue of Max Marx & Berndt, Berlin,
1928.*

254 Egyptians building a boat,
"Das Antike Seewesen" by August Koester,
Berlin, 1923.
Cross section of boat,
"The Mariner's Mirror" vol. 22, 1936,
and Capt. C. V. Solver, R. D. N.
Roman mosaic,
courtesy Mansell Collection.
Anchors,
all photographs GERHARD KAPITÄN.
Amphorae,
"Hommes et Dieux de la Gaule" by
H. P. Eydoux (Editions Plon),
drawing PETER SULLIVAN.

255 Harbour diagrams,
"Klio" supplement, 1923, vol. 19 edited by
Karl Lehman-Hartleben,
(Dietrische Verlagsbuchhandlung).
Diver with camera,
photograph SERGE DE SAZO-RAPHO.
Submarine vehicle
courtesy Dimitri Rebikoff.

256 Echo sounding,
"Oceanography and Marine Biology"
by H. Barnes (George Allen & Unwin).
Echo ranging,

courtesy A. H. Stride.
Neutral buoyancy float diagram,
Camera unit,
Echo tracings,
*all courtesy National Institute of
Oceanography, England.*
Corer,
"Westward Ho with the Albatross" by Hans
Pettersson (E. P. Dutton & Co., Inc.)

257 Thermometer,
*"The Oceans: Their Physics, Chemistry
and General Biology"* by Sverdrup, John-
son and Flemming (Prentice-Hall, Inc..
U.S.A.) © 1942, reprinted by permission.
Water sampler,
Salinity meter,
*both courtesy National Institute of
Oceanography, England.*
Ekman current meter,
"Science of the Sea" by G. H. Fowler and
E. J. Allen (Clarendon Press).
Roberts Current Meter,
photograph courtesy Kelvin Hughes.

258 Profiles,
Formation of a canyon (p. 259),
both "The Earth Beneath the Sea" by
F. P. Shepard (The John Hopkins Press).
Formation of a coral atoll,
"Exploring the Deep Pacific" by Helen Raitt
(W. W. Norton and Co., Inc.)
last two diagrams PETER SULLIVAN.
Formation of a guyot,
courtesy A. S. Laughton.

259 Monterey,
*"Possible Pre-Pleistocene deep sea fans off
Central California"* by H. W. Menard
(Bulletin of the Geological Society
of America, 1960)
diagram PETER SULLIVAN.
Mid ocean ridges,
courtesy "Scientific American," October,
1960.

260-1 All charts from *"Meteor"* Expedition
reports, 1925–27, vol. 6 text and atlas by
G. Wüst and A. Defant. (Walter de Gruyter).

262 Tide generating forces,
Distribution of tide forces,
Equilibrium tide,
*all courtesy K. F. Bowden, and
"New Scientist".*
Rotary tide movement,
"The Tide" by H. A. Marmer (D. Appleton
& Co.).

263 North Sea tides,
"Admiralty Manual of Tides"
by A. T. Doodson and H. D. Warburg
Crown copyright reserved, reproduction
by permission of the Controller of H.M.
Stationery Office.
Tidal current,
"An Introduction to Physical Oceanography"
1962, by W. S. von Arx (Addison Wesley,
Reading, Mass.)

264 Beach nomenclature, Rip current,
Dungeness (p. 265) and beach profiles
(p. 265)
all *"Beaches and Coasts"* by C. A. M. King
(Edward Arnold).
Construction of a wave,
"Beaches and Coastlines" by R. K. Gress-
well (Hulton Educational Publications).
Description of a wave,
courtesy M. J. Tucker.
Meteorological chart of the
North Atlantic,
*Crown copyright reserved, reproduction
by permission of the Controller of H.M.
Stationery Office.*

265 Cliff formations,
"Textbook of Geology" by Lake and Rastall
(Edward Arnold).

266 Salinity profiles,
*courtesy National Institute of
Oceanography, England.*
Distribution of phosphates,
courtesy A. C. Redfield.
Constituents of sea water,
courtesy R. A. Cox.

267 Benguela current,
diagram PETER SULLIVAN.
Organic cycle of life,
both diagrams courtesy R. I. Currie.

295

Key to Endpaper

1. Trumpet Shell, *Charonia tritonis.*
2. Spider Shell, *Lambis lambis.*
3. Baler Shell, *Melo diadema.*
4. Tiger Cowry, *Cypraea tigris.*
5. Black Cowry, *Mauritia mauritiana.*
6. Black Cowry, *Mauritia mauritiana,* extremely large specimen.
7. Egg Cowry, *Ovula ovum.*
8. Tiger Cowry, *Cypraea tigris.*
9. Tun Shell, *Tunna perdex.*
10. *Lambis chiagra.*
11. Geographer Cone Shell, *Rollus geographus.*
12. Textile Cone Shell, *Darioconus textile.*
13. Mole or Chocolate-banded Cowry, *Talparia talpa.*
14. Map Cowry, *Leporicypraea mappa.*
15. Carol's Volute, *Amoria caroli.*
16. Beautiful Volute, *Cymbiolacca pulchra woolacottae.*
17. Blood-red Volute, *Aulica rutila.*
18. Wiseman's Volute, *Cymbiolacca wisemani.*
19. Sophia's Volute, *Aulica sophiae.*
20. Court Cone, *Regiconus aulicus.*
21. Stiated Cone, *Dendroconus stiatus.*
22. Marble Cone, *Coronaxis Marmoreus.*
23. Giant Mitre, *Mitra mitra.*
24. Eyed Auger, *Terebra oculata.*
25. Divided Auger, *Terebra dimidiata.*
26. Fly-marked Auger, *Terebra muscaria.*
27. Spotted Auger, *Terebra maculata.*
28. Scorpion Shell, *Lambis scorpius.*
29. Lynx Cowry, *Lyncina vanelli.*
30. Luhu or Red-mouthed Stromb, *Conumurex luhuanus.*
31. Crested Stromb, *Strombus laciniatus.*
32. Tellen, *Laciolina quoyi.*
33. True Bubble Shell, *Bulla ampulla.*
34. Black-mouth Stromb, *Strombus melanostomus.*
35. Tulip Cone, *Tuliparia tulipa.*
36. Horse-hoofed Clam, *Hippopus hippopus.*
37. Painted Scallop, *Gloripallium pallium.*

Scale: The length of specimen 1, *Charonia tritonis,* is 9³/₄".

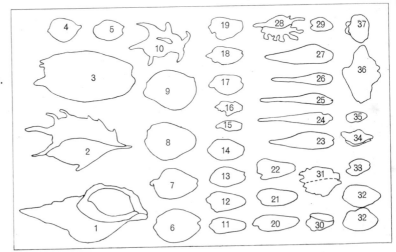